Daishi-san

Novels by ROBERT LUND

Daishi-san

The Odyssey of Thaddeus Baxter

The Alaskan

Hour of Glory

大師さん

Daishi-san

A NOVEL BY

Robert Lund

NEW YORK

THE JOHN DAY COMPANY

*The calligraphy on the title
page is by Tsai Tsao.*

Library of Congress Catalogue
Card Number: 61-8282

To

The Late JOSEPH N. WELCH

who had the rare and wonderful quality of tolerance
and also the courage to stand up and be counted,
I respectfully dedicate this book.

41890

PROLOGUE

I have spent part of the afternoon propped up with cushions behind me and for the first time in many years I have longed for the softness of a broad English bed. This sleeping mat, though of double thickness, gives no comfort to my emaciated frame.

Using an inkpot and brush, I have been translating into the English tongue the stipulation as to where I wish to be buried. The writing looks crude compared to the lovely brush strokes of Japanese calligraphy; but, as ever, I will make some excuse that English is bettered by the use of quill, and Shoki-san, in innate courtesy, will agree with me. To the eyes of both of us, though, the English writing has no more beauty than hen tracks. In this land of Nippon, calligraphy is an art, and Shoki-san, my friend and secretary for so many years, has a rare artistic touch. His hand has always been the one that has made my words look beautiful on paper. Though I have learned this complicated written language, my hand, being too large and insensitive, has never been able to bring beauty from a brush stroke.

But this, my burial request, reads as follows:

> *Having in my wanderings come to this land where I have until now lived in comfort and plenty, thanks to the Tokugawa Shogun, I have reached the end which all men must face. It is my wish that my friends may be so good as to bury me on the summit of Hemmi Hill, making my grave to face the east so that I may thus behold Yedo, and my soul, being in the underworld, shall ever have protection over this capital city.*

As befits a true Englishman, all my affairs are in order. My will is made and my properties are in the care of trusted friends. My will states that a division shall be made, giving half the value of my properties and possessions to my wife, Elizabeth, and my two children in England, should they still be alive. It has now been twenty-two long years since last I left England and, in truth, I do not know what has been their fortune.

To my Japanese wife, Magome Yuriko, this woman of Nippon

7

whom I cherish beyond words, and our two children, the flowers of our love, I leave the other half of what I possess.

My heart is at ease, more so than it has been for a long time; and though death is never a happy prospect to anyone, I have learned to accept with good face what cannot be avoided.

Through the efforts of my friends of noble lineage, holding high rank at the Shogun's court, the anger of Tokugawa Hidetada toward me has cooled. By his word and law I should have been put to death. But he has left me to end my remaining days in peace and has given his word that my lands and noble title of Daimyo of the Second Class will be inherited by my small son Joseph, and thereafter passed down through the generations. Though Hidetada has, heretofore, hurt me deeply, I hold no hatred against him.

Much to the objection of the doctor and Yuriko, my wife, I have spent the last days reading through the long pages of this manuscript on which I passed so many weeks and months remembering the events of my life. Many things now come to my mind that I should have told. But time is too short and perhaps it is better so. The writing has been my solace and comfort during the past two troubled years.

It is my vanity that perhaps, some day, my countrymen in England will read this chronicle of the things, both good and evil, that made up the days of my life. Through these words they may come to feel some kinship with me in my wanderings and share somewhat the joy I have found in living and the philosophy of life I have worked out. I know some will say that my tolerance toward men, even those who have done me harm, was weakness; that, had I the courage to stand forth and retaliate with violence, my life would have held fewer troubles. But they mistake tolerance for weakness. Of all things in life tolerance is the hardest principle to hold fast to. All mankind praise and esteem it until it conflicts with their own current desire, be that patriotism or religion, then they turn violently against it and any who practice it. Could man come to know that his view of the world is as narrow and limited as his own thoughts and that it cannot help but differ from the view of others, then we might realize tolerance.

It is a virtue I have tried always to cling to, yet I have failed as other men have. Once I went to visit a priest who had been thrown in prison for disobeying the Shogun's order against preaching the Christian religion in Japan. When I entered his cell he was on his scarred and bloody knees. I put out my hands to raise him up and he railed at me, calling me heretic and blasphemer. This man had caused me much trouble, and now, in anger at his fanaticism, I called to the guard to let me out, and I left him there to his fate.

No one can know how this has eaten at my heart. When I was young, the evils done in the name of religion sickened me. Later I came to understand that the very spirit of religion, which can never die, is that which puts man above the other creatures of the earth, and no matter how many distort it through bigotry and intolerance, it is the hope of the world.

Captain John Saris of HMS *Clove* accused me of becoming more Japanese than the Japanese, taking even their religion. His words held some truth. I have found solace and wisdom in the teachings of Buddha, which are indeed at little variance with the teaching of the gentle Christ. But Saris never accused me of being a coward; he carried a scar I put upon him in his youth until the day he died. My courage has been as great as the next man's, and proved often enough. And my honesty sits clear on my conscience; for although during the time I held great power I was accused by the Portugals, Spaniards, Dutch, and English of favoring the others, the charge was not true.

My life has not been overlong, having just reached fifty-nine years, yet I believe I have come to some knowledge of the world. But those who read this recounting shall be the final judges.

When I was young and first went to sea, traveling to foreign ports, I learned the basic truth that though these countries be strange to the eye there is a great similarity among all people, of whatever land. I am afraid my countrymen would not agree to this, for no Englishman worthy of his name would ever admit that any people or any land could ever compare with England or the English.

During those great days when England stood alone against most of the power of the Western world and defeated the Armada of Philip of Spain, I, too, had this pride in my country. But those days are long past and I have learned to love the people of this Morning Land as I never loved those of my own. In this there may be prejudice because, almost from the beginning, I held high honor here, much higher honor than I could ever have held in England even had I rivaled Drake himself.

In this land, as in many others, names are important. I have had many. They call me Daishi-san, or great teacher; Injin-san, meaning great pilot; Daimyo, Lord of the Second Class, which is the same as a lord in England. And the wise Abbot, Tenkai, who taught me of the Buddhist religion, has honored me with the Buddhist name Gerio Manen Benzui Kochi. Yes, I have many honorable titles.

The heights I once reached are in strange contrast to my humble beginning and my sad ending.

I am the son of an English tenant farmer. My birthplace was the village of Gillingham near Chatham, in Kent, where the Queen's ships used to lie, and the year was 1561.

It is strange to remember the years thus. To me, now, it is natural to count time in the Japanese fashion. Today is the tenth day of the fourth month of the sixth year of Genna. To translate, it would be counted in England as the sixth day of May, in the year of our Lord 1620.

The years of my life have been full and ever changing. I have known much hardship. Thirst, hunger, and fear have been familiar things. I have heard the thunder of cannon, the screams of men dying, the shouts of victory. I have survived storms beyond description, have given many shipmates to the hungry sea. I have enjoyed riches in plenty, eaten of the finest foods, drunk the best of wines, and known the delights of many and varied women. It has been my good fortune to have had great friendships, and my misfortune to have been violently hated. Most of the friends are gone, and life, in passing, has left me on this beach. But so be it.

Above all in the last years, it has been my fortune to have known, understood, and loved one woman without measure. There are many who will say I have led a sinful life, for even now I am a man with two wives. But I make no apology. In Magome Yuriko I found, during the seven years she has been my wife, something so beautiful, so rare, that there are not words in any language to convey the exquisite joy of her. I have loved her so that at times the depth of my feeling has frightened me. I believe it true that had I known her in the beginning there would never have been reason or need for any other woman; and had I had more time with her I could have become a very wise man.

This sickness that has eaten its way through me in the past year seems to have finished its work. Pain no longer wracks me. Though I feel like a hollow shell, I am now at peace.

Through the opened *shoji* screen I can look at the soft and lovely evening as I wait for Yuriko-san and little Susanna and Joseph to come and bid me good night as I bid good night to my countrymen.

And God bless you all.

PART ONE

The Apprenticeship

1

This journal was begun once before. When I left Europe as pilot major of a fleet of five Dutch ships in the year 1598, I set forth to sail through waters no Englishman had been on before. My hopes were high of returning to England with an account of new discoveries, new lands, and some knowledge of the people in the Far East. I kept track of the route, tides, wind and currents, all things I thought would be of interest to the geographers of the Royal Society and the Hakluyt Society. That journal was lost, but the value of it is now gone, too. Many men have come after me, finding easier and better routes than the one we took on that long and disastrous voyage.

On this journal I have begun at the beginning, which is always a good place. Though the events of my childhood are not important in themselves, I think there may be some value in drawing a picture of those early days. A man does not come full-blown into the world, but is developed and molded by the people and events around him, by what he sees, touches, hears, and learns. So that you may know me I must start from those two people who brought me into the world.

The first lucid memory of my childhood is of a sunny day on the

Kentish coast. My father and I had walked over to Chatham where the Queen's ships lay. We arrived there of an early morning with the sun just coming up out of the Channel. It was a bright, fresh day, such a day as, in England, only Kent can offer.

My father faced me to the east and told me that the world was round; that, if I traveled ever eastward, I would arrive sooner or later back at the same place where I had begun. He told me many things, whether on that day or other days is not clear in my memory. But his voice I remember so well—deep, pitched low, his words simple and thoughtful.

My father was a big man and I recollect how tall he stood beside me, how brown his face and how honest his far-seeing blue eyes. His hands were large and worn with toil, yet how gentle and kind they were.

John Adams, my father, was a tenant farmer on the elder Hakluyt's holdings that lay next to the village of Gillingham. He was lowly born, owning not even the house in which we lived. But he had a wondrous, trim, unsullied mind; and through listening and talking to the geographer and mapmaker, Hakluyt, and other geographers and sailors who visited the manor house, his mind had become enamored with the ever-widening horizon of the world. He had vowed on the day I was born that my life was to be wider than his. No father ever made a happier choice for his son, though it was always a sore point between my father and mother.

I think of my mother, Mary, with love and tolerance. Yet from my first awareness I could not hold to the narrowness with which she turned from life. My mother was bound and dominated by the Puritan sect to which she clung, ever engrossed by a fear of hell and a sense of sin in all the world about her. The few spare moments we had, we were forced to spend in church seeking forgiveness for the sins we had unwittingly committed.

My father liked to talk, to listen to people, to argue. Perhaps he spent more time than he should at the Inn of the White Bull; but if all men committed no more sins than my father, this would be a happy world.

Our small village of Gillingham was like England in miniature. The majority belonged to the Church of England, which looked with understanding on the little weaknesses of men. The Puritans, few as yet, would forgive no weakness. How my mother came to favor this group I know not. But this alliance of hers made for unhappiness in our house. The same disagreement prevailed in the village since the growth of the Puritan belief, and friends became enemies.

Being a kind and gentle man, my father had long since given up any attempt to change my mother's mode of thinking. He tried to live at peace, his good sense keeping the balance against her fear.

Though he could ill afford it, he had me taught the beginning of knowledge, how to read, and to set quill to paper. When I was of an age to read I had access to Master Hakluyt's library. Father and I would spend stolen hours together, he listening and I stumbling over the difficult words. In his eyes there was a hunger and a dream. I wish he had been able to come with me on all my later wanderings. He would have been a rare companion.

I was near the age of ten when I met the man who was to be as a second father. What character and understanding I have I owe to Nicholas Diggins.

On this day, by some excuse, my father kept me at home while my mother went off to a church meeting with my younger brother, Thomas. Sensing his mood of conspiracy, I was excited as we trudged across the field to the manor house. We entered through the back and a servant announced us to Squire Hakluyt. He greeted my father warmly, with no air of patronage of squire to tenant.

Hakluyt was a short, broad man with a deep voice and a great, bald head resembling one of the globes of the world that stood in his hall. Several other men were present.

I was somewhat afraid as Hakluyt said, "Ah, sit down, John. So this is the boy?"

And with this he introduced me to a Mr. Thomas Wickham and a Mr. Nicholas Diggins. I held on to my father's hand for security until he pushed me gently forward and I bowed to the gentlemen as I had been taught.

Wickham paid scant attention to me, but Diggins looked me over with an inquiring eye, then called me to him. He drew me close between his knees and, holding me in a strong grip by the arms, looked directly into my eyes.

"I am told that you want to know about ships and the sea." When I did not reply he asked, "Is that not true?"

"Aye, sir." I said.

He then asked me some questions relating to geography, searched out my meager knowledge of counting and figures, then, seeming satisfied, let me go.

I returned gratefully to my father who, upon invitation, had taken a chair and had in his hand a glass of port. I stood beside him and listened to the talk, feeling exceedingly proud that my father was accepted by these great men almost as an equal.

Some of the talk had to do with me, but I understood little of it. When we took our leave I was anxious to get outside where I could question him.

"What did they mean by 'apprentice,' Father?" I asked when we were some distance from the house.

"William," said he, "this is a great day in the lives of both of us, but do not tell your mother yet. Mr. Diggins has agreed to take you next year as apprentice, and to teach you the arts of shipbuilding and the sailing of ships."

His voice was warm and happy and I responded, not understanding wholly and still somewhat fearful.

"Will I have to go away to learn these things, Father?"

"Aye," he said. "You will be off to London and it is a great opportunity, Will. Once there you must study hard and do everything Master Diggins tells you."

"Will I see you and Mother and Thomas?"

"You'll see us. London is but a few hours away."

My memory serves me well the night our secret became known to my mother. With my brother Thomas asleep beside me, I was reading of the great voyages of Magellan. My light was a small stump of candle, which had been hard to come by. So engrossed in the book was I that I did not hear the footsteps on the ladder that led from the kitchen up to my small room. My mother's head appeared in the opening. Guiltily I tried to hide the book under my pillow.

"What hast thee there, William?"

"Nothing, Mother."

Mother always spoke in the manner of the Pilgrims, using "thee and thou," and one of my father's minor victories was that we did not. With her face in the shadow and framed by her dark hair that caught the light, Mother looked young and lovely. Yet her voice was sharp and dispelled the illusion.

"Tell me no lies, William. I have oft told thee thou art not to burn a tallow here. Now give me what thou has secreted."

"It is but a book borrowed from Squire Hakluyt, Mother."

As always, she wasted no more words with me. She held out her hand with a gesture that permitted no argument, and I handed the book to her.

"Now the light, William, and say thy prayers."

"I have said them, Mother."

"Once more; a thousand times more would not do thee hurt."

Crawling from my pallet and out on the rough boards I began to repeat the lengthy prayer she had taught me. Part of my mind, though, listened to her steps going below. I was fearful she would do harm to the book. Even young as I was, a book was a most precious thing to me.

From below I heard the deep voice of my father questioning her as to the trouble. She answered but I did not hear the words.

Then I heard her say in a louder voice, "Thou fill the boy's head with such nonsense that thee seems bent on his ruination."

"If knowledge be ruination, then ruined William will be. But he will have it, and with it a better life than I have known. And this I tell you now."

It was the first time I had heard my father's voice raised in anger.

"Thee wants to put the boy to where he does not belong and to instill in him the sin of pride."

"Mary," he said more gently, "I have ever tried to be a good husband to you. I give way too often, but I am a man, and in this nothing in all the world will sway me from the plans I hold for William. Come next year he goes to London to be apprenticed to Master Nicholas Diggins the shipbuilder."

There was silence for a moment as the words penetrated, then she fell to weeping as though her heart would break. And I prayed my father would not weaken. I heard no more of what was said between them that night. In the days that followed she was cold and distant to both of us.

2

It was a spring day in the year 1572 when I left the green fields of Kent and came to London. I remember standing in front of the Inn of the White Bull with my father. Some children of the village huddled in a group near to us, watching me start on my great adventure. Now that the time for me to leave had come I was afraid, and though my father's large hand was a comfort, still my heart longed for my mother. She had not answered my timid good-by, turning her face away, but I heard her weeping as we left. Now I caught myself looking down the lane hoping she would soften and come. I doubt not that she loved me but her rigid belief would admit to no turning from the path which she believed to be right.

My chin trembled when the coach rolled up. I wanted my father to put his arms around me, but he merely gripped my shoulder with his hand as he helped me into the coach. He was wiser than I, as I know now I would have wept had he hugged me.

"God be with you, William." Then he turned away to give instruction to the driver to let me off at Old Lime Street.

The coach was crowded with people, bales and boxes, live chickens, a pig or two, all bound for market. It was not the coach such as the gentry took, but my father could ill afford even the fare on this one.

I sat quietly huddled in one corner clutching my bundle and holding on to the stick I had brought with me as some sort of weapon against this unknown world I was entering.

The coach lumbered and lurched along, and once into the city I had my first smell of London. It was like a fist in my face. Even a pigsty didn't bruise the nose so. During all the years I lived in the city I could never accustom myself to the smell, nor my ears to the noise. Londoners always seemed to be talking, screaming, pounding on something.

As I stood on the street and watched the coach disappear, it was as if I was parting with my last and only friend. With my bundle over my shoulder I grasped the cudgel and started off down the street, keeping to the middle as I had been told was the safest thing to do. I walked along trying to avoid any attention.

The directions on how to get to Diggins' house were firmly etched on my mind and I plodded along purposefully. A number of dirty, ragged city children, noticing my country attire, began tagging behind me, hooting and jeering. When I paid no heed to them they became bolder, some going ahead of me.

The street was a bedlam of sounds, with more people than I had ever seen. The noise made my ears ring. I hung on to the bundle with one hand and took a firmer grip on the cudgel with my right. I was lonely and much afraid as if these weren't people but some strange, hostile animals. Suddenly I was tripped from behind and someone grabbed at my bundle. I hung on and, regaining my footing, rapped my assailant across the head with the stick. Then I was shoved again. As I fell I struck out and laid the cudgel across a pair of ankles whose owner set up a howling dance at the hardness of the blow.

Rolling over I came quickly to my feet, straddling the bundle and holding the stick with both hands ready to ward off the next attack. By this time I was surrounded by a large crowd, most of whom seemed to be urging the group of urchins to another attack. Though I was filled with fear, there was no place for me to run. I knew they could overwhelm me and take my few belongings but I promised myself they would have to earn what they took.

Suddenly a ratty sort of man pushed his way through the crowd and came to take a place beside me. At his interference the crowd turned angry, but he spoke in a cockney dialect which to me was as a foreign tongue. After a moment the crowd turned to laughter. I did not understand what he said but was comforted by his arm across my shoulders. The urchins now crowded around, slapping me on the back and shaking my hand.

Gratefully I thanked the man who had helped me and a path was now cleared so that I could make my way freely down the street. Some even followed me for a little way, laughing and making remarks which I took to be friendly. The strangeness of these people confused me, hostile one moment and laughing the next. It was not until I was well on my way that I discovered my pocket had been slit and the money which my father had so carefully hoarded to pay my expenses for the first year had been stolen.

I was shaken, wholly heartsick, angry, and knew not what to do. My first thought was to turn back and find the thief or thieves, but I knew instinctively that this was hopeless. I was sure now that the man who had so willingly stepped in to "protect" me was the thief. I swore if ever I saw him again he would answer for his thievery. Ashamed to go to Diggins, I was yet more ashamed to return home. It was not that my father would be angry, but he had sacrificed so much to accumulate that little store, I could not ask more of him. The lesser of the two dilemmas seemed to be Diggins, so I picked up my bundle and trudged downheartedly along the refuse-filled street ignoring the squalling children, shrill-voiced women, and the loud, drunken laughter of the men.

The quality of the houses began to improve as I neared the Thames and at last I came to the large, impressive house of Nicholas Diggins. It had been described so often and so well to me that I could not mistake it. It sat away from the street, behind a high, stone fence, rising to four stories. There was a wide, ornate heavy iron gate opening into a courtyard. To one side was a door in the gate which, after some hesitation, I tried and it opened under my hand. All was still within the courtyard and I stood for a long time before gaining courage enough to mount the steps and lift the large brass knocker.

3

The sound of the knocker reverberated hollowly through the house. Taking a firmer grip on my bundle, I waited. Hearing no answer, I banged it again. Finally footsteps sounded.

The door was opened by a dour, stern-faced woman clothed all in black. She had the appearance of a woman worn out by children without the pleasure of conceiving them or suffering the fulfillment of giving birth. She looked very large and forbidding.

"Master Nicholas Diggins, please ma'am," I said.

She peered at me for a long moment. Probably if I had not been so full of sorrow I would not have been able to meet her eye, but meet it I did, until she said, so harshly and abruptly that I jumped, "New apprentice, ain't it? And do you expect to be coming in the front door like a gentleman? Round to the back with you and come in the way you're supposed to." And with this kind welcome she slammed the door in my face.

Since there was little room in me for further misery, I turned and went through the courtyard to the back where a carriage house and stables of massive proportions sat as though they had been there forever and seen many such as me come and go. Finding the scullery door I put down my bag and surveyed this place that I had so often dreamed of seeing. It was even grander than I had visioned it.

As I stood forlornly looking about, a man came out of the stable carrying a pail of milk. He was a small, round man like a turnip with a fat, smooth jovial face that seemed to have never known trouble. When he came up to where I stood by the door he set down the pail and smiled at me so warmly that in spite of my unhappiness I had to smile wanly in return.

"Ah now, that's better, me lad," he said, looking at me quizzically. "From the first look ye gave I thought ye had either lost your fortune or found a wife. Could it be that you are waiting for an invitation to the castle of Master Diggins along with a royal reception?"

"I am to be apprenticed to Master Diggins," I said, my voice sounding far off even to my own ears.

"Ah now, that is a sad thing, lad, but there is that measure of trouble that must befall us all. But if the trouble begins early then the rest is bound to be better, or so I've been told. But come now, I will show you inside."

I held open the door while he carried the milk into a large kitchen. It was there I met the woman again who had greeted me at the front door. Surprisingly enough, it turned out she was the wife of the milkman.

"Molly," he said gaily, "look at what I found standing outside the scullery door looking lost and lonesome like some poor little dog that has been kicked."

"I met him already," she said. "And you will not be spoiling him, nor giving him the impression that this is a soft place. By that you will just make it all the harder for him. Now show him up to his place and get him settled before Master Diggins comes home."

I followed him up the back stair of the big house—up and up until he was puffing and blowing like a porpoise. Finally we entered a large attic room which held six or seven beds, all in a row and all neatly made up. Each bed had a small chest beside it and he showed me where to put my things, rambling on as I emptied my few belongings into the chest. Then I followed him down the stair again.

I stayed close to him for comfort as he seemed the only familiar thing in this strange world, but at the same time I was trying to think of what I would say to Master Diggins.

We went out back to the stables and he showed me around the barn, chattering away like a large and happy magpie. After a while there was the thunder of horses' hoofs on the cobblestoned street and a great wagon pulled into the yard. Out of it spilled a group of boys from my age up to near manhood. They lined up as Master Diggins descended from the front seat of the carriage.

The only other time I had seen Master Diggins he had been seated but he had impressed me as being a large man. Perhaps the stories I had heard about him made me picture him as being tall. But he was not; he was short, though heavy of frame. Master Diggins at that time was about fifty years of age. He was quick-moving in his gestures, his voice having a great firmness, giving an air of complete confidence.

He gave several orders and the boys went with the hostler to lead the horses into the stable while others emptied the wagon that appeared more like a caravan of various articles, papers and bundles. Each boy seemed to have a specific chore which he carried out with no wasted effort.

Diggins turned and started toward the house. As he came toward me he noticed me. With one quick look that covered me from head to foot, he said, "Adams?"

"Yes sir," I answered.

"Come inside." And with rapid steps he went through the door with myself half running to keep up with him. We passed through the kitchen with no more than a nod to the housekeeper, Molly, and entered a long passageway that led to the front of the house. Turning to his left he entered an enormous room containing long tables, piles of books, papers all scattered about, and many instruments for which I did not know the use.

Pulling off his hat and coat he handed them to me and went over to a table while I hung them on a rack. He ignored me for some time as he studied some papers. Then looking up, he gave a quick nod of his head, saying, "Come here, lad. I want to show you something."

I came over to look, and there on the table was a drawing of something which I could not make out. To me it looked like a long, curved platform of some sort.

"You know what this is?" he asked.

"No sir, I don't," I said.

"That, my boy, is the keel of a ship—a ship that is going to be the finest that was ever built in England."

"Yes sir," I said.

"You want to learn about ships?"

"Yes sir," I said.

"How much do you want to learn about ships?"

"I have dreamed about it for a long time, sir," I said.

He looked me up and down. "You have grown some. You'll be a big man like your father. I wish I could have had your father as an apprentice, but it may be you'll be as good a man as he in time. I hope there won't be the weakness in you I find in all the rest. Tell me, when did you arrive?"

I told him. Then all of a sudden I could hold back no longer. With words stumbling over one another I gave him the sad tale of how I had been robbed. He looked at me quickly for a minute.

"So you have no money?"

"No sir," I said.

"I don't suppose your father has any more?"

"No sir," I said.

He looked down and away, then back at me. "You know my rule. An apprentice for the first year must pay his own board and lodging."

"I could work for it, sir," I said.

"Ah, you will be working, me lad. You will be working twelve to fourteen hours a day, but that won't be providing your board and lodging. That will be paying me for what I am teaching you about shipbuilding."

There was no reply I could make to that. Not knowing what to do I just stood silent and heartsick.

He got up and walked to the window and stood there with his hands clasped behind him. After a long time he turned and faced me.

"Well, let me think about it. Have you said anything to anyone else about this?"

"No sir," I said.

"Then don't."

"I won't, sir."

"Then off with you. Find the others and ready yourself for supper. From the look of your face your stomach must be empty."

"Thank you, sir," I said, and left the room, my heart resting much easier.

4

That was the beginning, and for twelve long years I served under Master Diggins, learning much of all the arts of shipbuilding and shiphandling. He was not an easy master. One of his favorite maxims was, "You cannot reap a harvest of courage, thought and ability without the seeding and cultivating of character."

Finally there came the day when I had command of my own ship. I stood on the deck with Diggins and, on that proud moment, I reviewed the years that had gone before.

Nicholas Diggins had about thirty apprentices bound to him at the time I arrived, and over the years this number varied but little, though many came and went. By the time I had grown to manhood and finished my apprenticeship there was no one who had come all the way with me.

The six youngest apprentices lived in the attic. It was a crowded place, cold in winter and holding the heat of summer long after the sun had set. Our horseplay was held to a minimum. We were taught to keep our bed and belongings always shipshape. Those who had finished four years with Master Diggins moved to the floor below where they lived more comfortably, two to a room. After two more years the apprentices then had a room to themselves. At the end of the apprenticeship the boys who were well into manhood and working toward being shipmasters or shipbuilders were paid a small stipend and could either lodge in the big house or take lodgings in town.

The hours were long and the work hard. At first it seemed I could never find my way out of the confusion and learn anything. Those were the days when the great privateers were roaming the western seas and the trouble with Spain was building into a war. Our shipyard was always a beehive—a confusion of men, piles of sweet-smelling timber, mountains of sawdust, the acrid smell of coke fires and the odor of hot metal. Worst of all, I couldn't understand the language. Not only were most of the words and phrases unfamiliar, but the accents were like those of a foreign tongue. Yet, by the end of the first year, I learned my way about. I had been teased, sent after tools that did not exist, and on many fool's errands which made me the butt of jokes and laughter. I was not alone in this; the other apprentices were treated in the same manner.

The good part was the varied sounds and sights of the yards and of the ships abuilding. I was enamored of the skill of the men who formed the thousand parts going into the making of a ship. The giant trees brought in on ponderous wagons, cut to lengths, carved and molded to form the great keels. The huge cauldrons of steaming water where the oak was softened and bent to form the ribs; the planking for the sides, the solid decks, the rails, cabins, lockers, and all the finished work. The tall masts stepped into the ship and firmly made fast to stand the strain of the massive spreads of canvas. And then, finally, the ship fitted and standing tall in the water, proud and ready for the meeting with the seas.

There were shipbuilders in England who built ships faster than Nicholas Diggins, but those built by my master were sounder, whether they were ships of war or merchantmen, than any others. He was held in high esteem by all for his knowledge and ability.

In trying to recall names and faces of those apprentices with whom I ate and slept, worked and studied, I find most of them no more than faint shadows, their identities blending one into the other except for two whose friendship lasted for a considerable period in my life.

One was Roger Trient, the aristocrat of our group, who, in the beginning, made my life miserable. The other was Jamey Bryant, a feisty, small boy who, like me, was a new apprentice.

Trient had already been with Diggins for almost two years and was the leader of the young apprentices. Those first days were confused and lonely ones. I did not know how to make friends and when they mocked me I retreated inside myself. All of the boys came from better families than I. Trient's father held a commission in the Queen's ships. His uncle was a baronet, which in itself set him far above the rest of us. My country-like manner of speech, too, seemed to be cause for their laughter.

Jamey Bryant was also a butt, but he, being familiar with city ways, was able to meet their belligerence on their own terms. That was the basis for our friendship, and I was grateful that he made the original overtures, since I did not know how.

Though we two were opposite there came a deep bond between

us. As we grew older, Jamey's love for adventure and roaming caused us both some trouble, but through Jamey I learned the ways of the streets of London. Our characters were as dissimilar as our looks, he being short, fast of speech and wit, and I growing tall, awkward, slow-going, with a habit of thinking things out rather than talking them out.

My friendship with Roger Trient came later. But as we grew, our friendship grew so that he was like a brother to me.

Diggins was a hard taskmaster and when we were not working at the yard helping the various craftsmen, we were being taught the fundamentals of book learning. Many times my head would be anodding, or I would be dreaming of far voyages when I would find myself under the tongue of Diggins, and a sharp tongue it was.

Then, all at once, I discovered what my youth was searching for. Experiencing that, the transition from boy to man was hastened.

5

Both child and man need a woman's love. In my early years, when I needed it most, little of it ever came my way. The Puritan sect considered a show of affection a sign of weakness. When I entered my apprenticeship there was even less love to be had. Certainly none from the housekeeper, Mrs. Grandy, though she was kind enough in her own way.

Fortunately there was little time to think along these lines, the days being so full I scarcely desired anything save sleep. Diggins did his duty to God each Sunday and made sure we did the same. Returning from church, we had the heaviest and best meal of the week. Then the master rested.

Sunday afternoon was our free time to do more or less what we chose. Sometimes Bryant and I would set out adventuring through the city—sometimes to Bedlam to watch the antics of the poor mad things locked in cages, sometimes to follow the execution cart west to Tyburn Hill. Jamey delighted in these excursions but, in general, I preferred to go down to the Thames and wander up along the bank of the river where the land and the water were clean and free of the refuse of men.

It would take a wiser man than me to mark the dividing line between love and sex. In pondering it I have come to the conclusion the line moves back and forth, one time sex bringing love, and love, other times, bringing sex. In any event, of all the powers of life it is perhaps our only reason for being. It stirs and swells. There is no denying it else it cripples the soul and mind.

We were boys grouped together on the threshold of manhood and, like all boys, there was some experimenting with sex among us. There was also much talk of women. It was the one subject that could bring any ear to bear and hold attention. The older boys bragged of their experiences with the girls of the streets. Mostly imaginative, I'm afraid, but of great interest to all. We listened to each tale with open ears and with no doubting the truth of the detailed affairs.

Over the years there had been housemaids and scullery help who came and went and, I am sure, more than one apprentice had been taught the secret by them. But I never had the courage to even think about them until, during my fourteenth year, a new girl came to the house as scullery maid.

She was fresh from the country with a clean look to her, and this, to my mind, was in itself attractive. I could never accustom myself to dirt or the smell of dirty people. Her name was Harriet and, though shy of manner, she was already developed into a woman.

We all noticed her firm breasts and rounded hips and there were some comments made by various of the apprentices of what they would do could they be alone with her. Mrs. Grandy complained several times about the boys loitering around the kitchen. I, too, dreamed of being alone with her but never expected it to be a reality.

It was a Sunday afternoon. The house was quiet. Diggins was asleep and the older apprentices were off to the city, the younger ones playing a game of bowls in the rear courtyard. I had been in my room trying to work on a problem in mathematics. It was hot and, finding the water jug empty, I went to the scullery to refill it.

Master Diggins had a theory that water needed to be cooked to remove any poison from it. This seemed to be true, as we hardly ever suffered from fevers as did others in the city. We were forbidden to drink from the well but had to take the water from a cistern in the scullery after it had been boiled.

I came down in my bare feet and opened the door to the scullery and found the new maid standing in a wooden pail of water, washing herself. The light in the room was dim but a small shaft of sunshine coming from the window lay across her hair and shoulder, bringing to light the airy blond sheen of it and lighting one round breast. I stood for a long moment, breathless and entranced until she happened to look up. Our eyes met and I could feel the flame spread to my face. The water jug dropped from my hand. The sound of it breaking startled both of us. She covered herself with the washcloth and gave a cry of dismay, and I turned and fled.

In the safety of the attic room I stood for a long time. In my mind's eye she still stood there like a nymph in the loveliness of her youth. Throwing myself on the bed, I buried my face in the pillow, but finding no relief I jumped up and left the house to go down to the Thames. I wandered through the fields along the river bank until I came to a dell where the water from the river backed up to form a pool.

Stripping, I plunged in, letting the cold water lave me until the fever abated. For a time then I forgot the girl by reverting to the youthful pastime of diving deep and trying to catch the lazy carp with my hands.

After a long time my body was still and at peace with itself. I dressed and wandered back. In crossing the field, a patch of bright blue cornflowers caught my eye. I hesitated, then defiantly picked a bunch and carried them home. No one was about. I peeped into the scullery and, finding it empty, quickly ducked inside and put the flowers on a bench out of sight where I knew she would find them. The act was instinctive, with no planning behind it. After it was done I felt somewhat foolish, but excited nonetheless.

It was not until the end of the week that I saw Harriet again, though she was often in my mind. Living in the same house this would seem strange, but the house of Nicholas Diggins was no ordinary dwelling. The work done by the women—the cooking, cleaning, laundry and such household chores—went on during the day when we were at our own work. They were not participants in the life we led. The front of the house and the rooms were for us. The quarters for the women were above the kitchen and scullery.

Almost our only contact with the kitchen were certain duties done by the younger boys, such as filling the wood box in the kitchen, bringing logs for the fireplace and hauling in water. All of these chores I had done in my turn but now I had been promoted to taking care of the large front workroom where Master Diggins had his drawing boards, instruments, books, papers and souvenirs. This was a position of trust and everything had to be kept in strict order. The fine brush he used in his drawing had to be washed and dried. The charcoals he used had to be lined up, the quills sharpened and ready by the inkpot, paper at hand, along with his tobacco and pipes. Diggins had learned the use of tobacco from the voyagers who introduced it to London. A strange habit it appeared to us.

It was during a lecture in the evening on a problem in navigation. I was not paying attention and Diggins noted this. He always caught us when our attentions would wander.

"Adams!"

I lurched to my feet. "Sir?"

"Was not the new cross staff brought in?"

There was a silence, then I spoke up. "No, sir. I forgot it."

"Adams, you are dreaming too much," Diggins said, looking at me levelly, and with that he sent me to the carriage house to bring the cross staff inside.

As I came out I found Harriet carrying a heavy bucket of water toward the scullery. She hesitated as she saw me, then continued with her bucket. I caught up with her quickly and took it from her, though, in truth, I think she was stronger than I at the time.

"Why are you carrying water?" I asked.

"The boy forgot to fill the cistern," she said shyly.

"I will speak to him about that," I said as though I was master of the house.

"Thank you, sir," she said as I handed her the bucket at the door.

My heart swelled. That was the first time I had ever been called "sir." From her lips it held an added sweetness. Later, I found she thought me older, or so she told me; this pleased me much, as I was impatient for the years to pass me into manhood.

When I came back in, Master Diggins computed the distance between the room and the carriage house and return compared with the time it had taken me.

"Our learned mathematician, Mr. Adams, has not found practical use yet of the theory that the shortest distance between two points is a straight line," he said caustically.

My dazed condition must have been apparent, for after the lecture Diggins called me to the front and asked if I was not feeling well."

"Why, no sir. I am fine."

He looked at my eyes, put his hand to my head to see if I had a fever and told me to go off to bed. I insisted I was well and would take care of straightening the room, but he would have none of it.

Now I was in a fever for the days to pass and for it to be Sunday, and when Sunday finally came I could hardly sit through the service at church and the long meal after.

This, too, brought me to the eye of Diggins, as I had never before shown any lack of appetite and Sunday's meal was the one we all looked forward to.

Diggins had a worried look as he called me into his study before taking his Sunday nap. He looked searchingly at me and I was afraid he had discovered my secret. He shook his head slightly.

"You don't look right, William. Perhaps you have been working too hard."

"Oh, I feel fine, sir," I said, perhaps too quickly.

"London is full of sickness. I think it best this afternoon you rest rather than overheat yourself with play."

"Yes, sir. And thank you, sir," I said, and left to go upstairs. But there was neither calm nor peace within me. I could hardly contain myself and when Bryant came in with some plan of adventuring about the streets, I refused, offending him somewhat.

"God's blood, Will," he said. "You don't have to bite my head off. Keep studying like this and you will wear your brain out before you ever get a chance to use it."

I had a book open in front of me as if I meant to study. I said nothing, impatiently waiting for him to leave. He shuffled around for a moment.

"Well, you won't go. Then I'm off by myself. But it's no way for a friend to act," he said, offended.

He then left me, much to my relief. When the house was quiet I went downstairs and into the kitchen, but with my boots on this time, making enough noise so I couldn't be accused of behaving stealthily.

She was waiting there, busying herself with some small task as I hoped she would be. She even made a pretense of being a little startled.

"I came for water," I said awkwardly, then added, "Do they still have you working?"

"Oh no, sir," she said quickly as though expecting me to find fault with the housekeeper. "I'm all done, sir."

We stood for a moment facing each other. She was so young and lovely. I remarked about what a nice day it was. She agreed. Having no experience to call upon, I knew not what to say. I was enchanted by the pretty picture she made leaning against the mixing board by the window.

"Have you been through the field and down to the river yet?" I asked. "There are some fine fair places to bathe." Then I blushed at the memory of last week and she did also.

"No, sir," she said. "I have been nowhere since coming to London. I thought it would be so grand, but everything frightens me. I am afraid to go out on the streets; ruffians follow me and make rude remarks."

"If it would please you to see the river, I would walk with you."

"Oh, no," she said. "It is forbidden that we should go out together."

"We could go out separately and meet in back, in the fields," I said, and so she agreed.

The day was one of those bright days that come with England's summer; the sun dazzling but not too hot. The fields were not far away from the city and the woods beyond were of many pleasing shades of green.

Once over her shyness, it was as if a dam had broken. We walked together and she talked mostly. She had been born on a farm near Southampton, one of many children. Her mother's sister was in service in the city and was a friend of Mrs. Grandy. Through this connection she had gotten her job, but it was not at all as she had expected. She told me of once when, in her innocence of city ways, she had set out to visit her aunt. She had gone but a short distance up the street when men made obscene remarks to her. Then, coming nearer, they even attempted to take hold of her. Her obvious fright made them yet bolder until she turned and ran. They had chased her right to the gate of the house. Since then she had gone out only once, in the company of the housekeeper.

I was angered by her story; but at the same time it made me feel protective toward her. She took off her bonnet and swung it by the string, and I was so taken by the look of her I hardly heard another word she said. In helping her over a stile I reached up to take her hand. When we went on again I held her hand and the day was so sweet that my chest ached with the joy of it.

We started along the river bank, I leading the way, for I knew the path and how to stay out of sight of the cottages and the small habitations that lay close to the river.

I showed her the dell and the pool where I bathed. With some hesitation she was persuaded to go in. I stood guard while she splashed about. My back was toward her, my body much heated by the sound of her in water. When she emerged and dressed I went in to swim. When I came out she was gone. I called out softly, and when there was no answer I was sure she had gone home.

My heart was heavy, the day no longer bright. Then I saw her head appear for a moment above the tall grass where she had hidden. I hurried over, first making sure no one was in sight, and dropped down beside her.

She had not dressed, but just put on her shift. She was lying on her back with one white forearm covering her eyes as if in sleep. I sat looking at her, at a loss to do or say anything. After a time she took her arm away and looked at me. Her eyes were large and dark, the pupils distended so that there was almost a blind look about them. She reached up and touched my face and I leaned forward and clumsily kissed her, then buried my head in her soft shoulder.

Her hair was soft and damp and her skin had the odor of fresh milk. We lay together that way for a long time, still, unmoving. Then she stirred and said, "What's the matter? Is it that you do not like me?"

"I love you," I whispered; then, after a moment, confessed, "I know not what to do next."

Without words she showed me. That first time I thought surely I was dying. But I did not and it was as if some great weight had been taken from my shoulders. That day, in that green field outside of London, I made the transition from boy to man and I have been ever grateful to Harriet Grisham.

6

What happened later was inevitable. Had I been older, had I more knowledge, I might have been able to keep the secret longer. But once having tasted the delights of love, my whole mind was now centered on ways and means of seeing Harriet to the exclusion of all else. There were too many days between Sundays and not enough hours on a Sunday afternoon to satisfy my desires.

I took to staying awake until everyone was sleeping. Then I would sneak down to the tiny cubbyhole that was her room, only returning to my bed when dawn was breaking. For the first few days this did not bother me overmuch, but shortly my mind and body cried so for sleep that I began sneaking away from work to hide and sleep, even if only for a few minutes.

Such actions could not go unnoticed for long. Master Diggins being a man of great shrewdness, it did not take him long to arrive at the answer once he had noticed my actions. He said nothing to me nor questioned me. I, being so involved, gave no thought to him nor paid any mind to the quips and snickers and sidelong glances of the other apprentices.

The end came one night and I have long believed that Diggins had the kindness to let us finish with our love-making before breaking the spell. We were whispering to each other when the door opened. Master Diggins stood in the doorway with a candle casting lights and shadows on his stern face.

I was so shocked and frightened that I would have run for cover if there had been any place to run. Harriet grabbed the covers and pulled them over her face.

Diggins stood there for a long time looking at me, then said, "Up you go, William. Off to your room."

I stumbled out of bed and into my britches. "It was not her fault, sir," I mumbled after the first moment of fright had worn off. "She was sleeping and I came to her room."

"That's enough, William. I said off to your room."

I stood for a moment holding my shirt and boots in my hand. Under the bedclothes Harriet was sobbing so it tore at my heart.

33

I started to reach out to her but Diggins took me roughly by the shoulder and shoved me out of the room.

Heartsick, I went upstairs and crawled into bed and tried to think of what to do. We would run away together, I thought, and somewhere, somehow we would find a life of our own. Thinking thus soothed me a little and, I must confess, I fell into a deep sleep. The next thing I knew it was morning. And as fate would have it, it was the morning we had all been looking forward to for months. A new ship of the line, the *Rainbow*, built for Her Majesty, was finished with her sea trials and was to be turned over to the Navy that day. The Queen with all the court were to be down for the ceremony.

Every ship built in those days was important to England, as Spain was crowding more and more upon England and upon the men whom she called pirates. We in England called them heroes.

It was a day of celebration for which we had all waited in anticipation, and now to me it was the day of direst trouble.

I worried about what would happen to me, but more of what would happen to Harriet. Diggins had a cold attitude where women were concerned. He felt they had a necessary function but their lives were distinctly apart from the work and world of men.

All appeared normal at breakfast, we apprentices standing until Master Diggins came in, prompt as usual, and took his seat. He did not so much as glance at me. That morning, even asking the Lord's blessing seemed to take much longer than usual. I kept glancing up at him where he sat at the head of the table. He paid no attention to me.

I hung back, trying to have a word with him after the meal, but was ordered to go about my duties and prepare for the ceremony.

I felt the need to talk about this to someone, but Bryant, though he was my only close friend, would, I knew, treat my trouble with laughter. I felt this was nothing to laugh about because the pleasure I had had from Harriet had been something sweet and fine, not a thing either to brag of or to mock. I was thoroughly miserable and, after we were all dressed, unable to contain myself any longer, I went to look for Diggins.

He was in the large room with a number of merchants and naval officers and he gave me a look of thunder when I asked if I could speak to him alone.

He came out to the hall, closed the door behind him and then went to stand by the window, his hands clasped tightly behind his back. He was dressed for the ceremony, in a great ruff collar, short doublet, and the short balloon breeches of some striped material that was the current style. The white stockings he wore were of the finest linen. He looked solid and handsome there and I did admire him greatly but I had to say what I had come to say.

"I am sorry to disturb you, sir, but I must speak with you!"

"Well, get on with it."

"Sir, what has happened to her?"

He looked at me in anger. "William, I have treated you like a son and have been proud at the way you have developed, but I order you now to speak no more of this thing. Leave now and go about your duties or, by God's blood, I will send you packing back to the farm and the life of a clodhopper!"

There was nothing I could say in the face of his anger, so I bowed slightly and backed away. When he had returned to his company I ran below to the kitchen. I got no more satisfaction here than from Diggins. The housekeeper shoved me out before I could so much as ask a question and Mrs. Grandy, in her own right, was as formidable as Diggins when she was crossed.

By that time everyone was gathered outside by the carriage for Diggins' inspection, and in deep and heartfelt misery I went to join them, not knowing what else to do. I felt helpless, a fool, guilty, and there seemed no alternative but to go.

The last thing I wanted was to go home a failure to my father, nor did I want to leave Nicholas Diggins. Stern and distant as he was, my respect for him was unbounded.

That day was a long one. It seemed to stretch interminably. The pageantry, the sight of Queen Bess and the men and women around her dressed like peacocks held no interest for me. I was besieged by my woes and had neither the weapons nor the wit to dispel them.

The day over, Diggins did not return with us and I found the door to the kitchen barred against me. Next morning he called me in, and what he said then seemed harsh and cruel.

"William," he said among other things, "one of the great dangers of being a man is to let a woman trap you by the penis and, by it, hold you in bondage. You are no more than a baby as yet. Do not think I am not aware of what pain this has caused you. I hope a lesson learned so young will help you avoid pitfalls later. I have hopes for you. I was doubly surprised to find *you* in such a situation. In general, you have more sense than most but you have been growing fast, faster than I realized."

I listened as patiently as I could but finally blurted, "But what is to happen to her?"

He waved his hand as if it was a stupid question not deserving an answer. "She has been sent home, of course, and there will be no more pretty girls hired in this house. I have no intent to provide doxies for my apprentices."

"But she was not at fault, sir. It was I—"

In complete exasperation he turned on me. "Adams, pack your things. You will leave here this afternoon for your home. I will let you know in a fortnight whether you are to return or not. If I decide to let you return, then make damned sure that your mind is clear of this girl. I will have no more of it. You are here to work, study, and learn. If you cannot give full attention to your duties then there is no room in my house for you. When your things are packed Mistress Grandy will give you a shilling for the coach. That is all. You can go." And sternly he turned away from me.

As I packed my few belongings the world looked bleak. I dreaded what my father would say, after all the dreams he had built on me. I thought of finding a berth on a merchant ship. It would have been the easy way out of this situation, but my love for my father was too strong for me to leave like that, though I knew he would not condemn me.

I had been given the shilling and a letter addressed to my father. All through the long ride to Gillingham I wondered what was in the letter and whether or not Diggins had ended the relationship then and there.

I had never seen Master Diggins so angry as when he had sent me packing. If this door closed on me then I knew there would be no others to open. In England a man seldom steps above the position he is born to and I was old enough to know what a great opportunity had been given me. Now it seemed I had ruined everything. As to Harriet, I knew there was no hope there at all. In fact, by then, I had reached the point where I wished I had never seen her.

All men pass through days of darkness and trouble and worry. I have had many, but never a worse day than that one.

7

It was dark by the time the coach reached Gillingham. I was let out in front of the Inn of the White Bull to a lonely village. The small light by the tavern was the sole illumination in the entire place.

I shouldered my bundle and with no trouble walked up the dark lane toward our farm, my feet having made the journey so many times. On reaching home I stood outside the fence which encircled our garden, feeling lost and helpless. I had made several trips home before now, but this one was different. Then the moon emerged from behind a cloud and, at the same time, Buff, our dog, came around the corner of the house. Seeing me there, he bristled at first, then with a happy yelp of recognition he ran to me and all at once I felt better. When I opened the gate he whined and jumped around me until I had to kneel and hug his rough coat to my face.

From inside the house there was a stirring and a dip was lit. The door opened and my father peered out, tall and gaunt in the doorway.

"Who is there?" he called.

"It is I, Father."

"Well, Will! My boy." And with one arm he embraced me and drew me inside. "Ah, let me look at you, lad. My lord, how you have grown." He held me off with one hand on my shoulder and there was love and pride in his look.

It was true I had grown a great deal in the past year. Our eyes were now almost at a level. I was to grow a great deal more before I was finished. We stood looking at each other and I was struck with how old and careworn he seemed, but thought it was perhaps because of the light and shadows thrown by the dip he held.

The noise woke my mother and she called out a question.

" 'Tis Will come home, Mary."

"Will?"

"Yes, Mother," and putting down my belongings I went in to her. She gave me her cheek to kiss and held my hand for a moment. I had hoped she would give me a warmer welcome, but she released my hand.

"It is late, Will. Too late to be standing around chattering. Off to bed with thee and we can talk in the morning. Send thy father in else he will be up all night talking."

"Good night, Mother," I said.

The cottage was small, being no more than two rooms and a little attic reached by a ladder that was put out of the way when not in use. My father pressed my shoulder affectionately and held the light for me as I climbed up to where my younger brother, Thomas, lay sleeping. Father then said good night and left me in darkness, but in that familiar small attic I needed no light. I was very tired. Undressing quickly, I heaved Thomas over from where he lay sprawled. He did not waken, but made some soft noise and continued his uninterrupted breathing.

Tired as I was, I lay a long time thinking, my mind going around in circles until finally I drifted off into an uneasy sleep.

The next morning I went to the field where Father and Thomas were already at work. Father stopped and smiled and wiped his forehead when he saw me coming. I was struck again at how much he had aged since last I saw him.

"Good morning, Will. I see you brought a hoe. Put it down, you should rest. Thomas and I can manage this well enough."

Thomas looked over at me and smiled shyly. He was about eight years old at that time and we hardly knew each other.

"I am used to work, Father. It's good to get out in the fields again." I breathed deeply of the fresh clean air. I had left my shoes at the house and now, taking up my hoe, I worked with my father and brother in close and friendly silence until we had chopped our way down one row and back another.

I noticed from time to time that my father would stop and press his hand to his side for a moment as if in pain. Finally, at the end of a row, we put down our hoes and went over to sit on a bank beneath the shade of a large tree.

"Have you been ill, Father? You don't look well."

He scoffed. "No. There's a twitch in my gut that bothers me some. But it is nothing." He smiled at me in warm welcome. "I was surprised to see you home so early. How are things with Master Diggins?"

I looked away from him and down to my feet. "I have a letter for you from Diggins, Father."

He held it for a moment, turning it this way and that, then handed it back to me.

"You read it for me, Will."

Not knowing what to expect, I broke the seal with trembling fingers and glanced over the contents. It was short and abrupt, just like Diggins; he was not a man to waste words.

Dear Adams:
William has a problem troubling his mind which I hope a fortnight at home will settle one way or another for him.

My father sat peeling a willow stick as he pondered the contents of the letter. Thomas sat quietly some distance away.

"Master Diggins makes it sound as if you have a serious trouble, son. Do you want to tell me about it?"

"It is a girl, Father." Looking at his face as I said that, I could see the worry go out of it.

"Girl? Well now, let us see. You must be about the age for that. And who is this girl?"

"She's a maid, Father, in the employ of Master Diggins. He found out and he sent her packing." I told him part of the story then, omitting intimate details.

He did not pass it off lightly, but took it with the proper solemnity.

"It would seem to me, William, the best thing to do would be to leave it lie for a day or two until your mind is settled. Then we will talk it over and decide what is to be done. Master Diggins is a man of firm character and we must not forget what it would mean to your future if you left your apprenticeship now."

And so it was left. We worked in the fields, my strength was running strong and new inside me so that I had to slow down continually to keep from forging ahead of my father. Thomas and I went swimming in the evenings. We would walk over to Chatham where the big men o' war lay and there, boylike and proudly, I showed off my knowledge of them as to their size, guns and type while Thomas gazed at me with obvious hero worship.

The days passed quickly and, under the sun and the country air and familiar things, my heart began to heal. Then something happened on the twelfth day that colored my view of religion for all my days to come, making me also to believe that there is something akin to madness in love.

The Inn of the White Bull was a warm and friendly place holding always the odor of roasting beef, of fowl and all manner of good eatables blending with that of wine and beer—a place of laughter and the voices of men.

The innkeeper was a great, bluff and hearty man, as English as any Englishman could be, though his was a foreign name, being Monserat. I had never known his wife, as she died before I could remember. Monserat had a daughter, a lovely, dark beauty. It had always been a joy to walk to the tavern with my father where I would sit and watch Olympia's quick and graceful movements, her smile, and listen to the quips which brought laughter from the customers.

How she had ever come to know, let alone love Francis Ormsby, was one of those mysterious things that is without reason or sense. Ormsby was a morose and brooding man, belonging to the same Puritan group as my mother and filled with the teachings of Calvin. He was that type of fanatic that turns the teachings of God into a dark and dreadful thing.

Their love, somehow, had grown in secret, though what sort of love it was I cannot imagine. The first I knew of it was when we came home from the fields one evening and found Olympia Monserat sitting in our kitchen with a bundle at her feet and a most woebegone countenance.

Father was unable to conceal his surprise at her presence in our home. The tavern keeper's daughter was of the "devil's blight," in the opinion of my mother.

My mother, looking as happy as I had ever seen her, explained her presence.

"Olympia has broken from her life of sin. She hath now come to God, casting all evil from her. And Brother Ormsby hath consented to take her to wife."

My father looked from one to the other in complete stupefaction as if unable to believe his ears. "Ormsby? In the name of heaven, why?"

"Use not blasphemy in our house, John," Mother said sternly.

"Blasphemy? The blasphemy is the thought of her with him. Olympia, does your father know of this?"

"I left word," she whispered.

Just then Ormsby came to the door and was let inside. He was dressed in somber black and when Olympia ran to him I could see not even a fleeting expression of pleasure in his face. She tried to embrace him but was gently disengaged.

"Francis, we must hurry before Father comes."

"Worry not. God hath sent thee to me and thou art under His care."

From outside came heavy footsteps and the deep voice of Monserat calling his daughter's name."

"Let not that man in this house, John," my mother commanded.

My father, as if dazed, went to the door and I followed behind, Thomas holding on to my shirt sleeve. Leaning on our gate, Edward Monserat stood all out of breath.

"John, my daughter—have you seen her?"

My father walked slowly over and opened the gate. "She is here."

"Do you know what madness she thinks of?" From his pocket he took a crumpled paper.

Father nodded. Monserat looked at him, searching his face as if there was some answer to his confusion. "But how can this happen? When? Why? Let me speak to her, John." And Monserat started to push by.

My father took his arm gently and said, "I will bring her to you, Edward."

I stood and watched. From inside came voices and, after some considerable time, my father came out leading Olympia by the hand. She seemed greatly frightened, which surprised me, as her father had always loved her, perhaps even more than is good for a father to love his child.

"Olympia," he said and held out his arms. But she didn't come.

"Olympia, what madness are you about?"

"I love him, Father. Don't you understand? I love him."

"Love? Do you think, Olympia, that I am beyond the point where I remember what love is like? I know love only too well. But to love is not enough. Believe me, life and love must live together and his life and your life are too different to be made over." Anger came into his voice then as he said, "With lighter heart would I see you love a befuddled drunkard, for worse than a drunkard is this man."

"I will not listen, Father." And she covered her ears with her hands.

He fell silent then, as if knowing defeat. "Bring him out and let me speak with him."

"He will not speak with you, Father, for he says you are damned."

"Damned? I am a decent man. Never in all my life have I with malice hurt or harmed anyone."

"You persecute them, Father."

"Persecute? No. Dislike, yes. Stand against their teachings, always. For what would they do to me, to all England, to Englishmen? They would destroy our right as free men, forcing us to their distorted belief. They would close the theaters, the fairs, the taverns. Nor, if they had their way, would they allow the pleasure of a dance, or a man to travel on Sunday. And why? Because, say I, they are mad. And this black crow of a man? What can he give you of love when he believes that beauty itself is evil? Take for husband the swineherd, or anyone to be husband rather than this distortion of a man."

"I have sinned, Father, and he will help me to repent."

"He says this? Say I that *he* is the sinner. He who sees evil in everything beautiful that God has made must be of the devil and do the devil's work. For God is good and what He has made is good —the sun and the wind, and song, and your own beauty, these are God's work. And if he sees evil in these things then surely he is the one who is damned."

As he said these words Ormsby came to the door with my mother just behind. At the sight of him such fury came over Monserat that he lunged forward like a bull. Olympia stepped between them with her hands against his chest. Without stopping he lifted both fists and brought them down on her head like a hammer. She fell beneath the blow, all crumpled and broken.

With a cry, which was more emotion, I believe, than Ormsby had ever shown in his life, he fell to his knees and cradled her head in his arms. But the force of the blow had broken her neck and, like a man already dead, Monserat turned and stumbled off. I, taking Thomas by the hand, turned and fled with him across the field.

There we sat, I trying to comfort him. Yet I had no answer then or later to explain man's violence to others. All I could do was hold him and try to still his trembling. Darkness and hunger finally drove us home. We found all the village awake and milling about as if enjoying the tragedy.

8

The death of Olympia Monserat stirred the surrounding countryside, and, as anger grew, sides were taken. Friends became enemies and Olympia seemed almost forgotten in the controversy as to which religion was right. The Puritans cried murder against Edward Monserat. He was taken to prison, and the hatred of those in the established church mounted against the Puritans.

In our own house the bitterness between my father and mother that had grown over the years now increased so that there was no happiness at all in that small cottage. Whatever their love had been when they were young had long since died by the conflict so common to all mankind, the disagreement over good and evil.

Men congregated in front of the closed tavern and let their hatred feed on words. The Puritans, in turn, gathered grim and tight-lipped at meetings and prayed steadfastly to God to punish the evildoers.

Seeing all about me this hatred, confusion and anger, I longed with all my heart to return to the ordered life of my apprenticeship. I could not sleep from the terror that filled me. What if Diggins refused to take me back?

On the fourteenth day a letter arrived. In my eagerness I opened it even before I showed it to my father. It contained but a few lines stating the hope that two weeks of country air had rested me and cleared my mind and that I was now prepared to return to my studies.

Now it was far different from the first time we had waited for the London coach. There was happiness instead of fear in me, though my father's worn and troubled face tore at my heart so that I wished I could give him comfort.

When the time was come he gripped my hand. "God bless and keep you, William. Work hard so that you may rise above meanness and poverty. I only wish that Thomas could go along with you."

"I will do my best, Father." And releasing his hand I turned to say good-by to Thomas, hiding the tears that were close behind my eyes. Then the coach was away and I didn't look back.

Life changed for me then. It was as if nature, having completed my body, had put to test my organs and, once proved, they became dormant while my mind took all my energy. Where before my mind had become sluggish, it was now sharp. Problems that previously I had struggled over, seeming as if beyond my understanding, now became easy. From time to time in those first weeks there came sharp stabs of conscience and, several times during the nights, I would awaken with the memory of Harriet's soft, joyful body. But that was soon forgotten and I felt free as I had never been before.

That same year I had my first taste of a ship and the sea and it was as if I had finally come home. The sea has different faces for different men. To some it is cruel, with an unbearable monotony, a dreadful wasteland. To other men, myself among them, it has a beauty which enthralls and binds.

The feel of a ship and the sea was like the first kiss of a lovely woman. The crowded quarters, the hardship, the cold and wet meant nothing. I accepted as if they did not exist the discomforts that to others were unbearable.

Four of us were selected to sail as extra midshipmen on a new ship which was to go on a shakedown cruise along the Channel ports. Jamey Bryant, Roger Trient, and an apprentice named Wilson were selected. Both Bryant and Wilson came to hate the sea. Trient was of my mind, at home and happy with the ship and the sea.

The cruise was longer than intended. We ran stores and arms to the Dutch who had begun their rebellion against Philip of Spain, then we cruised the Channel in company of other ships, lying in port during the winter months. It was spring before we returned to London.

When I returned to Diggins' house it seemed to have shrunk in proportion to how I had grown. I stood then over six feet, and though there was not much weight to me, I was strong.

Diggins gave us as warm a welcome as his dignity would permit. When we had talked awhile he dismissed the other three saying he wished a word with me.

This pleased me, as I wanted permission to return to Gillingham as soon as possible to describe to my father, in person, the things I had seen and done. To Thomas, also, I would stand as a hero.

"William," Diggins said, "bad news is something no man likes to be the bearer of. I could have written you but there would have been little point, as it was already done and you would have grieved."

I couldn't imagine what he meant, though I was afraid, for his voice was very serious.

"What is it, sir?" I asked.

"Your father, William. He died during the winter."

"Dead? Dead? From what, sir?"

"Who knows, Will? Work, perhaps. Whatever it was, dead he is and you owe him a great debt, William, because he was a rare, good man."

It was a terrible blow—so terrible that I remained calm, even in my mind.

"I had best go to my mother, sir. She may need help."

"William, I am sorry. After your father died your mother went off to Holland with a Puritan group. They intend to form a colony somewhere in the Americas. They had a ship."

"Was there not a message left for me, sir?"

"Yes. I talked with her. She feels that your life, having already made its pattern, should go on as it is."

I knew these were not the words my mother had used. I tried not to feel bitter, for that was the way she was. I couldn't change her. For Thomas I felt a great pity. He would be small and lonely in that stern group of people. In time, though, the wound healed and that was the end of that part of my life.

9

I have ever been of the opinion that one of the great joys of life is when the mind is opened to learning. Once this happens, the thirst for knowledge can become almost like a fever.

Those few of us who were left now entered a period of study under Diggins, himself. Most of that which was taught was practical, though twice a week we were sent to the academy to be taught Latin and Greek by Master John Burroughs, and a most arid and pedantic man he was. At first I could see no value in these dry and ancient languages, yet learning the basic roots was to stand me in good stead in later years.

I did have an itch to be off to sea to make my fortune, as those squadrons under Drake, Hawkins and other privateers brought great wealth to England. Diggins, however, persuaded me against this foolish adventure. He spoke to me like a father.

"William," he said, "before you came to me your father spoke often of the ambition he held for you. These are good times for sailing the sea but it will not always be so. It seems, for sailors, it is always either a feast or a famine. Now we are taking the wealth of Spain. This is madness. It cannot last. It will either come to war or this privateering will be halted. Whatever trouble lies ahead, though, it will be resolved; and when times come bad, remember this, Will. Only the best of mariners will find a berth. I know your blood now runs hot, but you are just at the threshold of knowledge. Stay. Learn as much as I can teach you."

Placing his hand on my shoulder, he looked kindly at me. "You have a good head, Will, and I feel toward you as your father did. When you feel impatient, look at Roger Trient, who has a family with position high enough to obtain a commission for him. Yet he has taken his father's advice and stays."

This was not entirely true. Roger had the same itch as I, yet he had to obey his father. I felt, at first, I had no one to reckon with. In thinking it over, though, I stayed, for I did owe a great deal to Diggins. In taking my mind from the dream of wandering I settled down to study, thereby showing I was somewhat nearer to becoming a man.

Now the doors to the world opened about me. Diggins was a learned man and had access to many of the great private libraries including the Bodleian, and through ancient and obscure works we learned much of mankind's continual search for the limits of the expanding world. It was exciting to be alive during the time the world was giving up the secrets of unknown lands and its vastness.

In my mind's eye I can still see Diggins standing before us, imparting his own excitement in talking of the men who, one by one, added to the knowledge we now hold. He went all the way back, from the first cadastral surveys of property boundaries measured for tax purposes in ancient Egypt. Some of these surveys went back to the dawn of history. He told us of how Eratosthenes covered distances between Syrene and Alexandria to determine the length of a degree. His measurements showed a degree to have a length of seven hundred stadia; one stadia being equal to two hundred steps. Of Anaximander, born six hundred years before the birth of our Lord, who made the first map of the world. Anaximander thought of the world as a cylinder, suspended from the vault of the heavens.

The ancient Greeks considered the world to be a circular disk. Later, the men of that nation, including Aristotle, proved the world to be a sphere. The Egyptians of those times also considered the earth a sphere. Yet this was but a theory they could not prove.

We copied maps by Hacataeus and studied his geography, which was known as the *Periodus*. Hecataeus' maps depicted the earth as a disk with only two continents, Europe to the north and Asia to the south, all rimmed about by the vast ocean. When we laughed at the crudity of it, Master Diggins said:

"Remember this, knowledge of any sort does not come full-blown, but is added little by little, by many men, and it is a wondrous thing to see how the horizons have expanded. Remember this too, that long before the Spaniards proved the fact the world is round, Aristotle proved it by three observations: first, that matter tends to fall toward the common center; second, by observing that only a sphere could throw a circular shadow on the moon during an eclipse; and third, he pointed out that the shifting horizon and the appearance of new constellations or the disappearance of familiar constellations proved the hypothesis that the earth was a sphere. The one thing he could not do, and that Columbus did by ship, was to fit the habitable world into the shape of a sphere."

We could see Phyteus developing his theory of a parallel by giving the dimension of latitude, or Sicanearcus of Sicily discovering the equatorial line which he called the *diaphragm*, which divided the world into a northern and southern half. I pictured the surveyors who accompanied Alexander, pacing off distances and drawing their maps. And Ptolemy, the greatest of all, who, with his court mathematicians and geographers, found the prime meridian and summed up the then existent knowledge of the shape and location of the earth.

Ptolemy drew the prime meridian through the Fortunate Islands, and his equator was divided into 360 degrees. The collecting of the existent determinations of the latitude and longitude of places included all the then known distances by land or sea.

Diggins told us of how Columbus used the works of Aristotle

and the measurements of Ptolemy to explain to Ferdinand and Isa-
bella the correctness of his plan to reach India by westward voyage.

Diggins, himself, had translated Vasco da Gama's record of his
voyages. Da Gama had found that the pilots of India had charts
showing parallels measured by a pilot star with relation to the calves
of the Little Bear and the barrel of the Great Bear. Their meridians
were drawn at intervals of a *zam*, the zam being equal to three hours'
sailing time. Yet there was so much still unknown and the only true
maps and sailing directions we had were those of the portolano,
drawn by the Turkish geographers and mathematicians, covering all
of the area of the Mediterranean.

So many things to learn and such a great time in which to live.
For fourteen hundred years the world had been banded by narrow
dimensions. Here, in one hundred and fifty years, we had learned
more than all fifteen hundred years before. Perhaps some day mankind, by some unknown means, will have a chance to reach outward
toward the stars. If this should come to pass it will be no more exciting than my time when ship after ship sailed out on voyages of discovery.

We learned the history of the compass, which, though new to us,
had been known in the East for twice a thousand years. With this
prime instrument we now had the ability to know direction regardless whether the sun, moon or stars were obscured.

Each man added his bit or piece to knowledge. Columbus, on
discovering the compass was affected by the magnetism of the earth,
corrected his errors in navigation by taking bearings on the Pole Star
and also by bearings of the sun at sunrise and sunset.

In our classroom, we sailed again the voyages of discovery, following by their logbooks that from day to day told the story. We
learned to use the cross staff, an instrument that Ptolemy and the
navigators of that time had used to measure the altitude of the heavenly bodies.

The cross staff is but two sticks arranged at right angles to each
other, the horizontal staff being thirty-six inches long and the vertical staff twenty-six and a half inches. The vertical staff is so arranged that it can slide back and forth upon the horizontal staff,
the end of the horizontal staff being the sight.

By looking through the sight on the horizontal staff and sliding
the vertical staff back and forth until the upper side of the vertical

staff is in line with the heavenly body, and simultaneously in align-
ment with the horizon through the lower side of the vertical staff,
the observer's eye can read the arc. The lower and upper ends of the
vertical staff can then be read off from the horizontal staff, which is
calibrated in degrees and thus used to find the position.

We learned the use of the astrolabe, a circular disk with the upper
left quadrant calibrated in degrees, the lower right quadrant calibrated so that the two readings, one a check upon the other, could
be taken. Three of us were necessary to make observations with the
astrolabe, one to hold the instrument in the vertical plane of the
meridian; the second, to take the sight; and the third one, to read it
off. Since the highest altitude of the sun is found at noon, our observations would start a little before noon until the sun began to dip,
and, taking our readings, we would consult our table of the sun's
declination and deduce the ecliptic. It was not an easy instrument
to use, and, more than once, in taking our computations, instead of
our vessel in theory being somewhere off the Spanish coast, we
would find ourselves hard and fast aground in Wales.

All of these things were gained by traveling the hard road of learning, and I was more fortunate than most, having a facility and affin-
ity for both mathematics and the instruments used in navigation.

Since those days of study, other advances have been made. In
1581, from France, came another instrument, the nocturnal, by
which the relation of two stars, called the Guards, and the Little
Bear, farthest from the Pole Star, could be measured. By a table
showing eight positions, either by addition or subtraction, the altitude could be found.

In 1594, my good friend, John Davis, invented the back staff,
which was a great aid to navigators though, by then, I was far beyond
my apprenticeship and had some reputation of my own as a pilot.

The days and years passed, and on my eighth year of apprenticeship there were none left who had entered during my time but myself. Roger Trient had received permission from his father to sail
with Drake's squadron and I was now teaching the apprentices as I
had once been taught.

Restlessness now filled me. That which I had learned from books
was filed in orderly array in my head and it was my desire to use it.
I knew that Diggins wanted me to stay with the building of
ships. Being a wise man and understanding my restlessness, he came

one day to tell me that I could sail as second in command of the *Richard Duffield*, a merchant ship in which he owned a third interest.

She was to go on a trading venture to the coast of Barbary and, God willing, to Constantinople with woolens, tin, and iron to exchange for silks and spices.

Few merchants now had the courage to send their ships in these waters, as the Spaniards, Portugals and Italians were much angered at the raiding English privateers. They, in turn, and I doubt not there was certain right on their side, could take any English ship they came upon, sacking her cargo and selling the crews into most barbarous slavery.

I knew of these dangers, but on my young manhood they acted as a spur. Danger being ever an attraction to youth, I was most ready, nay anxious, for this first long voyage to a foreign land.

10

In my head there was crammed a great mass of detail. I knew every part, piece, spar and sail that made up a ship. In navigation and geography of the world I was an expert. I knew all the history of the sea and the voyages made upon it. Yet, in fact, I knew nothing, and I soon discovered that the captain and crew were aware of my pomposity.

When I was introduced to Captain John Emory by the merchant, Richard Duffield, one of the owners, I did notice that he looked upon me with somewhat of a jaundiced eye. But, resplendent in my ignorance, I thought it envy on his part.

As soon as we left the dock in London I found my knowledge was less than I had believed. Even now I blush to remember the mistakes I made.

The crew were a mixture of English, Dutch and Turks who were a hard-bitten lot. Captain Emory had been courteous to me in London but once we were in the Channel and our sails set, my ego became much deflated, not only by his attitude but by the sailing master and the crew, who referred to me as the "schoolbook sailor."

We had much heavy weather as we swung wide into blue water

to avoid all Spaniard or Portugal shipping. Since I was all but ignored I kept to myself and by watching and comparing the unused knowledge in my head with the actual working of the ship, things began to clarify so that, by the time we came about beyond the Canaries and swung toward the African shore, I knew the ship well.

The prime danger of the entire voyage lay within the area of the mouth of the Mediterranean Sea where the narrow passage is guarded by the high rock of Gibraltar on the left and the mountains of Africa on the right.

Luck was with us; we had a good tide and the morning wind bellied our sails. We were far beyond Ceuta when the sun came into our face. The wind then holding fast, we were in sight of the Cape of Bon, unmolested by the Spaniards or Italians. Yet in this area we faced further danger. Though we flew from our topmast the banner granted by the Sultan of Turkey, still these Tunisians had been but lately brought under Turkish rule. They were well-known pirates and the danger was ever present that they might ignore our safe pass.

We came to anchor safely at Tunis, however, without incident and soon were boarded by the officials of the Sultan, also by an Arab of most ill-begotten mien who was the agent of the English company.

Receiving permission to discharge that part of our cargo destined for this port, I supervised the unloading while the captain went ashore to pay his respects to the representative of the Caliph.

I was fascinated by these people, the first really foreign I had seen. Being of a trusting nature and desiring only to be friendly, I invited the cargo master to my cabin for a glass of wine. This he refused, being Mohammedan. However, we talked together as best we could for some time and parted in the most amiable manner. It was only later I discovered he had stolen a number of small articles. Though these were of no great value, his action shocked me. Later, I understood that though these people have honor of their own, to steal from a Christian is considered no sin at all. Having assimilated this, I became more careful in my dealings.

I had a great longing to see the city. From the bay the buildings stood white and clean. The crew, having come to some tolerance with me, the boteswane came with the request I seek the captain's permission to grant them shore leave.

When Captain Emory returned I approached him with due for-

mality and passed on the request, offering with it my promise to
go along to safeguard them. He looked at me for a moment, then
suddenly his face broke all apart and he dissolved into laughter that
shook him from stem to stern and sent the blood rising to my face
in anger. When finally he managed to catch his breath he jokingly
said:

"God's blood, Adams, that is the funniest thing I ever heard. You,
to protect these hard cases? Why there's not a one who doesn't carry
a scar of some kind from all the ports where ships put into."

Then, seeing my flushed face, he slapped me on the shoulder, saying:

"Adams, I will grant them shore leave but only on the following
conditions. The crew can draw lots, half to go ashore and half to
stay. You may go along with them so long as it is clear that *they* are
responsible for *you* and to keep you out of trouble, with the guarantee to bring you back with your head still on your shoulders. Adams,
given time, you may be a sailor. Even if not, I would carry you a
year just for such a laugh as I have had today."

I was highly indignant at Captain Emory's attitude and stalked
off with the full intent that I would not go ashore. I told myself it
did not concern me whether the crew came back whole or not. On
the other hand the desire to see this strange land and people was
more than I could withstand. Restraining my injured pride, I saw to
the drawing of lots. Before hiring a small four-oared galley, the boteswane and sailing master called a conference, making each man swear
that he would not leave the others. The understanding being when
we went to one place, we would all be in a body, keeping eyes alert
to the danger, of which I had no conception.

The city, from the distance looking so clean, changed its aspect
on a nearer approach. When we landed at the quay the smell that
struck my nose was as ripe as Southwark, the sailor section of London.
We were immediately besieged by a mob of peddlers, pimps, jugglers, and acrobats.

The sounds, the sights and the antlike activity had me somewhat
bewildered. Only the quick action of my shipmates kept me from
being swept off into the crowd and probably to my destruction, for
these people love to use a knife on a Christian.

Slightly subdued, I trailed along. We ventured not far from the
waterfront but were led through a narrow passageway and into a

most pleasant garden. The smell of the streets was left behind. From the outside no one would have thought such a place existed.

The owner of the establishment was a small, oily Assyrian, and as the crew spoke Lingua Franca, the common language in these ports, they bargained with him for wine and women. Pooling our money, we paid the Assyrian.

Flagons of sweet wine were then brought to us. Soon a number of girls appeared, small and veiled of face, very shapely, with breasts bare and wearing a sort of transparently voluminous form of britches tied at the ankles. At the sight of their bare breasts I was shocked yet intrigued. Curious at what was hidden, I began to wonder what their faces were like. Their eyes, shadowed with some dark cosmetic, were most attractive. Their hair hung in ringlets and they wore jewels on their fingers and also on their feet.

One came to sit next to me and I gazed on her with curiosity. She in turn seemed attracted by my height, the blondness of my hair and my youth. I drank of the wine but she would take none because of her religion. It was heady stuff and I, not yet accustomed to liquor in any great quantity, soon became boisterous, fondling her and trying to lift her veil, which she would not permit.

The more the wine heated my blood the more enamored I became of her but was too bashful to request her to bed with me. To build my courage I drank more and more of the wine. Finally lurching to my feet I took her hand and, wordlessly, pulled her toward the inner rooms. She went along willingly enough, and I remember the darkened room with a little bed and her closing the door. Then next I remember I was being carried back to the boat. The sailors being drunk by now, most of the time my bottom was bouncing on the rough cobblestones.

Finally I struggled so they let me come to my feet and, with the help of two seamen, I managed to get down into the boat where I became violently ill. I was filled with shame at my drunkenness, yet because of it they accepted me as one of them.

From Tunis we successfully ran the eastward passage, staying for the most part within sight of the African shore until we were beyond the island of Crete. We then swung northward, through the Greek Islands, and finally came to Constantinople. As we worked our way through the narrow strait toward the white and gleaming city I was spellbound by the sight. Here had been the seat of Christendom for centuries. By now the great churches had been changed to mosques and the Christians had lost all.

Our trade went briskly, and though we had to use some care in going about the city, the Turks for the most part were friendly. Here I used some discretion with wine and women.

In the Turkish capital there were women from all the world. Black Nubians, blond Muscovites, Tartars, Greeks, Italians, and small, slant-eyed women from the Far Eastern countries. These women were cheap of price and easily available and I tried many different ones but found not much difference between them.

When the time came to sail again I was more than ready. Now my confidence was backed somewhat by experience. Our luck ran well and we were back in England almost a month before we were expected. The profits from this voyage were great. The captain, myself and the sailing master made a large bonus so that, for the first time in my life, I had money in my pocket, more money than I had ever owned.

Diggins suggested I use part of this to buy goods on my own, and, from the Drapers Company, I bought several bolts of woolen cloth before we set sail again.

The second trip was as successful as the first, even though the storm clouds of war were thickening between England and Spain. No kingdom in all the world, except the Turks, had more power than Philip of Spain, but the piracy of England was bringing bloody war ever nearer.

On the third trip our captain fell ill of some fever and it was left to me to bring the ship from Constantinople back to London. The Turkish physician had told the captain to remain, but being an obstinate man, he refused.

From his cabin he directed the sailing of the ship until he was no longer able. It was then my total responsibility and, being young and full of pride, I was happy to prove my ability.

Captain Emory's desire was to live long enough to reach England, as he had a horror of being buried at sea. Each day he would ask me of the day's run. Always I added a league or so to my reckoning to make him happy. He held on until we were in sight of the Lizard, that ever-welcome sight of the outermost part of England. When I came down with the good news I found him dead.

Our carpenter made a box. On the bottom we packed a layer of damp salt. Then, placing Captain Emory in it, we used all the salt we had on the ship to pack him in, sealing the lid with tar, as I was determined that he should have his wish and be buried in England's soil.

I encountered some grumbling at this among the crew. Superstition made them believe that death stayed with a corpse and would take others. But I did not listen to their talk.

That homeward voyage changed me truly from a boy to a man, and when we eased alongside the dock and Diggins came aboard, it was the first thing he commented on. As we shook hands he looked up at me and smiled. "Well, William," he said, "I have watched you grow from a boy and looked forward to the day when you would reach maturity. Now I am a little sorry it is done. Let's go below and have a drink and tell me of the voyage."

11

There are many forms of happiness but to my mind there can be no joy so full as that when, for the first time, a man is given command of his own ship.

On that third trip when we came to London I wanted with all my heart to retain the captaincy of the *Richard Duffield* but was afraid my youth was the barrier. The taste of the sea was in my blood so that the only time I felt free was away from the land.

Things were becoming desperate for English shipping. More than half the ships that left England did not return. Others, surviving attack by the Spaniards, Portugals, Italians or the pirates of Africa, limped in, damaged and broken, with many seamen lost. Few mariners now had heart for the Mediterranean Sea.

Henry Duffield and Richard Martin were merchants and different men from Nicholas Diggins. They used the profits from trade to build ever greater wealth. Profits were their sole concern. Diggins used the money to put back into ships, for ships were his love, not money.

On the three voyages we had brought back goods enough to pay for the cost of the ship and more, so that now they had but little to lose and much to gain from another successful voyage.

I had, by then, made considerable money, as money was counted in my mind. To a rich man it would not have been much. Yet worse, I had the sea fever and the dream that some day I would have a ship of my own.

Duffield and Martin agreed that I should command the ship. Diggins had tried to dissuade me, pointing out the dangers. Seeing I was determined, he finally consented.

They began buying goods for the ship's cargo while I went in search of my crew. I had not been about much in Southwark, skirting only on the edges of that stinkhole of pimps, whores and thieves who lived off the seamen. The sailing master, Martin Johnson, was my guide and we went from ale house to bawdy house and brought men out, one by one. Then I sobered them up and kept them by the ship. For a mate I came by fortune to an old seaman, John Gordon. Gordon was that breed of man above the forecastle but without desire for the ultimate responsibility of master, preferring the status of mate. He was a very competent seaman, and from him I learned, as I was learning from all, adding bits of knowledge of ships and men. The sum of my ability was rising until I was to reach, not then but later, the ultimate confidence of knowing the sea and the ship and what I could expect from both.

In my youth danger was like salt to the meat of living and I faced it joyously. Before departing from England we had put aboard six long guns in addition to the four we normally carried. The gunner, whom I had stolen from the Queen's ships, drilled the crew daily until we had a ship which could strike back like a true man o' war.

We had a running fight with an Italian galleass but outsailed her around Cape Bon and into the safety of the harbor at Tunis. When we came out it was in the dead of night. Luck being with us, we soon reached Constantinople.

I knew that word had passed that an English merchantman was in the Mediterranean Sea. There would be many ships of war watching for us. Therefore, instead of running south from the Greek Islands, I came about between Greece and the island of Crete and sailed directly toward Sicily, holding off until the wind was right. We passed through the straits between Sicily and Italy, a most dangerous transit, as the sea is very narrow here. Silently, running on the tide, we successfully passed through the strait, then headed due west, far north of the African coast, and never did sight a sail.

The wind holding steady and the weather good, many of the crew complimented me on the wisdom of my course though there had been much murmuring before. Southward, we passed beyond sight of the island of Sardinia, everyone alert and none sleeping too soundly but still, with each day, gaining confidence. The wind held steady until we were almost abeam of the main of the Balearic Islands when, suddenly, the wind died. We began to drift all through the day, making no more than two or three leagues. The crew, by the end of the day, were going about the decks whistling, as sailors believe whistling will cause a gale to blow. But the sky remained clear, and it was not until night that we began to breathe easier. All during the night the moon shone bright on the sea. We stayed awake and watched for wind, but none came. Though morning brought a small breeze, it was from the wrong direction.

Our guns were all run out, loaded and ready, with a slow fire smoldering in the pots, and on the masthead I had two men keeping continuous watch. In the mid-afternoon came the signal we had all been dreading.

Six galleys of at least forty oar apiece had sighted our sails and were bearing swiftly down on us. As they neared, a light breeze came up which was a godsend. This gave us way to maneuver and bring our guns to bear. Each galley had one long gun mounted on the bow, as was the Italian custom. As they came in range, one by one, they fired and began to circle.

Our guns were loaded with round shot and we did little damage while they sprayed us with all manner of bolts and balls, so that all had to crouch behind the bulwarks. From that first round our sails and rigging were much damaged.

We then loaded our guns with many pieces and bits of metal and sprayed them back, causing much damage in return. They circled us, trying to keep us off balance, but I held the ship steady, sailing with the wind, and ordered the port and starboard gunners to fire upon a single galley at a time. In this manner we managed to sink two and damage the others so that they changed their tactics and tried to come astern where our guns could not bear. By this strategy they hoped to board us.

I was greatly afraid, yet at the same time exultant by the heat of the battle. I was proud of the way the men fought. Throughout the whole afternoon and until night fell we fought them off, and when it became dark they sent red-hot balls into the ship, starting several fires. These we managed to extinguish.

One galley pulled away from the others, and on her afterdeck set ablaze a barrel of pitch that lit a great beacon in the sky. I knew they were signaling for help. We were now in such a condition that another day would see us sunk. Already some of the shot had holed the *Duffield* near the water line.

As the galleys drew off, I surveyed the damage. It made me heartsick to see what ruin had been caused. I did what I could for those who were wounded and tried to keep a cheerful face before the men, yet my heart was heavy. All knew the miserable fate of those captured and sold into slavery.

Just before dawn a fair wind came up. God was with us and we managed to escape. The Italians, by then, being as tired as we, could not row with enough strength to keep pace. By daybreak we were out of their sight.

Taking count, I found eight dead, five wounded. Our sails were in tatters and much of our rigging shot through or damaged. Soundings showed we were taking water—how much, I could not tell.

We buried our dead and made the wounded as comfortable as possible, repaired our rigging, and brought out a new set of sail. Through the long day and into the night we worked. Once we had new sail on her, we divided in two, half of us falling into exhausted sleep while the other half manned the pumps.

Fate, or luck, is such an unknown thing that a seaman must learn to be a philosopher. Had not the wind died, the galleys would not have sighted us. Yet now, being so damaged and short-handed, our luck changed so that the wind held fair. We transversed a hundred leagues of the Mediterranean Sea without sighting another sail, passed the Strait of Gibraltar without incident and had a fair wind all the way home to England, even across the Bay of Biscay where always the winds are contrary.

When we picked up the river pilot, news of our arrival preceded us. Many people came down to view us when we were towed into Howland Dock. Diggins, with Duffield and Martin, were waiting, impatient to board us.

The *Duffield* was, in spite of the repairs we had made, a most derelict sight. The fires and shot had blackened all the superstructure. The masts were scarred and the caboose where the cook and boatswain lived was almost shot away.

I welcomed my guests aboard and, after they had surveyed the damage, took them below to the main cabin and opened a bottle of fine port.

Diggins raised his glass and said, "William, I am proud of you. Not many could have brought her in, holed as she is above and below the water. It must truly have been a bloody fight."

"It was bloody enough," I said. "Ten men dead and three crippled."

"Could you not have avoided the fight, Adams?"

At these words I looked at Duffield. I knew he was a merchant and understood where his interests lay, but yet it seemed a most stupid question.

"Nay, sir," I replied, trying to control my temper. "I did all in my power to avoid it. They knew we were in the vicinity. I set way clear of the African coast, taking a route which they would not expect. It was only ill fate that the wind died and the galleys sighted us. We had no choice but to fight. But I don't think your cargo is damaged overmuch."

I sat drinking my port wine and watched them, busy with their figures, and as they exclaimed over the profits they were to make I became sickened. After a while Duffield looked up at me with a contented smile and said, "Well done, Adams. It was a most successful voyage."

"I am happy to hear you say so, sir. And, as your profits are so great, I think something could be spared for those men who had families or relatives and died so that you might make this profit."

My voice was harsh. They looked at me in surprise, as if I had spoken some sort of blasphemy. To start reimbursing seamen for injuries, or their families for their death, was unheard of. Seamen were looked upon by men such as these as somewhat less than human. I turned my gaze from them to Diggins, who sat quietly while this interchange took place. On his face there was a half smile.

"Preposterous!" Duffield said. "Why, think, if we should do such a thing, every merchant in London having a ship would be about our ears. These men knew the danger and were willing to risk it."

"And you knew the danger and were willing to risk it also, though the circumstances were different. You sat safe and sound in your big houses in London."

Perhaps the strain of the voyage, the lack of understanding and the complacency of these two men, along with the sorrow I felt for those who died, made my anger more than it should have been. They could not know of the nights when I had no sleep. To hear them lightly dismiss the death of these brave men as if they were some low form of animal life galled me to the depth of my being. I could feel my anger boiling and had not Diggins interrupted at that point I might have done injury to these two merchants.

Diggins spoke quietly and said, "Captain Adams is right. We have made great profit over the last few voyages and a man's life cannot be computed in pence and pounds. In gratitude I, too, feel we should make some gesture to whatever survivors they do have. It will not be any great amount, as not many seamen can afford the luxury of family. This can be done quietly so that there will be no danger to the money bags of other merchants."

They grumbled and growled and I, being so filled with anger, said no more. Finally they agreed that those men who had kin would receive ten pounds and the three badly injured should receive ten pounds also, above their wages.

I saw to the issuing of the crew's wages for the voyage and the bonus which they had so bravely earned. Then, turning the ship's contents over to the merchant clerk in charge, I went with the boteswane and some of the crew to Southwark where I did get most boisterously drunk trying to wash away the memory of the merchants' greed which had filled me so with disgust.

Still being very young, without the understanding or acceptance of the world's ways, I had come to love the ship and those who sailed with her. They were a replacement for my own family. However, after two days of brawling and drinking and wenching, my stomach could no longer stand it and I had to seek fresh air. Drink is a strange thing. It can brighten the whole world, bringing forth song and laughter. Yet on the other side of the coin there is a sickness so great that a man could wish to die. All I wished for was a hot bath and a clean bed. When I had left the ship I had told Diggins I would be at his house that evening. I knew he would be worried about me. Sober, I emerged from Southwark sick, dirty and well-bitten by vermin, and went home to Diggins.

I thought he would be angry at me. He was a man who loved a drink, but taken in its proper proportion, in the manner of a man.

The apprentices had all gone to bed when I let myself in his house. Diggins was alone in his office. He looked at me sternly. Then he smiled.

"Well, William," he said. "Seems you took a most drastic cure for your anger. I have been worried about you. I'm happy to see you safe. Now don't tarry here. Go out the back and strip. I don't want my house contaminated with lice and fleas. Leave your clothes outside and I will see Mrs. Grandy lays out enough hot water to wash your sins away. Tell me, how did anyone manage to hit you in the eye? He must have been standing upon a chair ."

I felt of my bruised and cut eye and said, "I know not, sir."

After I had bathed and crawled into the clean and sweet-smelling bed, sleep closed over me and I was content.

PART TWO

The Armada

12

War is a strange sickness seeming to occur at regular intervals. War, or the scent of war, brings with it excitement, righteous anger against whoever the enemy happens to be. The people become as if drunk. All good sense is lost. Hatred, breeding fancied wrongs, makes the killing of other men an honorable and glorious thing.

Now London and all England spoke for war against Philip of Spain. There was much drinking and loud talk in the taverns, with discussion of Drake, Hawkins, Frobisher and other great commanders and how they would smash the Spaniards. Drake, however, sat at home in ill repute with Elizabeth the Queen while his squadron moldered at Plymouth.

I knew little of politics as yet, but it seemed as if the Queen varied with the wind, going first on the side of war and next attempting to make peace. As always, it is easy to find her mistakes in retrospect, but she should have known that, having challenged the might of Philip of Spain by taking his treasure ships and wrecking his commerce, he would do no less than to take England. And England regarded herself in a way no other people saw. She thought of herself as a nation. To the rest of the world England was but a poor little island.

Having now a considerable amount of money, I purchased some foppish clothing which the style of the day recommended and, in the evenings, began going about the city with other young men of my acquaintance. I drank more than was good for me and wasted money that had been hard to come by. Diggins looked upon my actions as foolish, but he neither condemned nor tried to persuade me from my way of life, which I considered as being that of a gay blade.

One evening four of us took a carriage to Burbage's playhouse, in the fields outside London. A new play by Christopher Marlowe was to be presented. Theaters had been much condemned by both the law and the clergy in the past years. For that reason both Burbage's and Braines theaters were built beyond the limits of the city, so that the law would not be enforced against them.

It was my first visit to this theater and I was astonished at its size and completeness. I was told that fully seven hundred pounds had gone into the building of it. We gathered in the inn proper to drink before the play was to start, then paid our fee and went into the yard, called a pit, because when there was no play scheduled, bulls were pitted here, also dogfights.

For those not wanting to stay below, rooms on the upper floor could be rented where the windows were built like boxes. There they could sit and drink and watch the play without being bothered by the noisy crowd below.

We were moving about, talking and laughing, when all of a sudden I was clapped on the back and, turning, came face to face with Roger Trient. We both being somewhat in our cups, embraced with loud greeting. I do not remember too much of the play except a deal of fencing and much slaughter took place. Afterward we went to an inn in the city. There Roger and I sat drinking and talking through the night, he telling of his adventures and I of mine.

Roger had been with Drake's squadron, which was called the Levant Squadron, in their last voyage to the Spanish Americas. They had taken many prizes. By comparison I was somewhat ashamed of my trading voyages, though I recounted the battle with the Italian galleys and perhaps embellished it somewhat. He exclaimed at how I had grown and changed. I had, by then, reached almost my full height, standing six feet four inches and weighing near fifteen stone.

As the night wore on, Roger became bitter at the actions of the Queen, speaking almost treason and condemning her for refusing even to see Drake and letting his squadron ride at anchor off Plymouth where the bottoms were fouling and the ships falling to pieces.

At that time the Queen had but a few ships of her own. All the men o' war owned privately were under her control by the issuing of permits to sail from England. The seamen, except for those few in the Queen's ships, were paid by a share from the profits taken in prizes. Laying to, like this, the seamen were almost starving.

Knowing that England and Englishmen looked upon Drake as a hero, I questioned Roger Trient as to why Drake seemed ever to be passing from one extreme of favor to the other, Elizabeth at one time proclaiming him a hero of England and bestowing upon him a knighthood, then but a short time later branding him a pirate and banishing him to his estate.

"I cannot understand this," I said to Roger.

"Nor anyone else," he replied. "My family, having some pretensions of nobility, positions me so that I can see what goes on at the court. Drake is a commoner. This is what stands mostly against him."

I smiled at these words. In the past, Roger and I had had many arguments on this subject. I, being lowly born, naturally had been somewhat bitter at the barriers erected by the nobility for the protection of their families. I had been irritated by Trient's snobbishness many times, even coming to bitter words on occasion. It had always seemed to me that too many weaklings lived in the reflected glory of the past strength of their family.

But I did not interrupt. I was pleased to hear of Drake from someone who had sailed with him.

"You must understand, Adams. Only Drake's genius has brought him to his present eminence. This also has brought him many enemies and much jealousy. There's no man like him in all England, though Hawkins does rate high. Still there's much hatred against him. The Queen, while she is a ruler, is also a woman. She shifts in the direction of whoever has her ear. For example, Sir Francis Drake may set upon a voyage with her full consent. He has orders from the Queen and permits to seize Spaniard and Portugal ships. This he does, returning with treasure of which she gets her full share. But then the ministers of France, Spain and Rome say that his actions have stirred up war. The only way she can pacify the Spaniard king is to disclaim, publicly, any responsibility. She then condemns Drake in most harsh words.

"It's madness, William. Of all men in England, Drake knows best there can be no peace with Spain. Would Elizabeth but listen, Drake would clear the seas of Spaniard ships and bring this papist bastard to his knees. But no, Elizabeth thinks by sweet words she will calm Philip's anger. She does, however, make no move to return the treasure which, on her orders, Drake brought to England. Philip has all the power of the Holy Roman Empire behind him, one army in France alone being twice as great as we have in all England. And, from the kingdom of Naples, from Portugal and from Spain he is gathering such a fleet that the weight of the ships alone will wash like a tide over England."

We had been talking until then between ourselves. But as he spoke his voice became louder and his passion grew so great that all in the inn were silent and listening. To speak against the Queen was a dangerous thing. London was full of spies and fear was abroad in the land. Cautioning him, we soon left the inn and I took him to his family's dwelling. He wanted me to stay with him but I begged off, leaving him at the door in care of a servant, and made my way home.

Roger came to the yard two days later. Now he was in a happy mood. Orders had finally come for Drake to return to Plymouth and refit his squadron.

"Damme, William, I have not been so excited in a long time. And I am to go as lieutenant in the *Bonaventure*, Drake's own ship."

Then, looking at me, his happiness faded somewhat. "William, I will speak for you," he said. "Perhaps I can get you a commission. But berths are hard to come by. It seems every seaman in England wants to sail with Drake."

"Thank you, Roger," I said. "But we have a great deal of work here. If, as you say, England does come to war, there will be room for me where, God willing, I can make a name for myself. Though the *Duffield* is by no means a man o' war, still I think they will find a use for her. I have had a taste of command and I don't care for the thought of being subordinate to so many others."

I bade Roger good-by with some envy. We clasped hands in friendship.

Each day I followed the accounts of Drake's squadron in the news sheets being hawked about the city. Then fate stepped in to advance my course. The merchants Martin and Duffield had obtained a contract with the Queen. The repairs on the *Duffield* being complete, she was to load stores for the Levant Squadron in London and proceed to join it at Plymouth. Though Diggins tried again to dissuade me I retained the berth as captain.

We moved over to the government naval stores and loaded a cargo of powder, ball, and food—if such it could be called. In the loading of barrels of salt beef, one barrel broke, spilling contents which looked as if it had no connection with anything that had ever been alive, being a dirty, gray sodden mess. The sight of it shocked me so I looked for someone to protest to. Whereupon I was politely but firmly told it was none of my affair, that I was not an inspector of pickled beef; my duties were solely to transport it.

We loaded and left London on the tide. With all sail set we came booming down the Channel to Plymouth only to find an empty harbor. Drake had sailed on April first, as rumor had reached him that the Queen was having another change of mind.

The day I arrived, a pinnace was being fitted out to catch the Levant Squadron and deliver the new orders. Coming ashore, I met with Captain Butterfield, who was in charge of stores. He had but just finished giving the Queen's messenger the course laid out by Drake. When the captain of the pinnace left I reported, handing the manifest of our cargo to him and requesting instructions.

He glanced quickly down the list of stores I carried and his face brightened visibly.

"We have sore need for this. Drake sailed with his ships half-stored. You will proceed in all haste to join with him." And he gave me the course and rendezvous point.

I glanced at it, then said, "Perhaps, sir, I am mistaken, but this seems not the course you gave to the other captain."

He looked directly at me and said, "You are mistaken. This is the same course."

Having by then gathered an inkling of the complexity of politics, I asked no further questions but said I would leave upon the hour as the tide was running in my favor.

Making sail, I watched with light heart the Channel shore recede behind me. Ahead of me was the pinnace, one of the largest of the sort I had seen. Most pinnaces carried but a main and a jib, but she had main and mizzen sail and must have been sixty ton where most pinnaces ranged but ten to twenty ton. She was fast, but I would be with Drake long before her.

13

I came up on the squadron on the fifth of April off Cape Finisterre. By flag I identified myself and was ordered ahead into the center of the fleet.

I had been given certain packets for the commander. Not wanting to miss the chance of meeting Drake, I took command of a small pinnace we had in tow and personally delivered the goods. While the seamen put the stores on deck I went aft with the packets to where Drake was in conference with his officers, meanwhile keeping a weather eye on the lowering mass of clouds that were speeding down on us from the direction of the cape.

"Captain Adams of the *Henry Duffield*, with stores and messages," the master at arms announced me to Drake.

When he turned toward me I was struck by his eyes, which were like the eyes of a hawk, penetrating as if no distance could dim their vision. Though he was of average height he seemed to be larger than the other men. His face, too, gave the appearance of a thirst for wild freedom. Once seeing him, I could not envision Drake being at home anywhere except on the deck of a ship.

"Captain Adams," he said, "you made a fine, fast sail from Plymouth."

"The wind was fair for us, sir. I was asked to deliver these messages."

He hastily scanned the seal and a look of relief crossed his face when he saw the seal of the Queen was not on them. He then turned to me as I said:

"There's a pinnace, sir, which set out the same day as the *Duffield* with a message from the Queen. I think it must be lost somewhere."

Drake looked searchingly at my face, then smiled in understanding. "Very good, Adams."

The wind now became stronger and I had to get back to my ship. Our orders were to keep position but, if separated, to rendezvous at the Rock of Lisbon. The gale that came up was of such force it scattered us over the sea.

By the sixteenth, however, we were gathered at the Rock. Here our scouting pinnaces picked up some homeward-bound Flemings. From them we learned that at Cadiz there was a great force of ships and stores ready to move to Lisbon.

Our Admiral lost no time in debate as to what course of action should be taken. He ordered his light squadron inshore to sweep up whatever shipping could be found.

The main ships of the line sailed at all speed for Cadiz. Once within striking distance, we gathered together on the sea and Drake called a council of captains. I, being in command of a store ship that was only lightly gunned, was not at the meeting. I learned later of the events.

Drake was a man who ever listened courteously to others' counsel, but followed his own. The Vice-Admiral suggested that they should wait for the slower ships to come up and attack in the morning. Drake bluntly replied he intended to attack immediately, while the wind was fair. He gave orders for them to return to their ships and make ready. This was hurtful to the dignity of Vice-Admiral Borough, ever a strong advocate of caution. Borough then quoted to Drake the standing orders which had been in effect since the time of our King Henry VIII, which said that an admiral shall not take any hand in exploit to land or enter into the harbor of the enemy, but that he shall call a council and make the captains privy to his advice.

Admiral Borough was an old man who had served well and faithfully for many years. He was held in great repute. Sir Francis looked at him, eyes blazing, then his gaze covered the others assembled.

"Gentlemen, I have but one order to give you. You are to follow me into the harbor at Cadiz and destroy what shipping we find at anchor there. Now the captains assembled will return to their ships."

To an old officer like Borough who had been Admiral of the

Fleet when Drake was in swaddling clothes, this order must have seemed madness. Cadiz is crowned by a summit of rock, well fortified. From the rock a low and narrow neck of land lies back for a distance of five miles to form a breakwater to the city. At the entrance lies a wide expanse of sea between the rock and the bay. But the entrance, deep enough for ships to pass, lies close to the rock and under the guns of the Matagorda. Inside the harbor lay galleys, armed and manned. This was ideal water for them to move in.

Sir Francis Drake, however, did not hesitate. His battle sails were unfurled and he made, direct as a shot, toward the harbor entrance. I, having no right to be with the main ships of the line, could not resist moving in to view the action.

As Drake's *Bonaventure* neared the bay entrance, two galleys came out from the inner harbor, which is named Port St. Mary. At this, Drake bore on with all speed, then luffed and gave them such a broadside that they were left shattered and broken. As he sailed on under the guns of the Matagorda it seemed that he passed through the fire as if by a miracle, remaining almost untouched.

The view from where I lay was a marvelous sight. At least sixty sail of ships filled the bay and, under the second battery, by the shore, lay a number of caravels and barques readying to join the Armada at Lisbon.

As Drake cut the first two galleys to pieces and sailed into the harbor it became a scene of mad confusion. Every vessel cut its cables and fled for refuge past the second battery. To cover their escape, ten galleys immediately put out boldly to challenge.

Drake signaled for the ships behind to take prizes, and he alone defiantly went on to meet the Spaniard attack. Turning to pass across the course of the advancing galleys, he received them with roaring broadsides. It was a lesson to the Spaniards not soon forgotten. Prior to this it had always been claimed that no ship of the line could fight and win against galleys in close water. Drake proved the fallacy of this claim.

Our other ships were now busy boarding and putting prize crews aboard the anchored vessels. As I and all of those in the crew would share in the prizes we took, I could not resist their pleas to join with those inside. Nor, truly, did I want to resist.

Taking the *Henry Duffield* in, past the Spaniard guns, I smiled to think of how Diggins' merchant partners would have wrung their hands had they seen me. Holding the ship in as close to the rock as I dared, we managed to pass the guns on the Matagorda with no more than a few holes in our topsails.

We took three prizes, one Italian and two Spaniard, with no more than a token fight. One had sail and Drake had ordered that those with sail were to be manned. On the other two, the men went below and stripped them of everything of value, and then set fire to them.

As the burning ships drifted in the shoal water, the Admiral ordered all his squadron to move up with their prizes farther into the bay and to anchor at the point named Puntales, just out of range of the city's guns.

Drake, with his *Bonaventure* and four Queen's ships, took a position more to seaward as protection against the galleys. The four royal ships moved in near him as if seeking protection rather than showing a warlike attitude toward the Spaniards.

Vice-Admiral Borough now insisted on a conference of captains. Having now two ships in my charge, I felt I could be counted among them. As further excuse I took four casks of fine port and some cheeses we had captured.

Keeping myself in the background, which with my height and yellow hair was hard to do, I listened to the proceedings and studied Drake who, after a battle such as he had fought, seemed hardly ruffled. He was calm and polite as Vice-Admiral Borough spoke.

"Let us be content with the havoc we have wrought. We are in a most perilous position lying here. If the wind should die we shall be helpless."

Drake was silent for a moment as if in thought, then said: "Our purpose, with the help of God and for our Queen, is to destroy these Spaniards or cripple them in such a manner that they cannot attack England. The destruction we have done today has been great, but there is more to be done. The great ships—the important ones—lie farther inside the harbor. I am not a man in love with wealth, but all except a few of the men who serve these ships are paid in prize money and we have small wage for them in payment for a battle so well fought. Gentlemen, we do not move to sea. You will lie quiet for the night. You will not move unless I do. I will give you my orders come morning." With that we were dismissed.

From a group of officers amongst whom I stood I caught sight of Roger Trient and signaled him. When we were dismissed we moved

together to shake hands. He looked fine and fit in every way. There
was an air about Trient which breathed greatness. I had no doubt he
was to have a great future.

"Roger," I said, "let us talk outside. I would prefer not to be noticed."

We turned away when Drake called to me.

"Adams, were not your orders to remain outside the harbor?"

"Sir," I said, "I was doing nothing and from where I lay it seemed
as if many of the ships could escape in the confusion. I felt that,
under the circumstances, I could not but lend my help."

"You took three ships. Were they worth the trouble?"

"Aye, sir. One with sail and two without. The loot was mostly
wines and cheese, though to sailors this is sometimes worth more
than gold."

He looked as if he would say more but then spoke good night, and I
was happy that my disobedience had been passed over.

We lay through the night watching the lights ashore. Not many of
us slept. At daylight, Drake picked up his light anchor and moved,
but not for the sea. He moved the *Bonaventure* in among the merchantmen and dropped anchor within a stone's throw of the *Duffield*. I watched him studying the shore through his glass and I could
see the prize he had in mind.

In the inner harbor lay the Spaniard admiral's own ship, a tall,
magnificent galleon. Drake called for the pinnaces to be manned. I
was fortunate enough to be put in command of one.

With seven pinnaces and twelve longboats of the fleet we gathered around the *Merchant Royal* which Captain Flick commanded.
She being an easy sailor, of shallow draft while yet well armed, Drake
took command of her. With us following, he led us in on the flood
tide as if the two galleys lying in wait were no more than two flies.

Drake's flag was flying from the yard of the *Merchant Royal*. His
name was so feared by now that not more than a half-hearted sortie
was made at us and our guns quickly drove them off.

While Drake was engaged with the two galleys, the pinnaces and
the longboat closed quickly with the great prize. Coming alongside
the *Santa Cruz*, she looked like a mountain in the water. We climbed
up on all sides, men going up the anchor chains and grappling lines.
Though the Spaniards put up a bitter fight, we took her within half
an hour.

It was here the trouble began between Borough and Drake that carried them up into the Queen's presence. To the old Vice-Admiral, Drake appeared a madman. Borough, leaving his ship, took a pinnace and ordered each ship he passed to put out to sea as quickly as it could up-anchor and make sail.

Almost mad with anxiety, he came by the *Merchant Royal* shouting for Drake. But Drake, the great galleon taken, had already returned to the *Bonaventure*. Vice-Admiral Borough returned to his ship and started to warp her around and out. By this time we had looted the *Santa Cruz* and set her afire, sending a mass of booty aboard the *Merchant Royal*.

The galleys, lying in wait, now took courage to attack Borough. Drake had then to send the *Rainbow*, *Edward*, *Bonaventure*, five merchantmen, and our seven pinnaces to his aid.

After a hard, sharp fight where it seemed for a time Borough would be run aground in spite of our help, Drake came up and the galleys retired to the protection of the batteries.

We continued on, with Borough, to the mouth of the harbor where we went to anchor. Lying there in sight of the helpless city, we revictualed all of the ships with food we had stolen from the Spaniards. We had wine, oil, biscuit, dried fruits and cheeses in abundance. We had taken six vessels laden with provisions and, from the great galleon and the others, there was considerable booty.

At a meeting aboard the *Bonaventure*, hard words passed between Borough and Drake. The inshore division was ordered back to their position and, in fine order, we prepared to make sail.

Then our luck seemed to turn. The wind changed, and there were many who thought that the Vice-Admiral, with all of his experience, had been right and Drake wrong because we were now helpless and exposed to all the devices the Spaniards could invent to destroy us.

We could see troops pouring into Cadiz and guns being moved down to the sand hills and brought to bear on the fleet. Fire ships were launched on the ebb tide and the galleys came out to attack again and again. Never had galleys a more fit place to fight, what with our fleet riding in a narrow gut with no wind. By all of the rules of naval warfare we should have been destroyed that day.

But we had Drake. When that day passed he had demonstrated how superior a well-handled ship, laying down a broadside, could be even against fast-moving galleys. Now, under his orders, all of the ships' boats were put out to maneuver the ships so their guns could bear. As the galleys would approach, the men would pull the ship around. The galleys with their one long gun were no match against a ship such as the *Bonaventure,* which had sixteen guns of culverins, cannons and demiculverins. By concentrating their fire on one galley at a time, the galleys were disabled and compelled to retire before coming within boarding range. The fire ships were no more successful. With the ships' boats we pulled our ships out of the way and the fire ships passed through the fleet to shoal on the reef and burn themselves out harmlessly.

The dead calm lasted through the day. We were continuously harassed by the shore guns, but we bore with it. At two in the morning a land wind sprang up. Drake immediately gave the signal to make sail, taking the lead with the *Bonaventure.* He swept the galleys from where they tried to block the channel, fighting his way through with the ships falling in behind, and we made it out of the Bay of Cadiz with losses hardly worth mentioning.

The wind fell off again, and the galleys once more came out to harass us. The action continued through the morning with little success. One ship was boarded and retaken. A southerly breeze came up and the galleys were forced to retire, leaving us to go to anchor peacefully, in full view of the town, triumphant and arrogant.

The next day was spent in further revictualing while Drake, on the *Bonaventure,* rode back and forth on a bravado in challenge to the galleys to come out and fight.

On the morning, we destroyed those ships which were of little value and sailed on the tide. We proceeded to sea and beat north toward Cape St. Vincent.

14

Like a shock of thunder, word passed through the fleet that Drake had decided to take Cape St. Vincent. We had headed north in search of the Spaniard Recalde and his squadron, from the Cape to fifteen leagues beyond. Recalde, it was said, had under his command a great ship of thirty-two guns and also six middling ships and five pinnaces.

Had the wind been with us, we might have reached Recalde's station and taken him, but he had arrived at Lisbon, his ships untouched.

At the news we were to take Cape St. Vincent only those of us who were very young, hot-blooded and full of confidence in our Admiral heard it with cheerful hearts. Most were afraid of such an idea. Cape St. Vincent was the point where all ships had to pass to bear north to Lisbon. This cape was the key that could lock the door to the Armada. Our poor Vice-Admiral was fairly aghast at the thought. He protested strongly to Drake against this insane move.

When Drake refused to listen, Borough returned to his ship and penned a long letter of protest to Drake. At the same time he dispatched a copy to England.

Looking back on this action of Borough's now, it makes some sense. Drake's intention violated every form of strategy the old seaman had learned and believed in. He was hidebound by tradition and, without doubt, resentful of being disregarded by this young upstart. But Drake was Admiral by the Queen's commission and Borough through his action at Cadiz and now questioning his orders was, in Drake's eyes, a traitor.

In high anger Drake sent a party to remove Borough from his flagship and set him aboard the *Bonaventure*. There, on the deck, before the chaplain, flag captain and the assembled officers, he charged Borough with treason. He gave the command of Borough's ship, the *Lion*, to Captain Philip Marchant and ordered him to hold "the traitor" under close arrest until our return to England.

The news was like a chord passing from ship to ship, shaking all of us. Borough had great standing in England. Soon, however, we had more things to occupy our minds than the fate of Borough.

Drake changed his initial strategy and decided to take the port of Lagos. Lagos would be used as a base against the Cape. On our first attempt, though, we found that Lagos had lately been heavily fortified. Drake, never being hidebound in any plan or decision, then rallied the ships and returned to his original decision.

Holding the ships back, we came up on the Cape before daylight and eight hundred men were landed at Cape Sagres. They proceeded to attack the fort called Avelera. The Spaniards put up no resistance here but left the fort and retired to the protection of Sagres Castle. This was Drake's prime objective. No one but Drake would have had any hope that it could be taken.

The castle sat out over the sea. On three sides the walls fell two hundred feet or more to the water. On the north side alone was there an approach. This was but one hundred fifty feet wide and covered by battlements and towers mounting heavy guns.

When Drake came ashore from the *Bonaventure*, his very air as he, personally, took charge of the assault was enough to give the weakest hearts courage. He seemed to have no doubt that he had but to walk in and take the castle.

The castle, so high and firm-standing, seemed to declare that nothing but a long siege of artillery and petards could possibly conquer it, and we had neither.

The men gathered on the open approach, out of range of the guns, to wait now and see what scheme Drake had. His only stratagem, we discovered, was the very simple method of firing the gate. Faggots from the countryside and timber from the houses and sheds and the woods about were gathered. Pitch was brought up from the ships.

Drake now divided his men, three-fourths being put to firing upon the castle walls while the other fourth followed the lead of the Admiral, who charged across the long causeway with a bundle of wood and, on reaching the gate, dropped his load of faggots at the base. The men following brought enough wood to start the gate burning. Back and forth they charged. Many were sore hurt during the two hours the gate was kept burning. But the Spaniards suffered also. Our fire was heavy and continuous and the Spaniard commander of the castle was killed.

Suddenly, above the burning gate, a white flag appeared. They called a parley. It was absolute madness for this to happen. Even though we burned the gate, strongly positioned as they were they could have held out for weeks. It was only the fear of "El Diablo," as they called Drake, that caused them to ask for truce. The only terms requested were that they be permitted to leave the castle. This Drake granted on the condition they take no arms with them nor destroy any of the castle's guns or fortifications.

And so it was. After a brisk fight of but two hours' duration we were in control of a castle formerly considered impregnable. As if by a miracle, we now had Sagres with all of its armaments and the castle stores. Once the Spaniards had marched off down the causeway, Drake left a token force and then turned his attention to the fortified monastery of St. Vincent.

They offered parley without even a shot being fired, as did the castle at Valliera. We ended the day with the loss of less than fifty men. Drake's planning alone was responsible for the taking of this impregnable and necessary arm of defense from Philip of Spain. I wondered what had happened to the spirit of the Spaniards that had bred such men as Cortez and Pizarro. They seemed to have changed from a virile breed to a race of eunuchs, having somewhere lost their manhood.

When the Spaniards had gone, straggling off like beaten dogs, all of the guns on the castle walls were dismantled and tumbled down to the beach below, where they were picked up by the ships' boats and carried out to the squadron that had moved close inshore. All the guns also were taken from the monastery and the castle at Valliera; and when all of the ammunition, foodstuffs and valuables were removed, the forts were razed and set afire.

I had taken no part in this battle. Those of us in the light squadron had not been idle, however. To the eastward of the Cape were eleven fishing villages. We swept these clean, sinking everything we found afloat. We took and sank more than one hundred small vessels, caravels, barques and coastal fishing boats. It was not pleasant work but every boat we sent down and every net destroyed meant less food for the Armada. It was work that had to be done, no matter that our stomachs turned against it.

Finishing our dirty, bloody work, we returned to the Cape and watered and stored with the main fleet and had a great celebration, though we didn't need much wine to lift our spirits.

The ninth of May we sailed for Lisbon. Now there was hardly a man in the fleet who thought any charge was too great for us. If Drake wanted to take Lisbon, then take her we would, even though all knew that Lisbon could not be taken from the sea. In all Europe Lisbon was the best fortified.

We came to anchor off Cacaes Bay, out of range of the guns of St. Julian's castle where Santa Cruz himself was in command. The wind fell calm. This would have been a good time for the Spaniards to attack with their large galleys, seven of which lay inside. But they did no more than sit and watch, making no move to attack. Cadiz must have set too raw in their bellies for them to challenge "El Diablo" again.

All day our great ships rode the challenge. When they showed no desire for a fight our Admiral sought to make an exchange of prisoners. Word came back that they had taken no English prisoners. Drake, knowing this for the lie it was, sent a message that he would sell those Spaniards we had to the Moors and use the money to ransom Englishmen, as the Spaniards seemed to have more love for gold than for their brothers.

In our position we controlled the entrance to Lisbon harbor. Any ships coming upon us, all unaware, were taken and sunk, or set afire and driven ashore as wrecks.

I have heard many men accuse Drake of being wild and reckless but it was not true. His actions now at Lisbon were proof. Drake ever knew the odds against his plans, and never moved except where he knew the odds were in his favor either by fear of his name, surprise, or some other element which he could use.

He now took count of his ships and the condition of the men. Many were weak and injured and sick from the scurvy. The ships' bottoms were foul and their bilges rotten. On order, we upped anchor and sailed for Cape St. Vincent to clean the ships and give the men a chance to rest ashore. So long as we held the Cape we could keep other parts of the Armada from joining with the main body at Lisbon.

Drake ordered pinnaces off to England for reinforcements, sending with them an account of his accomplishments and our position. He knew so long as Englishmen held the Cape, they held the key to Philip of Spain's downfall.

Day after day, week after week we held the Cape, waiting for reinforcements. None came. Time began to hang heavy on our hands. We all knew that a strong Spanish force could drive us into the sea as we had destroyed all the fortifications.

Then a scouting pinnace came in bearing news that ten galleys had arrived at Lagos. This promised us action. Orders were to proceed toward Lagos with the light squadron, sweeping everything inshore while the heavy ships bore a straight course farther out to sea.

But at Lagos the galleys retreated inside the reef and lay where we couldn't reach them except with small boats which the galleys could overmatch. We ran bravada, calling them Spanish Dogs, but they would not stir. Turning back to Cape St. Vincent we waited again, but no help came. The men were becoming tired and sick. Many now began to waver in their confidence in the Admiral. Then one day information was brought that a great carrack, the *San Felipe*, was homeward bound from the East Indies carrying much treasure.

Knowing we could not hold the Cape without help, the Admiral sent ships home with the sick. It was with some difficulty he persuaded those still strong to sail with him. To jolly us into accepting this new project, he made a great fandango ashore with wine and biscuit and much tough Spaniard beef to sharpen our teeth on. He spoke well to us, saying those who wished to return to England could do so and he would hold them to no blame.

"You have stood with me in the proudest tradition of Englishmen. I could but wish that those at home in England would support us so well. It has been many months since we left England and I know your heart cries out for home the same as mine. You who are sick and tired, take the ships to England. But ask other Englishmen to return them to me. Those of you who are strong and have confidence in my destiny, sail with me. With luck, we shall take such a prize as has never before been seen in England."

And so we parted. Many of the ships set sail. I sent the *Duffield* home and sailed for the Azores with Drake, feeling my fortune lay with him.

15

I had been transferred to the *Rainbow*, Drake's flagship, the *Bonaventure* having been sent home. The damage we had done to the Spaniards had been crippling, but there had been little prize money taken.

On our way toward the Azores a gale blew up scattering the entire fleet over the sea. When the storm abated there were only ten ships that came together again, and our commander was beset with many worries. Vice-Admiral Borough chose this time for his traitorous mutiny.

A sail was sighted, and the *Lion*, being closest, set out in pursuit. The sail turned out to be one of our own ships, but instead of joining us, the *Lion* continued on with her, sending a pinnace back to the fleet.

Aboard the pinnace was Captain Marchant, who had been mutinied against when he had ordered the ship to come about and rejoin the fleet. Vice-Admiral Borough had won the crew to his side and persuaded them to return to England. Captain Marchant confessed his laxity in allowing the Vice-Admiral the freedom of the decks, but he had pleaded earnestly with his crew not to do this. They had replied that they preferred the judgment of the Queen on whether this was mutiny, rather than face certain death with Drake. Marchant, with a few of his officers and crew, had been granted permission to take the pinnace and join the fleet.

Drake's anger was volcanic. He raged against the mutineers, then impaneled a jury to try them in absentia. The *Lion* was hardly over the horizon when he passed sentence of death immediately upon seizure on Borough and all the chief officers.

Deeply reduced in strength, we nevertheless continued on toward the Azores. It was evening when we came upon the island of St. Michaels. In the dusk, we could make out a large man o' war lying in near shore. On Drake's orders the *Rainbow* heaved to and waited for the two pinnaces that had fallen astern. When they came up we set sail again and continued on.

As dawn came over the sea we were in sight of the ship. She proved to be a great Portugal carrack. It was plain to see she had mistaken us for the Spaniard escort she had been waiting for. From the size of her and the guns she mounted she appeared strong enough to fight off almost any attack alone.

There was not much wind as we moved gently through the water. She came on, dipping her flag and ordering us to show our colors. We knew by her colors she was the great treasure ship from the east.

We made no overt move. As she bore down on us we could see her guns being run out, ready to fight her way through. And still her flag dipped, asking us to show our colors. This we did not do until we were within shot of her. Then we hung out streamers and pennants along with our flag so she would have no doubt as to who we were.

She was a monstrous ship. We greeted her with shot and she answered with sharp courage as we circled her like terriers about a bull. With our long guns we pierced her many times. She would fire first at one, then another of our ships. With her great amount of sail it seemed as if she would pass through us and go on. But our Admiral had no idea of permitting such a maneuver.

Drake then ordered our fly boat and a pinnace to push in and attach themselves athwart her bow. This they did, catching the Portugals unaware. Despite her attempts to destroy the two boats with shot and fire, she could not reach them, as they lay too far under her counter. In spite of her great sail this slowed her so that we had her in an encirclement and laid into her fire, so hurtful that we could see blood running from her decks and down her sides.

On Drake's order we now moved in to board her. It was then she struck, and we held in our hands such a prize as had never been taken on the sea before. She proved to be the *San Felipe,* the King of Spain's own merchantman and the greatest ship in the world.

Here was a blow that would hurt Philip of Spain more than any other. Here, too, was a windfall that would fill all of our pockets. Her crew was taken off and put aboard our ships. Then we began to see what she contained. In her holds were tons of spices, chests of precious gems, chest upon chest of costly china, great bales of silks and velvets and coffers of bullion and worked jewels. Truly this was a great fortune.

As for Drake, the only excitement he showed was when we brought him papers and charts disclosing the long-held secrets of the East India trade and the routes taken by the ships for the Far East. Drake knew the value of these charts. They would open the doors of the Far East to Englishmen.

The weather held good as we lay upon the sea and took count of our prize. Now there was no more to be done save return home to England. We were in dire need of stores and rest for the men and help for the sick and wounded. Drake would have preferred to return to beard *Santa Cruz* at Lisbon, but we were at the end of our rope. Fast pinnaces preceded us with the news of the prize we had taken and when we arrived off Plymouth it seemed all England was out to greet us. We were heroes and London opened its doors. There was nothing too good for Drake's men.

16

Since my first love I had ventured no more down that path. Once I had a ship of my own and came to manhood I took women casually as I took my drink. They came and went and left no imprint on me save the pleasure of the moment. On our return to Plymouth with the great carrack, I came to learn the more sophisticated pleasures London had to offer and I had a very able teacher.

On my transfer to the *Rainbow* after sending the *Duffield* home, Roger and I were at last on the same ship. He, too, had gone with Drake rather than return with the *Bonaventure*. During the long days at sea we had come to know each other, not as boys, but as men. Many times we disagreed yet between us there was respect. We had boarded the *San Felipe* together and exulted over the treasure. Now we set out to spend our share. Roger Trient was now a slim, graceful, dark-haired man, with a face as handsome and bold as a Toledo blade. He had an ease of manner, great charm and a reckless courage. Roger had learned the discipline of the sea but ashore, he acted with mad irresponsibility. This in itself was not unusual. It seemed the better the family, the more dissolute and rake-hell were the sons.

Through Roger I entered a part of society that had been closed to me and probably would have remained so but for Roger and the fact that we were a part of "Drake's band of heroes."

Trient now took me in hand. Our first chore was a visit to his tailor. Formal wear of the gentry was a foppish costume consisting of a high ruffled neckpiece, frilled coat with great balloon shoulders; ruffled, short britches, and skin-tight stockings reaching almost to the crotch. I felt like a fool but when I commented on the stupidity of the costume, Roger gave me a lecture.

"Certain men in high position," he said, "set the fashion. All must go along, for to do otherwise sets you apart. Making yourself conspicuous in a different costume shows you do not belong. The value of a costume such as this impresses people that you are a gentleman. By the time they find this not true, you have had the advantage of making their acquaintance. Then, already being friends, they forgive the lack in your birth."

"I am not ashamed of my birth," I replied.

"Damme, Will. Let's not revive these old arguments. Each trade has its costume. Without clothes all would appear equal."

"What an admission for you to make."

His face flushed, but he would not pick up the challenge. "Should you wish to attain some success, you will wear the proper costume with good grace," he replied.

Seeing his seriousness and knowing his unselfish desire to push me forward, I said no more about it. I felt, however, somewhat like a stork in the short britches. The padded and ruffled coat made me seem all shoulders on top, and the stockings revealed a length of leg that was seemingly endless. To say the least, I was a startling sight. I was not handsome in the face, being of large feature. The beard I wore in the style of Drake helped me a bit but I would have wished it to be dark rather than the yellow it was.

In time I got used to being dressed so, though the first time Diggins saw me he could not hold back his laughter. Diggins had held my room for me but made no comment when I moved in with Roger at his father's London house.

Roger's father had inherited a baronetcy on the death of his brother. His holdings were in Devonshire, but following the custom, they spent most of their time in London. They had a fine, large house on Pall Mall, with servants in livery at our disposal at any time of the day or night.

For a few weeks we drank a great deal and whored about the town, and most of the time I couldn't tell whether I was with a prostitute or a lady of fashion. Later on I learned to differentiate. The whores were generally the ones with a certain delicacy in their speech.

This was a trying time for England. Everyone was happy at the loot the seafarers brought to England and proud of the successes in the battles. Yet when Philip of Spain proclaimed his just anger, they shook in fear at the thought of war and blamed the very men they had just finished praising and called them pirates.

From the time we arrived in London we were caught up in a whirl of parties, balls and dinners, and though my share from the prize was more money than I had ever had, I found I was spending very little, for we were Drake's men and the guests of all.

It was one of these nights that I saw, for the first time, Elizabeth Howard. It is a strange part of man's nature that, out of thousands of people, there will appear one who strikes a spark and causes this emotion for which no better name has ever been found than love.

We had gone to the "theater in the round" to see a play that was bruited about to be a fine, lusty comedy. I loved the theater. It was one of the good parts of life and I had just learned to discriminate between the good and the ordinary. But of this play and the players themselves I remember nothing. My memory covers but the scene of me standing at the back of the box talking to Lady Trient and a young lady cousin to whom they had introduced me. The play had not yet started. Down below, in the pit, there was a mass of movement.

It was not considered good form for a young man to stay in the box. We had just come to pay our respects before going below to mingle with the young gentlemen of the city and their doxies. These ladies were like a group of colorful, chattering birds. The entire theater was abuzz with conversation and laughter. Wine was being consumed in quantity. From time to time a scuffle would start, half in anger, half in play, which was ignored by the ushers who stood by the walls holding staves. When a really serious fight would begin, the ushers would move in and efficiently bruise a few heads to restore order.

As we talked, the box next to ours filled and a girl selected the seat nearest to us. My eyes struck and held to the loveliness of her profile. I lost interest in the conversation and waited impatiently for her to turn so that I could see her in full face. Finally she did look around and I was not disappointed. As our eyes met I felt a shock that seared me like a broadside.

She had the largest, darkest eyes I have ever seen, with winged eyebrows above them. She had a short, straight nose and a graceful curve to her upper lip. Her skin was very white and clean, and good health seemed to shine outward from her. Her hair was caught in the back in what was called a snood. It shone black as a raven's wing. Our eyes held for a long time before I recovered myself enough to make a short bow.

She turned away as the lights were being damped. Roger took me by the arm and we went below. I had no chance to meet with the girl that night but the image of her stayed in my mind like a chord of music. By subtlety I tried to find from Roger who she was, but he wouldn't take the bait. Finally, I had to ask him outright.

He looked at me owlishly over the rim of his cup and shook his head.

"You are an ox, Adams, a great, ungainly ox. God's blood! London is full of willing wenches and you make eyes at that one."

Anger came up in me, though why, I couldn't say.

"I asked a question which you return with an insult. You presume too much on our friendship."

I knew it was childish to take offense, still I could not help myself.

His face flushed, then he laughed. "I'm sorry, Will. Your size makes me forget how thin your skin is. You want to know about the girl? Her name is Elizabeth Howard. Mind you, Howard is a great name in England but there are many Howards. She is one of the poor relations sent up to London from the country in order to make a good marriage. It is the way of our society, William. Sometimes the only hope a family has is a fair daughter to be shown off. Put on the block, as it were. By marrying well they can then recoup the family finances."

When I did not reply, he placed his hand on my arm in understanding.

"I'm sorry, Will. But that is not for you."

I made some remark to clear the air and we went on to a party where there was drink, laughter and music, but somehow it had lost its flavor.

The following evening Roger's mother insisted on our presence at a ball. She was so proud of Roger and looked upon me as a steadying influence. To stand by Roger and keep him somewhere on course was little enough repayment for the warmth and hospitality his family had given so freely to me.

Roger and I arrived late, having spent a great deal of time over a long and noisy dinner. I had had much difficulty in getting him to leave, as he had been smitten by one of the barmaids.

Being ushered in and announced, I saw Elizabeth Howard again. Her beauty was proved by the crowd of men paying court around her. She was dressed in very fashionable style of some gold cloth that had a great, high collar in back. In front it was cut so low the sweet rise of her breasts seemed ready to emerge from the gown at the slightest breath. The dress was pinched in at the waist so that I could have spanned her with my two hands. It billowed out into a wide circumference as if designed to entice yet keep her beyond reach of anything but admiring eyes.

As she turned from one to another, they leaned toward her, somewhat in the manner of a bird trying to peck at a morsel while keeping its legs firmly planted. It took some time before I was able to maneuver into a position to speak with her. But eventually I managed to separate her from her admirers and claim an introduction. For a moment or two I had her all to myself. I tried to keep my eyes from the lovely uncovered fullness of her bosom, but with each breath she took I could not resist glancing down to see if one or the other had popped out like the cork out of a bottle.

"You are a captain, Mr. Adams?" she asked.

"I have sailed my own ship," I said. "But with Drake I have been no more than sailing master." Then I added, "But to sail with Drake in any capacity is all any true seaman can ask."

"I know but little of ships," she said. "But my cousin, Lord Howard, seems to know somewhat of them."

"Aye, that he does," I replied, and wondered at the way she had emphasized "her cousin" as if it was necessary to impress me of her relationship with Howard. I remember thinking, though, that it was my imagination, as I was always sensitive at the mention of highborn family.

"Is your home here in London, my lady?"

"For the present I am staying in town. Our country house is in Chatham," she said. She had a sweet, childlike manner of speaking and my eyes watched the bowlike curve of her mouth. She was very small, so that I felt almost a giant beside her. Her soft hand resting on my forearm seemed not much larger than a child's.

"Chatham? Then we're almost neighbors," I said. "I was born in Gillingham."

A slight frown crossed her brow as she said, "I remember no Adams family at Gillingham."

"There is no one left there now," I said. "My father is dead and my mother somewhere in either Holland or the Americas with my only brother. But then you would hardly know us, my lady. My father was no more than a tenant farmer." I felt compelled to say this, though Roger would have called me fool.

I could not see her reaction to that, as someone interrupted us just then and she smiled and left. Roger came over with a group of friends almost at the same time and carried me off to a wine shop. But my mind was still so occupied with Elizabeth that I soon made excuse and went off by myself.

I walked all the way across town, not thinking of the dark streets or footpads, ignoring the whores that accosted me. Finally I came to the house on Lime Street. Letting myself in, I spent the night in my old familiar room.

I slept but little that night, my mind jumping with thoughts of this girl, of my status in life, and debating whether Roger was right and that I should perhaps not have mentioned I was lowborn. Drake was the best example of the results of being common born. Had he been of noble lineage, there would have been no one to stand above him. But, though knighted by the Queen, there remained this barrier which not even he could surmount. His descendants, perhaps, but not Drake. And so it would be for me. What thought I had given to the subject before was that I would marry a girl somewhat near my own station, raise myself as far as I could, and then let my sons, if they were able, continue on.

The memory of Elizabeth wound about my mind like a lovely perfume. I argued vehemently with myself, saying this was a foolish dream. Such dreams, for me, just at the beginning of my career, were childish. I had hardly started to make my way. All the wealth I had in the world was not more than two thousand pounds—a great deal of money to me but, in a comparative sense, it was nothing. Some of the wealthy women of London would pay that much on adornment for the year.

I tossed and turned and argued. Yet love is a strange thing with no relation to reason or logic, and I could not help dreaming. Finally I dropped off to sleep, my last thoughts being that perhaps, with Drake, some great thing would occur whereby, at one single stroke, I could gain recognition and wealth. Man is ever beset by such dreams.

I came awake in the morning with the well-loved and familiar face of Diggins smiling down at me as he shook me. He asked no questions, merely making some jesting comment that there was herring and ale on the table suitable for the settling of a drinking man's stomach.

After we had breakfasted I sent a message to Roger saying I had some business to take care of and would see him in a day or two. In the light of day I dismissed my dream and resolved I would see Elizabeth no more. Diggins and I went to the shipyard where a new ship of the *Rainbow* type was nearing completion.

The next several days I spent in the workrooms and down at the yard, going over the plans for the new ship Nicholas was building for our Queen. His designs for the *Rainbow* and the *Vanguard* were so far ahead of the time that, to the seamen, they were almost unacceptable. He had lowered the poop and slimmed the lines. Besides the regular sail of mainsail, main topsail, foresail, foretopsail, mizzen and spritsail, he had added topgallant sails, which was considered completely impractical as far back as the time of Henry VIII. But Nicholas had set them so it was a practical design. Many of the sailors who claimed to wisdom of the sea swore they would founder in the first gale. The *Rainbow* had proved this was untrue. No ship in the fleet handled better than the *Rainbow*, nor could outsail her. Now, on this new ship, Diggins had become even more radical.

I had learned my trade well from Diggins and evolved some theories that were even more advanced than his. I discussed them with him and he agreed.

"William," he said, "in each step it is necessary that we prove ourselves. In order to continue building ships, I must build them for a profit. To do that I must cater to the wish of the purchaser, whether merchant or Queen. For this reason I cannot move too fast. You well know what happened to the *Rainbow* before Drake took her out. For a full two years she lay at Chatham, sailing no farther than Plymouth because our good Queen believed what her other admirals had told her, that the ship could not live in a storm. They did admit, though, that she could outsail anything else in good weather. It was Drake who insisted that she go with the fleet to Corunna. You know then how well she proved herself.

"God bless Drake, he has finally convinced the Queen that this was the best ship ever built in England. Now, to prove his faith in me, he has commissioned us to build a ship of a thousand tons, mounting at least fifty guns. These are the plans, William. I have been saving them for your eyes to see first."

He showed them to me with such pride and love that I responded in kind, being so honored at this display of confidence in me. I remember how we sat that night studying the drawings. He had done something which profoundly excited me. She would be a ship so mighty that nothing on the sea could stand against her. The plans were almost completed.

Nicholas asked me to stay with him until they were finished and then carry them to Drake, personally. In spite of the great prize, the *San Felipe*, that Drake had taken, the Queen was once more at odds with him. On this occasion he was in disrepute because of his actions toward Vice-Admiral Lord Borough. His angry insistence that Borough and the others be tried for mutiny angered Queen Elizabeth. On her refusal to follow his demands, Drake spoke his mind, a very dangerous thing to do.

On his return to England, Lord Borough had given a distorted version of the events. He had charged that Drake was insane, citing his reckless behavior as proof. Borough had many friends at court and, in truth, had we not taken the great carrack, the *San Felipe*, Drake's head most assuredly would have fallen this time.

The vast wealth the ship contained, of which the Queen made sure she received her share, coupled with the tremendous popularity of Drake, could not be taken lightly, even by a queen as strong-minded as Bess. Yet she pardoned Borough and completely exonerated him, thereby placing Drake in an untenable position.

We, who had sailed with Drake, knew that had it not been for the last, devastating cruise, King Philip could have sailed from Lisbon against an England totally unprepared. Drake had bought time. Had he been given the weapons and reinforcements he had asked for, the Armada would never have been able to sail.

Our Queen was a strong woman, hard, arrogant and miserly, constantly disputing over her share of all prizes taken. She even resented giving the seamen a fair portion of the profits. Strangely enough, she was loved by all as no monarch had ever been before— a complete paradox.

The thought that I would have the privilege of bringing the drawings to Drake excited me. Fortune permitting, I would be able to have some further conversation with him.

On the third day, when we had almost completed our work, Roger Trient came to see me. He found me dirty, with pitch beneath my fingernails like any common laborer.

"God's blood, Adams!" he said angrily. "Here I set you up in the best society and now find you run away to muck in the dirt. We have a dozen invitations to balls and parties."

I greeted him warmly but told him I had decided to forego society. I felt out of place, as some sort of impostor.

"Nonsense," he said. "You cannot pass up a chance to better yourself. I will not let up on you. I know you have learned as much of your trade of shipbuilding as Master Diggins, and you sail a ship better than any man I know. But that will not put you where *you* belong. And the women, now, with the threat of war hanging over us, are as ready to make love as rabbits. This, truly, you cannot pass up."

Taking his arm, I led him away from the work area.

"This is no place for you and your fancy ruffles, Roger. Anyway, I have had enough of wine and wenching for the time. Diggins has just completed the plans for a new ship and she will be like no ship ever built. I am to carry them to Drake in a day or two."

"Very well, muck about in the daytime, but tonight there is a ball. My mother has specifically asked that you come. No one turns down my mother's request. Also, there's been a certain young female asking for you."

My heart lurched. "Not Mistress Howard?"

"The same. But what she sees in a lout such as you I cannot understand."

"All right. Let me see Diggins and wash some of the dirt away and we'll be off."

I am sure I would not have gone had it not been that Elizabeth had asked about me. A man's mind can overcome almost everything except that deep, primitive urge of selecting a mate. I knew there was no possible hope of a union between Elizabeth and myself but she attracted me beyond any ordinary woman hunger. Once, at a later time, when we were anchored off the coast of Africa, I watched moths throwing themselves to destruction in a lamp and wondered why. There was no more sense in my action than in the moths', but we had this in common. Once attracted, we could not turn away.

That night there was a small gathering for dinner before the ball. Whether by design or good fortune, I had the place next to Elizabeth. My tongue, which ordinarily was hesitant, became loose at both ends. I talked of things, including my ambitions. Her head leaned toward me and the curve of her neck and the rise of her breasts drove me to such a state of passion that I was unaware of anyone else. We stayed together as much as it was in my power to arrange that evening. The following day we met and went to the maze, losing her chaperone and ourselves, and I kissed her and she accepted the kiss.

There is no point in recounting the nights I could not sleep, the hunger that ate at me, my dreams and hopes. All who have loved know what I felt, though I doubt in such measure. She was never for a moment out of my mind; though, in our more calm moments, we both agreed that this love was an impossibility and would be foolish.

The plans for the new ship were finally finished, though I had been little help to Diggins. The day after their completion, he asked me to take them to Drake. I hated the thought of leaving London, but could not refuse.

That night I asked Elizabeth to accompany me. Under ordinary circumstances such a suggestion would have been impermissible, but we were on the verge of war—and war, as if nature knew the danger to the strength of the race, caused even the most virtuous women to behave with freedom unthinkable in ordinary times.

I know not why her family had not nipped this affair in the bud, for undoubtedly they had heard of it; probably they credited Elizabeth with better sense. She would not consent to go until Roger and his girl of the moment consented to accompany us as chaperons. In this manner she gained permission. As for me, I felt more wealth had come to me than the day we took the *San Felipe*.

I picked up the designs of the ship from Diggins and we set out. It was a bright and lovely day. We started our journey as if on a pleasure jaunt. I felt as if the whole world was filled with happy laughter. The beauty of this girl was such that it made my heart ache each time I looked at her. Woman-like, she was well aware of the power she had over me.

She teased me, and flirted with Roger, bringing me to the point of anger, then melting me with no more than a secret glance or a touch of her hand. I knew not much of women then. I know not much of them now, except that their outward behavior gives little indication of what goes on inside them.

As she told me later, she loved my ungainly size and quiet manner despite the knowledge I had neither grace, family, nor any of the things upon which her ambitions had set. But it was a day to remember. Our mood and the journey were delightful. The small discomforts were not even noticed. Before going on to Drake's manor house we stopped at an inn to refresh ourselves. From the inn I sent a messenger to announce our arrival to the great Admiral. The messenger returned promptly with orders to repair to the house. There the Admiral received us with warmth, almost as if he was lonely.

Drake met us in the large hall. It struck me that he seemed not so tall away from his ship. Drake ashore was strangely different, as if only half the man was in attendance.

While our baggage was taken by the servants to our rooms we had a glass of wine and Drake talked and bantered with the ladies, making us feel welcome and at ease. Then Roger and I retired to his study to go over the plans. They were so radical that I wanted to be with him to answer any questions while he studied them.

Ah, how that man knew and loved ships! He bent over the parchment drawings, scanning them the way some men would look at the portrait of a beautiful woman. Little was said except for an occasional question. Finally he straightened up and looked at me and there was a gleam of laughter at the back of his eyes.

"Damn my soul, Adams, Nicholas Diggins must be mad! It would seem he thinks I am of his own ken. How can she hold to a sea with so narrow a beam and hardly any poop? Ask any man and he would tell you she would broach with the first wave."

"I would stake my life that she won't, Sir Francis."

"You had a hand in this, Adams?"

"Some small part. Diggins and I talked often of such a ship even before I sailed with you."

I removed a parchment from the pile—the one that showed her masts and rigging.

"If you will study carefully the design of this rig and the setting we can give the sail, she will be able to sail much closer into the wind."

He studied it again, asking me several questions before he put the drawings aside. "What a ship!" he said, admiringly. "But the cost? What estimates has Diggins for her building?"

"Ten thousand pounds will do it, Sir Francis. But there will be slight profit for Diggins in it. I know how close he has calculated because he will not skimp on the ship; this he will never do. Further, he feels England needs this ship now."

"Ten thousand pounds. That is more than my share from the San Felipe and I have many debts."

"Perhaps, knowing the need England has for this ship, the Queen will advance part of this sum."

He looked at me in grim amusement. "Our Queen has turned away from me again. But perhaps . . ." he mused, more to himself than to me, as he once again leafed through the various drawings. "It is a great sum, but with a ship such as this I could sail round and about any fleet, cutting out ships as a dog cuts out sheep. What does Diggins estimate her speed?"

"Diggins reckons—and I do not doubt him—that with the wind she will sail at twelve land miles each hour."

Drake laughed joyously. "Tell your master I think him mad!" And taking the sting away, he laid a hand on my arm. "But tell him also that I am mad enough to believe in such a ship. Had I the money I would order the building of her tomorrow. I will give him my answer in a fortnight. Damn my eyes, this should be the Queen's business. She refuses to see England's danger, hoping she may not have to empty some of her money bags. Adams, was there ever a ruler who expected so much from her ships and sailors? Yet she shares hugely in whatever profits we return."

He had spoken bitterly and freely. Now he looked at me to measure the effect of his words, which were close to treason.

I answered him frankly. "I am honored that you speak so honestly to me. Those of us who follow the sea know how England stands. Though you well know the truth of what I am about to say, I say it again. There is no sailor in all England who would not follow you with open heart to any place you would lead them. One of the proudest things I shall ever tell my grandchildren is that I was with Drake at Cape St. Vincent and Lagos and trod upon the bloody decks of the *San Felipe* when she was taken off St. Michaels."

He bowed silently toward me, smiling, and said, "Adams, do not make a hero of me. I am but an Englishman." Then, in a more serious mood, he turned and looked toward the sea that shimmered in the last rays of the evening sun. "I speak my mind too freely for our Queen and those who surround her. There are some who would like to see my head on a pike. But though good Queen Bess may banish me to the country intermittently, so long as there is danger to England my head will sit safely on my shoulders. In that there's some satisfaction. But enough. Come, we will join your friends lest they think we're fighting those past cruises, station by station. From the look of the filly you brought, I am sure there is another battle you have in mind which has nothing to do with ships."

"You are right, Sir Francis. Trient calls me a fool and Diggins has told me, since a boy, that marriage is not for a sailor. But I find my heart is in dire straits."

Smiling, he said, "All of our hearts have this weakness. But you listen to Diggins and take his advice. Marriage is for those who live with the land. Diggins and I, being old bachelors, well know the dangers."

"My mind argues with my heart in the same fashion," I answered. "But my heart has no logic and I do not know how this battle will end."

Drake laughed and poked me in the ribs. "God's blood, man, it is not your heart. Take the pressure off your balls and you will forget this love, I warrant."

"I doubt that there is much cause for worry in this. She is a sensible girl and I hardly think marriage with one so lowborn as I would enter her mind." I felt ashamed at the reference to birth as I said it, but Sir Francis did not seem to notice it.

"Don't depend upon a woman's reason," he answered. "If she does desire marriage with you there will be little that you, her family, or anyone else can do about it."

We were laughing together as we re-entered the main hall. The beautiful face of Elizabeth set my heart to jumping as she came forward and curtsied before us.

"My lords, we had almost given up on you. I thought you were gone off on some sea battle leaving me a sailor's widow while yet a virgin."

"God's blood, lass. If you are still virgin after being around this one then I say he needs some further lessons in the art of love. He should have had you grappled and boarded by now."

"It is not through lack of his trying, my lord. From my cousin, Lord Howard, I have learned somewhat about slipping by the wind. When he boards me it will not be by force of arms, but an alliance." As she said this she took my arm and smiled up at me with such warmth that my heart seemed to reach outward toward her, and the vexation I felt at her mention of Lord Howard being kin vanished.

"It is true, Sir Francis," she went on, "that he has a certain attraction for me, a maid from a seafaring family, and perhaps some of the luck which you, my lord, carry like a shield will rub off on him. I would say he shows promise not only as a lover but as a sailor. What say you, sir?"

"I say, my lady, don't discount the talent of this giant. I know much of him. I say he sails a ship with more skill than any man I have seen. And though he blush at the compliment, I also say that in designing and building ships he will outstrip his master. As to his ability in the arms of Venus, I am afraid you will have to find out for yourself, Mistress Howard."

I blushed, in fact, at these words, and at the same time wondered how Drake knew so much of me. Yet his genius was to know men. Sir Francis then took her other arm and we walked over to where Roger and his girl, Peggy Thomas, stood by the fireplace.

"I am afraid now," Elizabeth said, "your servants have been holding up supper."

"Your beauty gives me appetite. This night we will drink of the best wine of Spain and to the chagrin of King Philip."

As we passed into the dining room set with glass, plate and silver, all part of the loot of Drake's raids, he dropped behind a bit and said:

"Damme, Adams, I begin to understand your problem the better the more I look at this lass. She is a lovely morsel. I insist she sit next to me and listen to my great exploits while you three chatter as you will."

Holding to the mood I bowed slightly, saying, "You are my captain but if she signals for help I will come to her aid, even for no more reward than her smile."

"Well said, Adams. But don't worry. I have no intent to board her. Not that I would slight the prize she carries but she's English and therefore safe against my guns."

Our dinner was light and merry and full of laughter. All through dinner when our eyes met she returned my glances with an ardor that burned me so I could hardly eat. To try and still my turbulent blood I drank of the wine to such an extent that even Drake commented on it. But the wine made no drunkenness in me. It neither thickened my tongue nor spoiled the clarity of my thoughts.

After dinner, Peggy played the lute and sang, and as she sang Elizabeth and I had an opportunity to go off to a darkened corner unnoticed.

She came into my arms so willingly that it took me by surprise. Ardently she pressed herself against me as if confessing she was mine for the taking. Where the wine I had consumed had no effect, I now became drunk on her lips.

When the time came to retire we parted to go our different ways. With Drake lighting the way I could snatch no more than a hasty kiss from Elizabeth. Once in my bed I tossed feverishly, unable to sleep. I wanted to go to her yet felt it would be taking an unfair advantage. I tossed and turned, trying to make up my mind, listening to hear if the house was yet asleep. Finally I reached a decision. If Elizabeth was still awake I would claim a further good-night kiss. Just as I had made up my mind the door opened slowly and Elizabeth came to me.

I held my breath as she closed the door and removed her robe, letting it fall gently in a pile at her feet. She stood before me in the faint light, so rounded, so light of skin that she seemed to gleam luminously as if brightened by a candle within her. Her eyes and mouth were but shadows as were the points of her breasts. My eyes slowly traveled downward, savoring all of the exquisite beauty of her. I whispered her name and started up. She made a faint gesture, cautioning me to silence, and then, all in one soft, free movement, she came into the bed beside me.

From that moment on, the world could have come asunder and I would not have heard it. The only clear thought I retain of that night was the wonder that so much fire, passion and energy could be contained in so small a body.

The relationship between man and woman has always interested me and particularly when man changes from pursuer to the pursued. Once back in London, I found myself now not quite so anxious for a hasty marriage. Having enjoyed the fruits of that which I had pursued so ardently, I was quite willing to proceed slowly

I knew the storm we faced with her family. She could have looked long and hard and not found a poorer prospect for a husband than I. Yet knowing this, when her family said it bluntly to my face, I was resentful.

All I knew of Elizabeth then was the outward endowments of

beauty nature had given her. Her family should have known that, when crossed, she had a whim of iron. Had they taken a different tack she might have looked at me with cooler eyes, but they set against me and their contempt also brought forth my own stubbornness.

We met each afternoon in London and she would tell me to what affair she would be that night. The memories of those days stay warm even now. Caught up as we were and bound together by this emotion, nothing else existed. The secret hours spent together in some prearranged room at an inn or house did not cool us but increased our desire. Then, one afternoon, she told me her family had forbidden her meeting me again. The news had reached them as I had known it must.

She held to me and asked, "What are we to do, William?"

"We have not much choice. I have put off thinking on it. But now we must. We will find a small church where the banns can be read without attracting any attention. There we can be married and, once done, they can't turn it back."

"You will never let me go?"

"Never so long as I breathe."

She drew away from me, thoughtfully biting her lip. "I have a better plan," she said. "You will come to call tonight, early."

"This may wreck everything. Seeing us together they will know our love in a moment. Your heart stands in your eyes when you look at me. They will put such a guard on you I will never reach you."

"Don't worry, William," she replied softly, "I know how to beat them." And she would say no more. When we kissed at parting she reminded me, "Early in the evening, William."

I had not met her father; but her mother I knew, and she would be a dangerous opponent. She was a broad-beamed woman, built close to the ground, with a force to her when she moved that reminded me of a Portugal carrack under full sail. It was with trepidation that I approached the house that evening.

Roger was in on our secret, and though he held little hope for my chances, he had encouraged me—not because of love but that marrying into even this far-removed branch of the Howards would increase my chance for position. I angrily rejected this motive and he spoke no more of it. He had offered to accompany me but I felt this was my problem to solve.

Being let in by a servant, I was met in the hall by Elizabeth. With a smile and press of the hand she brought me inside a room where the clan was gathered in array against us. I remember the eyes centered on me, cold and unwavering. Elizabeth curtsied before her mother and father.

"Father, this is Captain Adams."

Her father was a short, quiet man with the look of being more comfortable in a field than a town house. He nodded briefly to me and seemed on the verge of saying something when Elizabeth's mother spoke:

"This meeting was Elizabeth's choosing, but there is no need to indulge in dishonest politeness. Will Adams of Gillingham, we know all about you. No tenant farmer's son is welcome in our family. You will not raise yourself to high estate on the foolish passion of our daughter!"

Her harsh voice and words angered me.

"Madam," I said, "I seek nothing from you or your family, now or ever. To love Elizabeth and to cherish her is my only wish. My feeling toward her is based not on intent, but on emotion. Over this I have no control. As to my low birth, I make no apology. This was not of my doing either. Nor do I make apology for my father, who was one of the finest men ever born, high or low."

Elizabeth now broke in, and it seemed everyone spoke in angry loudness that reminded me of a sharp squall at sea. I was ordered from the house. As I turned to go, Elizabeth uttered words that brought instant silence:

"Send him forth and he leaves behind a bastard. I am with child."

I looked at her, then at her mother's pale face. Her father stared first at her and then dropped his eyes in sorrow. Taking Elizabeth's arm, I led her out of the room.

"Elizabeth—"

She looked around to see if we were alone, then hugged me gleefully.

"Did you see their faces?"

"But why didn't you tell me?"

"Because," she whispered, "it is not true. But they don't know. They can't refuse us now."

I was disturbed at the unhesitating ease with which she resorted to trickery. But she proved right. We came back again to find a different air. It was not *if* we could marry, but how soon.

Now the family closed ranks and the wedding plans under Elizabeth and her mother's direction went apace. Never have I undergone such a trying time. The only one who suffered more was her father.

It was a lavish affair with the bridesmaids and musicians and a huge dinner for none of which had I any enjoyment. I felt like an impostor. Such a wedding was too grand for the station in life which we would have to enter and more than they could afford. Still, I could not chide her for it nor spoil her enjoyment. It seemed half of London was there, of whom I knew not more than a dozen.

Roger stood with me and, of course, Diggins was at hand. He wished me happiness and treated my bride with warmth. He was like my own father in this.

For our holiday we went to a country place near Chatham that one of the Howards had lent to us. The days there were bright, joyous and full of love. Yet in the background I had a nagging worry of what I knew must come into the open between Elizabeth and myself.

I had never, to Elizabeth nor anyone else, made any false claims as to my background or status and I had no intent to seek position or favor from her family nor anyone else, for that matter. Yet Elizabeth had the attitude that, in truth, I was a prince in disguise who had wooed her under the pretense of being a poor man, just to test her love. It was on this point I had to disillusion her and it caused our first quarrel.

During these last days when the time neared for our return to London, she began to chatter of the house we would take, the furniture to buy, and of the parties we would attend. On this I gently chided her.

"Elizabeth, there's a time to dream and a time when we must face life as it is. I thought it well understood between us that I have not the funds for such things. I must go to work for Diggins or else go back to sea in order for us to live."

She looked at me like a child. "But the prize money you got from the voyage. You still have that?"

"But Elizabeth, I have told you it was but six hundred pounds.

Five hundred of that I gave to Nicholas to invest in a ship. I have, in all, less than two thousand pounds which Diggins has invested for me. Please understand this is not money to be spent. In London, living the way you want to live, it would not last six months. We have to think further ahead than that."

"William," she said, coldly, "there is a time for pride and a time to think of the future. To attain rank we must live among people with rank. So we have only enough for half a year. In half a year we will have established ourselves. Remember, I am a Howard."

"No, Elizabeth. You are an Adams. Whatever fortune comes to us will come through my own efforts, not by favor from your family."

She wept and said many bitter, biting words, but in me was a stubbornness all her tears could not overcome. We came to know each other better. Finally she melted, blamed herself for being selfish, agreeing that I was right. She promised to follow my course because she had confidence that someday the name of Adams would be more honored than Drake or Howard.

She accepted the loss of the first engagement, but never gave up the fight.

And so we moved in with Nicholas Diggins on his insistence. He made us more than welcome, turning over one whole wing of the house to us. I knew he thought my marriage a mistake, but he would never, by word or deed, interfere.

He accepted Elizabeth. For a time, they appeared to be great friends. She couldn't do enough for him, and I think Nicholas enjoyed having someone as lovely and young as Elizabeth in his house where no woman had ever reigned before. She even won over Mrs. Grandy and I was happy.

One day I received notice from Drake of my recall. I would be given a command in Drake's squadron. Though neither Nicholas nor Elizabeth wanted me to go I used the excuse of duty to the Queen and England. But in truth, it was the need to feel a live ship under me again and the wondrous joy of the wind and the sea that sent me out. That, and the fact I was not yet broken to marriage.

Elizabeth was beautiful, but even beauty can be wearing. The nightly necessities of appearing at some function or other bored me now. I was not unaware of her intent. Always it was with the motive of advancing me. She would not give up. Nor would I. With her help

I could have obtained a better ship and position, but I was determined to make my way alone.

I joined the squadron off Plymouth, and after a time I longed to be back in London enjoying Elizabeth's passion. Our parting had been sweet, she giving everything to me so that I would have memories of our love during the long days at sea. Not knowing the plans, I could not ask her to come to Plymouth. The weather was brawly and cold. I contented myself with the writing of long letters and trying to keep my spirits up.

Our stores were ever low. The monotony of waiting day after day brought such discontent amongst the entire squadron that all about me almost treasonable words were spoken against our Queen by officers and men. But Englishmen are a strange breed; no matter how foolishly the Queen acted, we remained steadfast.

Day after day, great debates raged in London until Drake, in fury, went there personally to speak the truth of the danger England faced. Drake's furious charges that it was absolute madness to allow the Spaniards to come to us seemed to have no effect on the Queen and the court, until one day the last peace mission Elizabeth had sent out returned to England. Philip would make no compromise. The Spaniard King's message was brutally phrased. Now, in high anger, the Queen ordered her squadrons out. By then it was too late.

Governments work in odd ways. Now that we had orders to sail I was put second in command of the *Rainbow*, but we were taken from the fleet and ordered back to London for new sails, rigging, and more guns. All were greatly disappointed at this. Just when it looked as if the fleets were to engage, we were to be left out.

17

We spent much time fitting out the *Rainbow*. As fate willed, we lost nothing but monotony; all during the time we were in London the fleet still lay off Plymouth, at anchor.

The day our fitting-out was completed and we had our orders to sail, Captain Marchant, Diggins and myself made a complete round of the ship. She was much changed from the older galleons of the same tonnage, carrying more sail and better guns.

The older ships carried no more than thirty pieces, throwing weight of ball of 426 pounds. We had aboard now guns of much longer range and higher penetration, throwing a total weight of 670 pounds from our thirty-six pieces. Also, our light, quick-firing guns had been changed to all of the same caliber whereas, in the older ships such as the *Lion*, there were from three to four different types, which made for much confusion in the serving.

After making the final survey, Captain Marchant left us. Diggins and I stayed, leaning on the rail of the high poop, talking and looking ashore at the activity going on at the Howland Dock.

"Soon now the battle will be joined, William," Diggins said. "I pray each day to God that both you and England survive, for both are important to me."

"We will, sir. Have no fear of that." But in my heart I was afraid. Both for myself and my country. I had seen the might of Spain. Our countrymen talked bravely yet milled back and forth with no more sense than a herd of frightened sheep.

"No man in the world, William, knows what fate holds and whether England shall become a great, strong nation or be defeated. Our only solace is that we, as Englishmen, shall do our best. But go now and say your good-by to Elizabeth. I shall see to her every comfort as much as is in my power."

Elizabeth's claim of being with child came true sooner than she would have wished. She was very bitter about it. On my return, she hadn't shown at all, but now, even with tight stays, there was no doubt.

She loved so to be among people. Admiration, to her, was important as food and drink. Her swelling stomach disgusted her. When she tried to bind it so she could get into her dresses I protested, fearing she would injure the child. This led to bitter quarrels, besides the fact that I would not give up the *Rainbow* for a position with Admiral Lord Howard of Effingham, who was in charge of the fleet.

Elizabeth thought me a fool. Perhaps she was right. Yet I could not do as she wished and remain a man. Knowing this did not make me feel less guilty, therefore I had gone with her wherever she wished.

Up to the last day I had not told her when we were to leave. Saying good-by to Diggins, I went to Bess with full knowledge of how hard this parting would be for her—and for me. I loved her so much.

To hurt her tore at me so that, like a coward, I wished to be gone. When I rejoined the fleet I looked forward to action to take my mind from my problem.

The Inn of the White Dolphin, in Plymouth, was a popular wine shop where many of the officers of the fleet gathered to while away the time and to thrash out the rumors that passed back and forth.

My relationship with Drake and the promotion I had received caused jealousy in some. Lieutenant John Saris was one of the most persistently bitter against me. He had been on the *Rainbow* before and it was I who had replaced him. Now he was on one of the older galleons. He was a pompous, undersized man, not more than twenty-one years of age, with a sharp, insulting tongue. He had a gift for words to cause anger, yet he was oversensitive to slights toward himself. Coming of good family, he expected to rise faster than he had.

Each time we met, his insults grew more bitter so that I was sorely tempted to lay hands on him. He had found my sensitive spot, saying I had married a Howard in order to advance myself. His charge that my connections were the reason for my fast promotion, after all the trouble my refusal of favors had caused between Elizabeth and myself, was too much. I resolved to have no more of it.

This night I was talking with a Scot soldier named MacGruder and some other officers in the fleet when Saris came over and, interrupting our conversation, said:

"What ho, Adams! What word does Drake's pogue bring from the Admiral? Do we sail or do we not?"

Pogue was a vulgar, insulting word relating to sodomy. The use of it angered me further. My temper was short and I could hold no reason to listen to his remarks, nor have him cast aspersions on my birth or my relationship with Drake.

"Once, Saris," I said in anger, "and only once shall I tell you. Never speak to me like that again, for if you do I shall stop you with my fist." Whereupon I turned my back, picked up my pot of ale, and resumed the conversation. There was a scuffling behind me and I turned to find two of Saris' friends holding his arms. His face was flushed with anger.

He shouted, "Adams, you lowborn scum. Are you of the mind that I fear you?"

I said, "You must be in fear or you would not so strongly try to prove otherwise."

At this he broke away and drew his sword, giving me no chance to draw, but lunged forward so that it was with luck that I managed to slap the blade to one side. Seizing his hand, I forced him to drop the weapon. I then pulled him toward me, drew the poinard from his belt, and forced his hand flat on the table. Then I drove the blade through his hand and deep into the table.

"Now," I said, "you have proved you are not afraid of me. But now, by God, be afraid, for if you ever draw on me again I will kill you."

I left him thus and went outside to cool my temper while his friends withdrew the blade and bandaged his hand. John Saris carried that scar all of his life. Never did he forgive me for that night.

The next morning a message came that we were to make ready for sea. Drake sent a note to be drummed throughout the squadron.

On Whitsunday, Lord Howard and myself took the sacrament together to bid God's blessing on the affair at hand. Our great and good Queen has given us permission to sail. Store ships are on the way from Portsmouth and London and may God give us wind to put us out to the sea, for go we will, even though our store ships arrive not in time. The fault is not mine and we must do as God will provide for us. I do say in my squadron is the gallantest company of men, captains, soldiers and mariners that has ever been seen in England.

I do claim it a pity that they should lack meat when they are so desirous to spend their lives in Her Majesty's service, but though we starve, we will win. God Bless you all.

Drake.

With all speed now we made ready for sea. The majority of ships were short of victuals and stores, and the store ships did not arrive on the promised date. However, we proceeded with the hope that the victualers would be able to catch up with us later.

A pinnace had delivered the news that the great Armada had left Lisbon with a number of ships estimated at 150 to 200 sail. We all prayed they were not sailing for England, but merely moving to rendezvous at Vigo or Corunna, which would give us still a chance to meet them at sea, away from our own shores.

Then, in some form of madness, the Queen sent word we were to lay on and off our own coast and not to leave the shores of England. This would put us to the leeward of the Armada and they could traverse the coast of England as far as Ireland or Scotland, always keeping us at a disadvantage to the prevailing winds. Now our hands were tied. We laid on and off, doing nothing, with despair gradually taking hold of even the bravest English hearts.

At that time we were unaware that the great Admiral, Santa Cruz, had died and the Duke of Medina-Sidonia had been given command. The Armada sailed from Lisbon and a mighty force it was. The Portugal squadron consisted of ten royal galleons and two pinnaces. The Castile squadron contained ten great galleons and four ships of the *flota* of New Spain. These two squadrons were the command ships under the command of Medina-Sidonia and Don Pedro de Valdez. There were four Lisbon galleys under Don Hugo de Moncada and, also under his squadron, four galleasses of Naples.

There were forty armed merchantmen in four squadrons; the Biscayne squadron, under Recalde, and the Andalusian under another De Valdez. Guipuscoan, commanded by Oquendo, the Levant squadron of ten Italian argosies under Don Martin de Bertendona. Besides these capital ships and many pinnaces, there was a light division under Hurtada de Mendoza of twenty-two sail; finally, a non-effective division of twenty-three hulks carrying troops and stores.

This fleet of 130 sail, with almost 58,000 tons burden, carried 2,500 cannon, 19,000 soldiers and 8,000 sailors. The organization bore out the Spaniards' reputation of the science of war but had two flaws which helped us greatly, despite the fact we knew not of them.

Philip of Spain had given command to Medina-Sidonia. But the Duke was to be guided by the advice of Don Pedro de Valdez, who, fortunately for us, was a vain man lacking experience; yet, by orders of King Philip, he was the true commander of the Armada. Though we had great difficulty with sickness, lack of stores and bad weather, these conditions also affected the Armada.

Had Drake been granted a free hand to leave when he wished, we would have had them at our mercy. But we could not disobey orders from the Queen. It was a time to try men's souls.

We waited. Each day brought new rumors: Drake was to take our squadron once again, to try to find the Armada instead of staying off the coast. We were to scatter and harass them so that when they reached England they would be much weakened. Then the following day we would hear yet another rumor contradicting the previous one completely. Nothing ever came of any of them.

I do not know whether the following story is true. The commanders of the squadrons were gathered at the Inn of the Golden Hind, playing at bowls, when a pinnace came scudding in at the harbor with word that the Armada had been sighted off the Lizard. Captain Flemming came bursting through the door with the news. There was shocked silence. Drake stood with a ball in his hand, about to make a roll. He glanced around at the others, then at the ball.

"Gentlemen," he said, "there's time for the game and to beat the Spaniards after." And he made his roll as calmly as if the word had merely been that it had begun to rain.

True or not, this is the sort of tale men love to hear about a commander they adore.

And now the long-awaited battle was to be joined.

18

From here there was no turning back. The fate of England lay in her ships. Those of us who knew their condition looked darkly and fearfully at the set of things. Lord Howard had to strip sixteen ships of their crews to bring up the others somewhere near their full complement. At that time it was reported—and believed—the Spaniards came toward us with more than one hundred fifty sail and we, with all effort, numbered but ninety, and one-third of those not even in fit condition to put to sea.

The great Spaniard fleet came on toward us. They hove to at Dodman Point. All along the coast of England the signal fires burned, passing the word from hill to hill.

The Spaniards had the wind from the southwest and the main body of our fleet was at their mercy at Plymouth Sound. Had they pressed their advantage, first with fire ships, then followed by the great ships, a different tale would be told in England today. But the Duke of Medina-Sidonia ran up the holy banner of Spain on the main truck which held the picture of Christ at one side and the

Holy Mother at the other, and stopped to pray for their success. By this, they lost their advantage.

Dusk brought with it a lowering sky and rain. Never in the history of the world did men work harder than we did on that night. We warped our ships out against the tide and the wind by carrying the anchors forward in longboats, dropping them overside and heaving on the windlass. It was slow, brutal work, but by morning we had beat out of the sound and there were fifty-four English sail lying in near Eddystone.

This was Drake's move, but not even Drake would have tried it save for the grave danger that we lay in. By afternoon we were in a better position and the Spanish still lay, busy at their council of war, thinking that they held us harbor-bound at Plymouth. We hove to under bare poles, sending out only pinnaces to inform us of the Spaniards' next move. If they should come in farther they would be to leeward and we would have the advantage.

During the night the Spaniards lifted anchor and moved in closer to Plymouth. We crossed farther over their flank until, by morning, we were off Eddystone where Lord Howard ordered us to come about. By morning the Spaniards found us bearing down on them on the port tack. The wind had shifted, and each of our great ships that had been able to come out was ready now.

The battle flags went up in the great Armada. Their ships now swung into what was called the eagle formation, being like two great outspread wings. It was a practical battle plan and would have been successful but for Drake, who had evolved a new strategy in which we followed the line of battle formation by division, pouring our fire into ship after ship as we passed in line, and leaving them no chance to engage singly or to recover from the insistent battering.

Our orders were to follow our Admiral in line, tack after his broad-side, each ship in turn giving a broadside until the Spaniard fleet was in utter confusion. So great was the shock of our fire it gave the Spaniards no chance for relief. Soon they showed panic and began crowding the ships ahead.

Recalde, coming about from the left wing of the formation, tried to bring his squadron into battle, but Drake's tactics completely confused him and his ship soon was almost helpless. Before the Duke of Medina-Sidonia could wheel and come up to his rescue, his great ship, the *San Mateo*, was met by the same hammer blows and he, too, was in bad condition. No other ships could relieve him.

The sound of the guns was like constant thunder. When, under Drake's orders, we pulled back, both the *San Juan* and the *San Mateo*, two of the greatest of the Spaniards' galleons, were in a broken and sinking plight.

Then the main body of the Spaniards rallied and Lord Howard signaled to all the squadrons to break off the engagement. In the heat of battle it was hard to get the Englishmen to clear. There was much cursing Lord Howard's decision, we feeling that shortly we could have had the Spaniards in full rout. But Howard was well advised in this maneuver. Our ships were outnumbered more than two to one, undermanned, short of powder as well as stores.

Drake followed Lord Howard's command. Our squadron pulled back. Though the day's work had not been as successful as it might have been, we had saved Plymouth. By now the Spaniards had come about again and were moving down the Channel.

It was a strange maneuver for the Spaniards. Not until the battle was long over did we learn that Medina-Sidonia had been given strict orders from Philip of Spain not to cast their full force into battle until they had joined forces with the Duke of Parma, who waited for them at Calais.

They tightened together and, as night fell, the Spaniard fleet still stood upon the water, not much hurt.

Our orders for that night were to keep light sail and follow in lines of three behind Drake's ship, the *Revenge*. He was to keep a bright stern light burning so that we would not be lost. During the night the stern light on the *Revenge* suddenly disappeared and we were thrown into confusion.

By morning our squadron was scattered out of formation. It was then that Drake appeared. Aboard his ship he held Don Pedro de Valdez and forty officers and men, with all the treasure of the great Andalusian galleon.

Drake was severely censured for his actions, Frobisher claiming that this move was nothing more than that of a pirate. Elizabeth, however, liked treasure more than strict adherence to orders. Later she forgave the charge.

Being so scattered, we were not able to do any damage to the Spaniards that day. It was late afternoon before we could reassemble. By then the wind had fallen almost to a dead calm and both fleets came to a halt between Portland and St. Alban's Head. The sole gain for that day was the taking of Admiral Recalde's ship, the *San Salvador*, after he had abandoned her. Once he was clear, a number of Spanish feluccas went in to set her afire, but our ships managed to drive them off, and the *San Salvador* was towed into Weymouth.

The wind changed during the night. By morning, the Spaniards had the weather, and Medina-Sidonia unfurled his battle flags and ordered an attack. We tried to gain the weather by changing back and working inshore but Levya's division countered us. When they approached us in wing formation, at Drake's orders we came up on line ahead and poured such fire into their lead ships that they were content to fall astern of us. The Spaniards seemed bewildered by our tactics. They would fire a broadside, then try to close in and board. We kept our distance, while our long guns hurt them sorely.

My whole time and energy was spent with the sailing crew, handling the ship in the various maneuvers while the gunners and soldiers did their part. At times the smoke of battle was so thick that the topmast was hidden. It was only in later days, in talking to men of the other ships and to Spaniards who survived, that I could get a clear understanding of what happened.

The battle off Portland was so confused that I do not think even Howard's orders and maneuvers were wholly understood. After breaking away from Levya's division our squadron joined Lord Howard's. Working around, we took the weather gauge from the Spaniards. Being scattered, they had to turn and flee eastward in order to re-form. The whole sea was covered with the smoke from the guns. To me it seemed that the fire came from all directions so that friend and foe were hardly distinguishable. I do know that the right wing of the Armada was turned back by Drake's squadron though he never got credit for it. He, seeing that Howard's attempt to turn the Spanish would fall short, ordered a more southerly course to get a better offing. Once we had weathered the main part of the Spanish fleet—and this was only due to the great smoke and confusion—we were able to join once again. By now we had the full weather gauge.

They broke from us and re-formed to the northeast. Frobisher moved in too close to shore with his division and was now to their lee, under a heavy attack by galleasses. Howard's division turned to

come to his aid, and the Spaniard Admiral came about and bore
down on Howard with his full division. It was then he discovered
that Drake's division had Recalde once again under heavy fire.
The Spaniard Admiral ordered Levya's division to come to his rescue,
but they were too far to leeward and could not come up to help with
sufficient speed.

Medina-Sidonia then made the mistake of sending most of his
squadron down from windward to Recalde's rescue while he continued with his ship and two others, intending to sink Frobisher.
Lord Howard's ship being the closest to the Spaniard Admiral, he
sent direct challenge. Medina-Sidonia, heeding the Spanish code of
honor, could not refuse. He signaled his acceptance and came up
into the wind to await battle. Lord Howard attacked, but brought his
whole squadron with him, and Medina-Sidonia stood alone fighting
back as well as he could.

It was a hard day for Spaniard honor, as our fleet refused to fight
by their rules. As soon as the galleons the Spaniard Admiral had sent
to assist Recalde arrived, Drake ordered our squadron to break
away and led our ships up to where the Spaniard Admiral was beset
and besieged. The Spaniards, seeing the dilemma their Admiral was
in, had their finest captains fight through to Sidonia's assistance, but
before they could come up and take some of the shock, the rigging
of his galleon was shot to pieces, the royal standard of Spain was
down, and the ship was taking water fast. As we came about, the
Spaniard ships were now between our squadron and the Admiral and
they took our broadsides in his protection. They held fast together,
giving way slowly. Now the tragedy was that we had to break off the
engagement. There was hardly a ship holding enough powder and
shot for one more broadside.

As the light wind from the French coast dispersed the smoke of
the long day's engagement, the Armada was almost as formidable as
ever. Help now was coming from those who had previously held
tightly to their purse strings. England would now have to provide us
with the equipment with which to fight or else go down to defeat.

I have heard many Englishmen say that it was only the Spaniards
who made mistakes and that Englishmen and English ships were far
superior. But those who followed closely this great engagement
know mistakes were made on both sides. Had the Spaniards concen-

trated on Frobisher when they had him close inshore, instead of breaking off and sending help to Recalde, the Admiral could have forced Lord Howard to come in to fight or else leave Frobisher and his ships to their fate of being sunk by the Spaniard guns or being run ashore. On our part, we had been split in three different directions, Howard, Drake and Frobisher being on their own without any tight organization.

That night we received enough stores to continue. Next day, while taking on stores and powder and shot, the fleet was reorganized into four divisions, each composed both of ships of war and merchantmen. Hawkins took command of the fourth squadron. Now there were Hawkins, Howard, Drake, and Frobisher, who, by his action the day before, had soared to great esteem, though I always considered him to have been outmaneuvered. I felt he had been forced to fight so well only due to his precarious position.

This reorganization was done not only because of the previous day's events, but because now we were being reinforced by all sorts of sail. Howard's plan of four divisions was to use each division in sequence, to break the solid ranks of the enemy. Our only hope was to keep them on the defensive. Thus, by attacking four places in turn, we could keep them from rest. Therefore, during the night, each squadron was given different orders. Frobisher's squadron, to keep the enemy busy under steady fire, thereby lessening his ranks. Then, at daylight, the three rested squadrons could be thrown in.

The plan was good, but the wind failed during the night. Morning found us becalmed, with no action except a short attack by three of our closest ships on Admiral Recalde, whose vessel had been badly hurt. Though the Spaniards had repaired her as best they could, she was not able to keep up. But this action did not last long. Recalde was cut off until the Duke of Medina-Sidonia sent galleasses to his support. Lord Howard signaled to cut off the action.

We harassed the Spaniard fleet in every way possible, keeping their rear guard crowding into the mass of the Armada. This lasted until the Admiral of the enemy fleet changed his formation and put forty heavy ships of the line to protect his rear guard.

The two great masses of ships continued, slowly, down the Channel until we were all becalmed about six leagues from the Isle of Wight. Being unaware of the orders they had to join with the Duke of Parma at Calais, it was thought their intent was to attempt a landing off the Isle of Wight, seizing the port through which they would then invade England.

Our orders were given: "Attack despite all hazards!"

We did all in our power to engage them. The wind being of no consequence, we put longboats over and hauled our ships until we were within musket shot of the rearmost Spaniards.

Soon our squadron was in close to a great galleon of the Portugals. The Portugal, showing great bravery, had his boats tow the galleon toward us, and for a long time fought three of our ships. Those of us too far away to close, sat on the calm sea and watched.

Meanwhile Medina-Sidonia had ordered his galleasses to attack Lord Thomas Howard on the *Golden Lion* and Hawkins on the *Ark*. The galleasses had the advantage of maneuverability, due to their banks of oars. With the quick-firing guns that had been put aboard the *Ark* and the *Lion* we were able to fend them off. These two separate battles were fought for a long time. The galleasses were badly damaged, one of them almost carried away on the careen. Another lost her main lantern, which came floating by the *Rainbow*. We fished it out of the water. Another galleass lost her nose and was forced to withdraw from battle by rowing astern to prevent her from sinking.

There were many good shots by all our ships close enough to engage. The Spaniards finally had to withdraw.

Before the engagement was finished, a signal flag on Drake's ship went up and our squadron began to work to the southward. Finally we got some wind so that we moved up. The Spanish fleet was forced to shallow water. With Howard and Hawkins besetting them and we flanking them, they had no choice but to flee to the eastward again and therefore could make no landing nor take any stand on the Isle of Wight.

By late afternoon the Armada was beyond the Isle of Wight. Though I have heard much discussion of that day I have never heard much credit given. Truly here was a great victory of maneuver, even discounting the fact that the Spaniards had no intent to make a landing.

Many an argument have I had of this action and much disagreement of my theory, but I did feel had Frobisher and Howard come in with a hammer at the rear guard while our squadron was turning the van, the Spaniards would have come out with something more than a bloody nose. Even so, the end result that day was a great victory for us.

Now the Spaniards were being chased, and the only place they could move was to the North Sea and Calais. Yet in England there was panic. It was claimed in London that the Armada had sailed through us without our being able to damage them and that, once joined with the Duke of Parma, that mighty force would turn and head for England. As the Armada moved up the Channel in all its majesty, it looked whole and intact, indomitable. Yet it was not. Seven of their great ships had been lost since they left the Corunna, and in the past day's engagement they had been much damaged due to the longer range of our guns and the superiority of our seamanship. Their strength lay in closing and boarding, but not one of our ships had they been able to board. God knows, they had tried desperately. Yet every time they felt they were closing, our ships would come about and slip out of their clutches.

We now were being supplied with all necessities—food and stores and shot and powder. There was no stint. The Spaniards having expended much, there was no place they could re-store unless they had supplies at Calais. Our seamen were aware their shot and powder must be low, for they had expended shiploads of it. Putting ourselves in the place of the Spaniard seamen, we knew they must be losing heart.

As for us, not only were we swamped with food, powder and shot, but by recruits also—so many that we had to turn them away else they would have sunk us with their weight. We had suffered some damage, but thus far had lost not one single ship nor many men.

As the Spanish fleet sailed down the Channel, the Duke of Medina-Sidonia sent a cry for help to the Duke of Parma, begging him to send heavy shot and powder and a squadron of small, fast boats with which he could outsail the English.

Once again we were becalmed. While the two great fleets lay close to each other, Lord Howard called all his captains together and, under orders from the Queen, knighted some of his kinsmen. It seemed no time for such ceremony, but this was a holdover from the old days of chivalry when the bravest were knighted on the field.

Drake attended and saw the knighting of Thomas Howard, Lord Sheffield, Roger Townshend, Hawkins, Frobisher, and Captain

George Baston of the dreadnaught which, it was claimed, had sailed with great bravery and skill. Perhaps this was so, but we on the *Rainbow* had not seen her at all. As to the most deserving, he was rewarded not at all. The Lord Admiral did say that he had not the power to further reward Drake. I did not think this bothered our commander overmuch. What did irk him was the time consumed in such ceremony when more pressing problems faced the commanders.

We lay to all day watching the Spaniard ships and waiting for the return of our captains. As the sun set over the English coast a south-westerly breeze blew up. There was great excitement from Lord Howard's ship. Signals came to close once again for the attack. But due to the delay of the captains' return to their ships—with many somewhat under the weather from wine—the Spaniards got away from us.

Through the dark and stormy night we held to the chase and, by morning, found ourselves within cannon shot of the rear guard of the Spaniards. They continued on under all sail, showing no desire to come about and join. By mid-afternoon they were off Calais and there, instead of searching for sea room and trying to get the weather of us, they went into anchor off the French port.

Much later we learned that the Duke of Parma, on whom Philip of Spain had placed such high hope, was in dire straits. A scourge of fever had decimated his troops. His army was in short supply, disorganized, and he could give no assistance. This put Medina-Sidonia in such a position as to break a man's heart. At Plymouth he could have taken us, but could not because of Don Pedro de Valdez. Now all was lost.

We dropped our anchor off the foremost Spaniard ships, almost within shot of them. And now further good news arrived. Our fleet was joined by Lord Seymour, commanding a fleet of thirty-eight sail. Seymour brought his ships in under full sail between us and the Spaniards. To show his contempt of the enemy, and his happiness at being pulled off the Dover Station, he gave a broadside to the Spaniard rear guard, then passed on.

Some say all battles are like a game of chess. The Spaniards had made a sorry move, enabling us to have them in check. They had played into our hands, yet somehow it was sad to see them sitting like frightened chicks, huddled close to the shore. Medina-Sidonia should have made every effort to stop Seymour from joining us, as with Seymour he had had the weather and could have done much damage to them. They now had thirty-eight more sail to worry about. They lay anchored in a port with no protection. The first bad weather would scatter their fleet over the North Sea.

With our lack of knowledge of his orders, it seemed such a stupid mistake for a brave and competent seaman to make. But Philip's orders had crippled the thinking of the Spaniard Duke. He had now no place to run, no sea room to move in, expending all his hope of help from the Duke of Parma, whose whereabouts he was not even sure of, and holding him in check were 130 sail flying the flag of St. George.

As we lay facing each other, I was ordered to take a pinnace and scout the length of the Spaniard fleet, then return to report their accurate positions to Drake. We were waiting for Sir William Winter to come up with his ships and a number of fishing vessels laden with pitch and faggots.

I was highly complimented by being assigned to the scouting pinnace. I sailed her with a small, picked crew, in and about and around the heavy, high-standing Spaniards, taking some small shot through the sails. After plotting the position of all the ships, I returned to Drake and reported my findings. By this time the fire ships, made up not only of the fishing vessels but all our numerous small ships, were being brought into position, shielded by our foreguard so that the Spaniards could not see our intent.

The Spaniards now were dead to windward. If the wind held into the night they would be at our mercy. When all was in readiness, I delivered a message to Lord Howard from Drake, then returned.

The wind was right and, as I had to pass along the front of the entire Spaniard fleet, on impulse, as we came by Medina-Sidonia's *Capitana*, I ordered the long gun on the pinnace to be run out. With what must have seemed the utmost impertinence, I wheeled in as close as I could to the great ship, laid four shot into her and came about before she could do more than put a culverin ball through my topsail. My four shot did no damage to the great ship, but this small challenge set the whole of the English fleet to cheering.

As I reported back to the *Revenge*, Drake made some remark about my foolishness and ordered me back to the *Rainbow*, but I could tell he was not ill pleased at the deed.

God was on our side that night. Everything went our way. We

could not tell what the Spaniards were doing to prevent our move though it was impossible to think they were unaware that we were readying to send in fire ships. We were in an ideal position for such a maneuver.

The tide turned just before midnight. In that section of the coast it runs like a millrace. In the dim overcast light we could see the huge ships swinging at their anchors to face the oncoming tide. The wind held for us, and to greet the anchored Spaniards we fired eight large ships that had their guns loaded with powder almost to the whole barrel, and the remainder stuffed with small shot. They were so charged that they would blow up when the fire touched them. Probably they would do no great damage, but the noise would be terrifying.

The Spanish had put out a patrol to stop our fire ships, but those eight ships came on fast, and by the time they reached the Spaniard patrol they were eight gigantic towers of flame. The guns exploded when the fire reached them, and the patrol, instead of trying to attach to the stern to direct them through the Armada toward shore, as was logical, turned tail and ran. The tide was running so fast that the ships seemed to fly at the center of the Armada. All at once they began to break like panicked sheep. Unable to get their anchors up fast enough, they cut their cables. Immediately on release from the anchor, the ships started to drift before sail could be raised. It became a scene of indescribable confusion that worsened by the minute.

Being held head into the wind by their anchors, the ships should have been prepared to put sail on immediately instead of falling off into each other, doing more damage than the fire ships could. The fire ships, by some trick of fate, swept merrily through the fleet without touching one ship, and burned themselves out ashore. Now more ships came in, all aflame—and then more—feeding the panic the way the fire fed on the doomed ships. The morning found the Armada scattered all along the coast as far as Dunkirk.

Medina-Sidonia ordered his ships to come about and anchor again, but many of them had cut the cables on both their anchors and could not get to their spare anchors in time. The Duke of Medina-Sidonia, seeing they could not come up with him and form battle lines properly, weighed anchor and carried those ships with him down toward Gravelines to form a battle order on the most leewardly ships, which Lord Howard had no intent to allow. Our plan of battle had already been made.

Thomas Howard was to lead the attack. At a signal, our great mass of ships weighed anchor and led off toward the enemy. Here a mistake was made that could have been our undoing. Drake, as usual, caught it in time and corrected it.

Thomas Howard, being in the lead, as his ship came athwart of Calais, saw in the early morning light the *Capitana* of the galleons laboring along the French shore, trying to reach the shelter of the guns of Calais. This ship was called the finest vessel on the face of the sea and it was too much of a temptation for Howard. Suddenly he broke toward the *Capitana* like a knight unable to withstand the chance for individual glory in combat. These were different times, however, and Drake had proved that only by using a squadron as a single unit could a battle be won.

As Thomas Howard's ship wheeled toward the shore, only part of his squadron followed. The rest knew not what to do. Unhesitatingly Drake signaled for all ships in his squadron to press on all sail. Thus our squadron was brought up to replace Howard. Then Drake led the fleet to the grand attack.

With the *Revenge* in the lead, we swept down on the Spaniards like hawks. The Spaniard Duke found himself once again in an untenable position. He could not maintain his line of battle without danger of going ashore on the Dunkirk banks. He therefore sent orders for the fleet to re-form back to where they would have more sea room while he turned his broadside to us and, with only two other vessels to lend him assistance, bravely waited for the hammer of Drake's squadron.

From the *Revenge* came orders to hold our fire. We sailed in on them in deadly silence, all guns run out and ready, the men standing by with slow fires awaiting the word to touch off. Then the *Revenge* turned, and, as she swung by, gave the great *San Martin* a tremendous broadside, then came about and gave her another. Then she moved on, and we did the same to the other two ships. As the greatest part of the English fleet was now crowding behind, Drake ordered his squadron not to delay but to bear out to where the Armada was attempting to form a line of battle and come to the assistance of Medina-Sidonia.

Hawkins held his squadron back to fight the three isolated ships while the others came on behind us. It was Drake's hope to cut off the main body of the Spaniards and drive them to the lee. It was a sharp, hard fight, and it would have succeeded had not the weather gauge gone to the Spaniards and about fifty ships managed to flank us and join with Medina-Sidonia. With such masses of men and ships it is hard to say what could and should have been done. In my opinion, and many have agreed with me, if Howard had not gone off, the Spaniards would have been ours that day and history would have called it the greatest sea battle of all time.

That day Drake's ship, the *Revenge*, fought like a tiger. She was shot through and through, above and below decks, yet from her poured broadside after broadside that made us wonder how the guns could be charged and fired so fast. To the rest of the squadron, the *Revenge* was like a clarion call for courage and effort on every man's part. The longer the battle continued, the more it became like fighting in a fog. We would emerge for a moment into clear sunshine and see the ships wheeling and turning, and then we maneuvered back into the thick of the smoke again where we could see not much more than the outline of our enemy. But of all the ships that fought that day, the Duke of Medina-Sidonia's *San Martin* and the two ships that stood with him—the *San Marcos* and the *San Juan*—took the brunt of the English squadron. They held on with much high courage until the bulk of the Spaniards could get by our squadrons and re-form behind the Duke. The Spaniard Admiral took the fire of all our ships that made a try for him, and yet kept luffing back and forth, shrouded in smoke, spitting back fire and shot from every gun. He held so well that his fleet got offing. If it had not been for the Spaniard Duke we would have run the greatest part of the Armada ashore on the Dunkirk banks. But even so the Spaniards were lost that day. All hope of taking England was gone for them. We had driven them beyond Calais, beyond Dunkirk, and now they could move nowhere except into the North Sea.

Then began a running fight, moving always away from the French coast. We cut out one ship at a time; and once cut out, we would circle her, pour shot into her and try to drag her down. For eight long hours the battle raged. All our squadrons had joined by now—Seymour, Winter, Frobisher, Drake, Howard and Hawkins—and we kept always moving, forcing the Spaniard ships in on each other when we could not isolate them.

We separated the *San Mateo*, *San Felipe*, *Señora Debona*, and the *San Juan de Sicilia*. On this last ship we were following behind. As she came about we poured a broadside into her. She was crowded with troops. How many broadsides she had taken before, I know not, but such was the slaughter that blood poured from the holes in her sides and colored the water where she stood. Still the Spaniards fought back with great and proud courage.

Coming up on the *San Felipe*—for a moment the wind cleared the sea—I counted fifteen ships, including ours, all pouring shot into her. She was so shattered, so full of shot holes it was a pity to see, yet they would not surrender. The *San Mateo*, all her cannon gone, still fought on with nothing but the musketry of the soldiers. Dying, she would try from one to the other, to close and grapple, even in the face of the greatest cannonade, but she could not come in, nor would we close with her.

We circled and wheeled. I had but little time to catch more than a fleeting look at the Spaniard ships dying all over the sea. There was so much to be done in giving orders to maneuver the ship under our fighting sail, coming about and watching closely so that we did not come afoul of one of our own ships and, at the same time, closing in far enough for our broadsides to do the utmost damage. Sometimes we would come in so close we were not more than a pike's length by which we would send a broadside but always keeping just enough distance so they could not grapple with us. Had our gunnery been as efficient as the nimbleness and sailing skill of our ships, the Spaniards would have been worse off than they now found themselves.

They were broken into individual ships. We were still in our squadron formation, everything under control and able to move from point to point wherever needed to do the greatest damage. Fifteen of their ships were in such distress only a few more broadsides would have seen them at the bottom of the sea, when a sudden, vicious squall came down the Channel and swept up on us. So suddenly did it blow up that we had to break off and send every unwounded man aloft to take in sail and prepare to meet the danger, many of our ships being badly wounded.

The Spaniards fled and the squall finished off what we had started. Ship after ship of theirs foundered. Though the squall lasted no more than two hours, it afforded those Spaniards still afloat the opportunity to join together again.

They fled to leeward and all those prizes which had been within our grasp were lost. Our sole hope was that further wind would make up and drive them, crippled as they were, to founder on the Zealand banks.

On the *Rainbow*, as throughout almost all our ships, we had many wounded, damage to our rigging, and were almost without powder and shot.

Admiral Lord Howard sent back to England desperate orders to rush shot and powder to us, then signaled for the fleet to re-form. We set out to follow the remains of the Armada.

It was a great day for England in spite of the mistakes that had been made and we were content to hang on the weather quarter, moving slowly behind them, holding a course northeast by east.

As night came upon us, working under what lights we could provide, we tried to repair our damage. The *San Felipe* and the *San Mateo* were driven on shore and taken by some of the fleet ordered over to them.

It had been a long day. Not knowing what tomorrow would hold, men slept by their guns or wherever they could find a clear space on the shattered decks, while those of us whose duties would grant no rest kept on, holding our formation in the squadron, and waited for the dawn to break and the final taking of the Armada.

19

By morning it was blowing half a gale and the crippled Spaniards kept on toward shoal water. We did our utmost to keep them from pulling up. Medina-Sidonia, realizing his circumstance, came about in the *San Martin* followed by three of his ships, making a barrier while the Spaniards a league or so distant tried desperately to tack away from the nearing shore. But the wind and water kept driving them headlong toward the banks. For Medina-Sidonia this must have been a terribly sad day. It was told to me later how he confessed himself along with his crew and prepared to die. But under Lord Howard's orders we held off. It seemed all we had to do was wait and let them run aground, thereby taking the fleet without having to fire another shot.

We drifted with them, watching as they neared the shore until the foremost ship could not have been in more than four or five fathoms of water. In a few more minutes they would have been aground. Then the wind changed, first only a point or two, but enough so that, instead of striking, they were able to maintain their distance from shore. In desperation, the Duke of Medina-Sidonia put on all sail and, coming to the head of the fleet, took a course we dared not follow. It must have been that the tides were extremely high, as the water in that area was too shallow to allow their passage.

We followed behind, losing time in trying to work outward so we would not endanger ourselves. In truth, it seemed as if God had stretched out His hand to save the battered remnants of the great Armada. The wind picked up, changing now to give them more sea room. Many cursed our luck but others bowed their heads in acceptance. With the sea one never knows what will happen next. I think too, at least those of us who were seamen had lost our belly for more blood, and the sight of those proud shops striking would not have been a pleasant one. Still, by their escape we lost much in way of prizes, as aboard some of those ships were great treasures.

All day we had waited for store ships to come to our relief with shot and powder and provisions, but there was no sight of them. A council of war was called by Lord Howard, and Seymour was ordered to give all of his stores to Drake and return to Dover to resupply his ships and go back to Channel guard.

Lord Seymour's fury at this order was violent. He accused Drake of seeking the final drop of glory. For a man of his spirits it must have been difficult to retire at this time, but it was a sensible order.

So Seymour's squadron came about after unloading their small supply of stores and started beating their way back to England. Drake's squadron moved up in the post of honor as we kept on in pursuit of the Spaniards.

On assuming our new position, Drake sent a message through his squadron saying, "We have the army of Spain before us and would, with the grace of God, wrestle a further pole with him. It pleases me muchly as it must please you all, to see the enemy flying from us to the northward. I doubt not that we will close in such a manner with Sidonia that he will wish himself in St. Mary's Port among his orange trees. God give us grace and may we depend on Him, as our cause is good. God bless you all."

Twice our squadron caught the wind enough where it appeared as if we would be able to close. We were willing, though we had no more ammunition on any of the ships to fire more than two broadsides. It was thought that Medina-Sidonia might have some plan to land his force on Scotland. To counter any such move, our squadron followed the Spaniards while the others broke off and made for the Firth of Forth.

But the Spaniards continued farther and farther, out away from the land. Their condition was worse than ours. We had hardly any water and no food. As the wind and the sea would prevent them from coming about, it was decided to break off and go in for stores. The Armada seemed bound as if for the Orkneys or the Shetland Islands.

To make certain there was no change in their plans, Drake stripped the other ships of what little food and water they had and sent us on the *Rainbow* in company with a caravel under Captain Berringer, to follow the Armada and to report any attempted change.

It seemed very lonely on the sea after being in the midst of so many ships. Now the weather thickened, with the wind high and variable, until we had a hard time keeping in sight of the Spaniards. As the gale increased in intensity, Drake's squadron was scattered from Norwich to the Downs and had to make any port they could, having many sick and wounded.

Ashore in England there was great celebration as our fleet came in, fully intended to take stores and go out again in the event the Armada was able to turn and take refuge into the Danish ports. Any such plan was stopped by Queen Elizabeth. Again she showed her miserliness by ordering the fleet to be paid off at once and disbanded. Many were wounded and sick, yet were given their few shillings and cast aside with no further thought.

We were unaware of this as we followed the Spaniards, mostly by the bits and pieces of flotsam that littered the sea from some one or the other of their badly hurt ships that foundered.

Dutifully, day after day, we pursued their track, bone-weary, dogtired, short of water and stores. Should we have come upon any part of the Armada we could have done them no harm, as there was much of the scurvy sickness aboard the *Rainbow*.

Finally we came to the conclusion the Armada was scattering around the high coast of Scotland. Here there would be no place for them to land, so Captain Marchant signaled Captain Berringer to come about and we broke off and made our way to the nearest port, this being in Scotland.

We were received royally. The people had been in great fear. By horse, dispatches were sent to London, giving the route, the conditions, and what we surmised to be the Spaniard's intent—which was to pass north of Scotland and Ireland and make their way home as best they could.

We rested for some days, enjoying the Scotsmen's hospitality, took on stores and water, and returned to England thinking we would be joined to cut off the Armada below the Irish Sea.

At the first port in England we received orders to proceed to London. On our arrival we found all the ships, except for Seymour's small squadron, had been paid off. The Queen counted upon God, the sea, and the iron-bound western coast to wreak the further destruction of the Spaniards.

For her and England it could have been a most expensive gamble. But her luck held as almost all the Armada was lost off the Irish coast and most of the survivors who managed to come ashore were brutally murdered by the people.

So ended the great battle which, largely by luck, saved England and made her strong and weakened Spain. I still remember vividly the blood of the men pouring from the shot holes in the sides of the *San Juan de Sicilia*. It was a time to remember, yet I would not care to ever see such sights again.

20

We expected a similar welcome to the one we had received in the Scottish ports. But hardly anyone even noticed our arrival. Having been away so long I was now in haste to go home. The time for the arrival of Elizabeth's baby had come and I had received no news.

I left the ship as soon as possible. At home I found Diggins' house in a state of complete confusion.

Nicholas met me at the door. I was caught by the strain that showed on his face and a little surprised by the fervor of his welcome. He embraced me and said, "Thank God you are home at last, William, and safe."

There was the sound of scurrying upstairs and I heard Elizabeth's voice raised in petulant anger.

My first question to Diggins was, "Did she have the baby?"

"Aye," he said. "It is a fine boy, William, a fine boy. God's blood, I never thought the birth of a child could be such a painful process or raise such a stir. I am afraid to move about the house."

My first thought being to see Elizabeth and the boy, I turned to run up the stairs. Elizabeth was in the chamber, soundly berating the maid. At the sight of me her face dissolved like water pouring over a cake of sugar. She flew into my arms with a great weeping.

"William," she sobbed. "You don't know what I've been through. You cannot imagine. What with having a baby without even the comfort of my husband. Oh, William! Having a baby is a terrible ordeal."

Her words tumbled one over the other, what with worrying about me and being left out of the gaiety and celebration of victory. Giving birth to a child to Elizabeth had been a catastrophe.

Guiltily I tried to comfort her. After a time I asked to see the boy and found him a healthy specimen, though both Mrs. Grandy and the maid hovered over him as if, should they relax in their vigilance, he would dissolve.

When I attempted to pick him up words of caution poured like an avalanche simultaneously from all three of them. He was bundled up into so many garments and coverings I wondered how he could breathe. I picked him up gently enough and, unwrapping the layers of swaddling, looked to see if all his parts were there.

"Put him down, William," Elizabeth protested. "After what I've been through, I will not have him catch cold."

The baby started to cry and they took him from me with looks plainly saying I was a clumsy oaf.

It was not until late that night was I able to sit down with Nicholas and talk over the great events that had passed and brought England safe out of danger. Nicholas alone seemed interested.

It was then I learned that Roger Trient had been killed aboard the *Ark*. The news struck me like a blow to the belly, knocking all breath from me. I had loved Roger, admired him, enjoyed him. I could not bear the thought. It seemed incredible that this vital, forceful, handsome man was no longer here—that no more would I be able to argue or disagree with him. This was not only my loss but England's. It was more than I could endure.

"The Trients, Nicholas—how are they taking this?"

"Badly, naturally. They not only loved Roger so, as did we all, but their title now will go to some other branch of the family, Roger being the only son. You must see them soon, William; they love you dearly."

The second day home I visited them, taking Elizabeth with me. We were welcomed with open arms and the tears flowed, mine with theirs. They clung to me as a sort of replacement for Roger. After that first visit I had to force myself to go again, for each time it kept open the wound of his death for all of us. It was so final. Nothing could replace Roger. Even though they hinted that they would like to take me in, I felt the kindest act I could do was to stay away.

London itself broke my heart. The conditions of those seamen who had fought so valiantly were now shameful. The crippled, the sick, the hungry, wandered about the streets begging. Hardly any would give them even a crust of bread. Now none were heroes. There was no longer need for them.

We took the *Rainbow* down to Chatham and paid off the crew. From there I went to see Drake. Incredibly, those to whom so much credit should have gone for the defeat of the Spaniards were now in ill repute at the court. Queen Elizabeth had demanded a complete accounting of all prizes and values taken.

To the penny she claimed her share. Because Lord Howard had spent monies for stores, using some of the prize money, he had been the same as accused of thievery. Drake, himself, had fallen deep into debt. Still she wanted more from him. In justice, Drake and the others should have been able to ask, and been granted, whatever of England's wealth they desired. This was a good lesson to me.

I, too, was in a very awkward position. It would be a long, long time before any accounting was made to the lower officers and seamen. When that accounting was made, I was sure there would be very little left of the prizes.

Exhausted, disillusioned, I had thought to go into the shipyard with Diggins, to stay home with Elizabeth and be a good husband. Now that I was sick of the sea, I found there was neither the need for ships nor for shipbuilding. After the enormous effort expended, shipping had now come to a standstill. For every merchant brave enough to send out a ship, there were a thousand well-trained seamen hungering for each job.

I had found that Elizabeth, for all her beauty and endearing traits, had no understanding of money. I had turned over to her whatever monies I had before I left. She had none of it left. Any discussion of money brought forth great argument between us.

England's celebration at the defeat of the Armada was over, including the parade of the Queen and all the court through the streets to St. Paul's Cathedral, where thanks were given to God for the victory. All of the credit was the Queen's and the people worshiped her. She had the ability to weave a spell over all but a few. Even those who had fought so well and been treated so meanly cheered her. Now England drew back to take stock of her condition.

Victory had proved costly. We had won but had not gained much of the Spaniard's treasures.

As for me, I could not take my responsibility lightly now I was father of a son. The only course open to me was to find a ship, return to the merchant trade and, with luck, repair our fortunes. I was determined to give Elizabeth all she so dearly craved. I tried to explain this to her, but since the beginning of time when men first set sail upon the seas, women have fought against their going.

"It is your stubbornness," she charged. "Had you thought of the ends you could have had high position and no worries. We could have everything but for you and your tender skin and foolish pride."

She was probably right, but that changed nothing.

Duffield and Martin retained their high opinion of my ability. They were anxious to renew trade to the eastern Mediterranean. By much effort they had obtained a pass from the Sublime Porte, and though well aware of the danger from the Spaniards, they were ready to chance their money for promise of great profits. As for me and my crew, we had no choice but to practice our trade.

I was beset on all sides by conflicting pressures. Diggins had made no fortune as others had. He had said, "William, you well know that you are as a son to me. True, shipbuilding has come to a standstill, but we can wait it out. Within a year there will be need for more ships and repair. The danger is too great now for me to rest easy in my mind about you if you do go out again."

I would not stay and live on his bounty.

Elizabeth exerted all her female store of wiles. "It is easy for you to go away now that we are really paupers. You do not have to stay and suffer. Now I have the burden of bringing up a child. I will not live in this house. Either I have a house of my own, which certainly is little recompense for what I have suffered, or we can accept the Trients' offer. They, at least, are of noble lineage. You are selfish. It isn't pride, it is selfishness."

Patiently, again and again I explained to her. "I do not wish to leave you or our son, Elizabeth. It isn't easy for me to do so. But I must. If we are ever to attain that which you desire so greatly, then I must do so in the only way I know. Please, dear, bear with it. By next year we will have a house and be well on our way."

But she would not listen. She kept harping on the Trients' offer and their nobility. It took many bitter words and much time before she finally understood I would not consider it, that I would not make such use of friends. We would have to face our fate and depend on my efforts and ability alone.

I thought much about my relationship with Elizabeth. I had tried to see London through her eyes—the great, fine place she thought it. When we went about the streets I could see nothing but sickness, poverty, and smell the stench. But Elizabeth, somehow, did not see this. Her world was a dream world of great houses, balls and parties attended by people of noble lineage, although we could not even afford the clothing to attend these functions.

The tension in the house, finally, became so great that she would stay no longer. She would move back to Chatham, with her family. They had been right about me and our marriage, she said.

All such things and others upset me so that I became thoroughly sick of England. I hated to go about the streets for fear of running into shipmates in need of help, and I had already done more than I could. I was ashamed of the Queen and of my country, who could treat her sailors and soldiers with such brutal indifference. I longed for the sea and its cleanliness as some men thirst for wine.

21

My parting with Elizabeth was greatly strained. She was past the point of tears and when I said good-by she would hardly speak to me. Then she cried out angrily, "You are bound and tied by your mother!"

This seemed an odd statement. I had last seen my mother at the age of fourteen. When I mentioned this she shouted, "Damn you, I do not mean your birth mother, but your bitch mother, the sea! To her you always must return as a baby to the breast."

Anger forced me to answer. "And what do you mean to make of me? You knew what I was when first we met. As for the sea, she is not my mother. My mistress, perhaps. Cruel mistress, but I love her, and shall as long as I live. You are nothing but a contrary woman who must have everything, including my manhood. But you will not have that. I am a man, and you will go my way or it follows that we will go different ways. My father was an excellent example of what a woman can do to a man. I will not let you do that to me. I will provide whatever I can for your comfort and living, but I will do it in my way."

Words in anger never solve anything. They bring, instead, a sense of guilt.

I reached the ship as a refuge. She was the *Dolphin*. Diggins had built her and I had some part in her design. She was fast, well-gunned, and I had great pride in her. Never did I feel so free as when we had dropped off our pilot and the two galleys which had taken us, against the tide, down the Thames.

The first breath of sea air was sweet. Within no more than a day or two we had the ship washed and clean with all the land smell gone from her. Our sails bellied and engulfed me with pleasure. The song of the wind in her rigging gave me that sense of completeness that only a man who has had a ship of his own can understand. I rejoiced in it. I felt whole, free, unfettered.

We swung wide, passing far to the outside of the Azores, not coming about until we reached the coast of Africa. The weather was favorable and our luck held. We had spied nothing larger than a fishing vessel until we were beyond the boot of Italy. Once past Sicily we were in safer water.

With the Sultan's flag which had been issued to us by the Sublime Porte flying at our masthead, few would dare interfere with our passing. The Sublime Porte was a man with almost the same power as was the Grand Vizir, just below the Sultan.

During the past two years of these troubled times hardly any trade had been carried on between the Turks and the English. In my previous journeys I had made friends in Constantinople. Now, as captain of a fine ship, I was treated with honor. The Turks were as anxious as the English merchants to resume trade.

As is the custom in that country, I was presented with many valuable gifts and gave some in return. All dealings in that country are carried on in a leisurely fashion. One must abide by the rules, for to rush the dealings is considered barbaric and bad taste.

After viewing our goods, they gave me a house ashore, lavishly furnished in Oriental style. The beds were low affairs with many cushions, and the furniture built also close to the ground so that, instead of sitting up, everyone lounged about, which lends itself well to the leisurely atmosphere. This can be most disconcerting, though, as these people are sharp traders.

In time I found it a very comfortable manner of living. Through an official of the Sublime Porte I was provided with a chair and six servants to carry me about, and one other to run ahead, singing out to the people in the streets to make way for me, calling out my various titles. Later, after I was able to interpret the language, I found that I was "the Supreme Navigator of a Massive Vessel—a Lord in My Own Land, and Under the Protection of the Most Glorious Divine Sultan, Himself."

We were bound to lie there for almost three months, waiting for certain goods, especially spices and silks, which I had been told to purchase. We expected the arrival of a caravan bearing some of these articles. This gave me leisure to look about.

I visited some of the famous Christian churches, now changed to mosques. All the magnificent paintings had been covered over with blues and greens, and all the statuary of the saints had been destroyed, as Moslems consider such things as idols. Yet they had not destroyed the magnificence of many of the buildings. Being advised to change into Turkish costume, I managed to get about the city without too much difficulty.

I gave my crew as much freedom as I could. Those who became drunken and boisterous, I managed to keep from serious trouble, punishing them by keeping them by the ship for a number of days. All in all, I had little to complain of.

I enjoyed this land, so different from ours, somehow not minding the beggars and dirt and smells as I did in London. I attended many feasts where they had lavish entertainment of jugglers, sword swallowers, fire eaters, magicians, and dancing girls. These girls danced so lewdly, in clothing so sheer it stirred my blood, though having assumed the responsibility of marriage and a family, I was resolved to keep myself from other women.

This resolution continued until one day, after negotiating on some further purchases of goods, I received a gift which I dared not refuse, yet I knew not what to do with her. That afternoon, on my return to the house, I found an emissary from the Sublime Porte with a gift for me—a Greek slave girl of astonishing beauty.

"Lord of the Sea and Master of the Winds," he said, bowing low, "my Supreme Master, His Eminence the Sublime Porte, who in his infinite wisdom knows all, deems it is not fit we should be lacking in hospitality, and it is against the will of Allah for you, a guest in our land, to be without a woman. He has therefore personally selected this feminine morsel especially for you. Master, she has been examined and is virgin. She is unblemished, as you can see."

As he talked he pointed up her virtues and qualities, pulling aside her robe and showing me how round and firm her breasts were, the width of her hips, and the roundness of her belly. The girl stood motionless during the explanation.

I dared not refuse her. Thanking him as warmly as I could, I gave him, as a gift for the Porte, a sword with a jeweled hilt that had been part of my prize from the great Portugal treasure ship.

After he had gone I thought frantically of what to do with her. I could not sell her, nor could I give her away without the grave danger of insulting the Porte and possibly endangering the entire venture. I decided it best to let her stay at the house until our departure. By then, perhaps I would think of some tactful way to dispose of the problem.

She sat quietly in the corner, saying nothing, watching me as I paced back and forth trying to think.

Mealtime arrived and the servants brought in food. As I sat down at the low table and she still made no move, I motioned for her to join me. She misunderstood and came quietly over and attempted to feed me. As I motioned for her to eat, she looked at me in great puzzlement, as it is not the custom in that country for women to eat in the presence of men. I tried to speak with her, using what fragments of Oriental tongue I was familiar with, but she seemed to understand nothing. Finally I called the servant and told him to take her into another room and give her food.

In each house there is one head servant, similar to a majordomo. Mine was by name of Ali, loaned to me along with the rest of the servants. He was as great a rascal as ever lived, a thief who claimed to be an honest man.

He would not steal very much from me for, as he said in his broken Spanish, I was a great and honorable captain and lucky, he assured me, to have one so honest working for me and seeing to my comfort. Perhaps I was.

Ali returned to inform me that he had ordered the other servants to prepare a bath for the girl and that she would be ready at my pleasure. I informed him that this was unnecessary, as I was tired and would have no use for her. He looked at me in great astonishment.

"But," he said, "she is a most pleasing girl and it is claimed the Greeks have a great natural talent. Of course, for myself, I prefer one with more width across her belly, but we can fatten her on rich foods and accomplish this in not too long a time."

Knowing it was useless, I still attempted to explain that I had a wife and that, in my country, other women are not deemed necessary, nor are they permissible.

He looked at me wordlessly for a long time and scratched his beard, as if such an attitude was beyond the point of reason, even for a strange foreigner such as I. Finally he said, "She will not like it."

I replied, "She is a virgin and will not miss what she has never known."

He watched me, slowly shaking his head. He was most forward, feeling his duty was to teach me some amount of sense.

"It is plain," he said, "you know nothing whatever about women. It is true she might resist your advances, but that is only the normal way for a woman to act. But to make no attempt would be a deep insult to her and I, for one, would not sleep well, not knowing what she might do to you."

I tried to dismiss the subject by saying, "It is not the custom in my country and I do not want her."

Ali became upset at these last words. "But, Master," he said, "such actions as these cannot be hidden. The other servants will talk. This house will become a laughingstock. To the storytellers in the streets, such a tale would be too good to keep hidden and it would injure you greatly, as your appearance denotes that you are a strong man and much admired."

Tiring of the conversation, I dismissed him abruptly. For a time I worked over accounts, putting the subject of the girl from my mind.

When I prepared to retire I found the girl kneeling at the foot of my bed. Her hair was unloosed and was a black shimmering wave down her back. The one garment she wore was sheer, so that her charms were not hidden but merely enhanced. She was very beautiful. My nature urged me to take such good luck as it came. My conscience, however, would not allow me to do so. As gently as I could, I made known to her that she was to leave.

At my touch she began to tremble violently. But when she understood what I meant her eyes darkened and her face flushed as if I had insulted her by some crude and obscene suggestion. When I pulled her to her feet as gently as I could and guided her out the door, she turned to face me with a look of despair and, bursting into tears, she crouched at my feet and wept as bitterly as any child.

Not knowing what else to do I drew the curtain and went to bed. Whereupon she set up such a wailing that the whole house was awakened. I could hear Ali outside remonstrating angrily with her. His words only made her weep the louder. A crowd gathered in the street. I had been an object of much interest to the natives. They happily seemed to think I was beating her to show my manhood.

At last, in complete desperation, I went to the outer room and brought her back inside with me where I tried to explain by gestures, that she could sleep at the foot of my bed. This quieted her somewhat, but every once in a while she would sob deeply like a child, and my heart was much torn by the desire to bring her to bed and comfort her. Finally her sobbing stilled and she slept. And now I was awake, wondering whether my attitude made any sense.

In England our teaching was that once two people were joined in marriage, they were to forsake all others—though I admitted to myself this was not always held to. England, however, was many months away and my manhood was strong within me. Without resolving the moral principles, I fell asleep at last.

When I awakened in the morning, she lay crouched at the foot of the bed, curled up with one hand under her face and the other hand outstretched as if reaching out to me. There were still tear streaks on her cheeks. Lovely as she was, my heart went out to her.

Picking her up, I placed her in the bed and covered her without waking her, and began to prepare for the day's activities.

Ali seemed happy over the way things had turned out. He, taking for granted that I had bedded with her, with many winks and coarse jests tried to learn if I was pleased with her. I refused to take any notice of his insinuations and brusquely ordered the chair brought around by the time I had finished my breakfast.

When I left the house the street beggars, shopkeepers, and all others in the vicinity met me with knowing glances and comments which I only half understood. The gist of them was somewhat similar to the remarks made to a bridegroom in England after the first night of wedlock.

On my return that afternoon, I was met with silence and puzzled frowns. Ali was cold toward me as he took my robe and brought me a bottle of wine and a glass. I paid no attention to him.

"Our house is in disgrace," he finally said.

"What foolishness are you saying now?" I demanded.

"It is common knowledge now that the girl is still virgin, though she spent the night in your bed. One shopkeeper questioned me if it was that you were a eunuch. I thrashed him soundly. Master, all day the girl has been weeping. Why are you so cruel as to treat her in such a manner?"

To try to explain would be hopeless. Already feeling that my attitude made no sense, I refused to discuss it further and dismissed him. He went reluctantly, shrugging his shoulders hopelessly and looking to the sky as if awaiting an explanation for my madness.

I had been pleased that day in being able to purchase a number of bolts of fine silk which I knew would bring a good price in England. Now the pleasure of this was dissipated. Hearing a small sound, I turned to see the girl crouched in the corner, her eyes red from weeping and looking at me as if I had beaten her. She seemed so forlorn and pretty that I called her to me.

She came as happily as a small dog being forgiven by its master. That night I broke her maidenhead to the great satisfaction of the servants and all the neighborhood, and mine also. I found her to be the warmest, fairest creature, and, for all her innocence, of such a natural-born skill that I thought if all Greek women were such as she, then the Greeks should have a greater reputation than they held.

Once the act was done I stilled my conscience. My days were busy and my nights filled with pleasure. The problem I knew I had to face I put out of my mind, enjoying the days that were left before it was time to sail again for England.

22

I found in this girl such a womanliness, such a joy in pleasing me that I felt as if I were some sort of god. I could not resist her and often caught myself thinking of her during the daytime. My conscience distressed me when I thought of Elizabeth, but it did not keep me from the Greek maiden.

As we could not converse, I found a Spaniard-speaking Turk who knew Greek. Each night he would instruct us. She had no great facility for language but I had been born with a gift as some men are born with the gift for music. Soon we were able to talk together haltingly.

Her name was Procopia. She was the daughter of a Greek merchant who, with his family, had been captured and all his goods taken. Being young, beautiful and a virgin, Procopia had been shipped to Constantinople where the great slave markets were located. She knew nothing of the fate of her family and wept when she spoke of them. If they had not been killed, they would have been sold also.

The agent of the Sublime Porte had bought Procopia, for he kept many such women either as gifts for his friends or to add to his seraglio should one take his eye. Those of whom he tired were resold to merchants who transported them to other ports. A cruel, inhuman business, this trade in people as if they were animals, but it had been going on from the beginning of time. As there was nothing I could do to end it, I closed my eyes to the painful condition, promising myself that Procopia would be freed.

When the time neared for our departure, I searched about for some means to send her back to her own people. I could find no trace of her family. I was doubtful of entrusting her to Ali. Nothing would prevent his taking my money and selling her, I knew. Yet I could think of no other way.

When I told her she would soon be free I expected to be greeted with joy for my kindness. Instead I was treated to a well of tears and protestations that her sole desire was to love and serve me. I told her I thought it best she should return home and find a husband, whereupon she threatened to kill herself. For me to act this way meant she had failed to please me. Tearfully she promised she would try to do more to make me happy.

I thought then, as I have thought many times since, for all the enjoyment a woman can give a man, she also brings with her sorrow and trouble.

Since I wanted to believe she meant what she said, I did the next best thing, after pondering all other courses. As the house in which we had been living had been put at my disposal as a guest, I instructed Ali to find lodgings where Procopia could stay until my return.

Ali, having attached himself to me, I provided him with a certain wage. Not trusting him too far, however, I made arrangements with the agents of the Sublime Porte to see that she did not lack for food and supplies.

I encountered the most trying scene in attempting to explain to Procopia that I could not take her with me. She swore she would do whatever work I gave her and also comfort me during the long days at sea. I was tempted. But a woman on board a ship is like an open fire around combustibles. Also, I couldn't very well explain her presence when I arrived in England.

I told her nothing about sailing plans. On the day we were to leave we had a feast and I got her to drink enough strong wine to make her sleepy. I left her that night without sight of her tears.

Once out to sea, I missed Procopia more than I had missed Elizabeth. This angered me and I said many harsh things to myself. My wife had given up much for me. But no matter how disgusted with myself I was in the daytime, at night I would awaken, reaching out in search of her. This I could not control.

Twice, before reaching Gibraltar, we had running fights—once with a galley off Sicily, and a second with three small, fast corsairs that tried to come up on us in the night. We had learned well from Drake. With our long guns and the maneuvering of our ship, we managed to beat them off. Once beyond Gibraltar we had little more to worry us than wind and weather. It was with great rejoicing that we finally passed the Lizard and started down the Channel.

The news of our arrival spread throughout London, not only because we were one of the first merchant ships that had made a successful trip to the East, but also for the wealth of cargo with which we returned.

After the formalities of receiving the congratulations of the merchants and turning over my cargo manifest to them, Diggins and I managed to have a glass of wine and a short talk in my cabin. The joy he felt in seeing me again was as great as mine in seeing him. He smiled at me over the wine glass, saying, "Well, William, by tomorrow you will be the hero of London."

This seemed rather an odd statement. I asked him why he should think so.

"England is in terrible condition, William. There is such poverty and sickness. The people are so without hope, it seems as if half of London are pimps and whores or thieves and beggars. This voyage of ours will stir the Queen and our good Englishmen to loosen up. There are no ships abuilding. No work at all. There seems to be no money to be had. Yet I am sure there is as much money in England as there ever was." Indeed he painted a sad and sober picture of England. I changed the subject by asking that which was closest to my mind. "Elizabeth and the boy—how are they? I thought she would be down to the ship. There is nothing wrong?"

"No, William. She is awaiting you at the home of her uncle. She left the boy in Chatham."

"Has she been all right, Nicholas?"

"As far as I know. She doesn't come to see me any more. I am sorry that it should be so, William. I have given her as much money as I could but she seems to feel that my aim in life is to cheat you."

Though he said these words lightly I could see the hurt in his eyes. This pained me, too.

"Nicholas, a few voyages like this and we will all be rich," I told him.

After nine months I thought Elizabeth would be changed. As I entered the house of her uncle she came flying toward me more beautiful than I remembered her. She was crying and laughing and so filled with emotion she could hardly talk. And when she did talk she tried to say all things at once so I could do little more than kiss her soft cheek, stroke her hair, and listen.

In remembering back, I believe it was during the two months before the next voyage that Elizabeth and I began to draw apart. As I came to know her better, there were many things about her that annoyed me. My "stiff-necked pride," as she called it, angered her also.

My son, a sturdy boy with large, dark eyes, was always too much trouble for her. She wanted to leave him at Chatham. On my refusal to permit this, she sulked. Thus his care and the love he needed fell to me. Of these I gave him plenty, but the time I spent with him was far too short. Elizabeth's attitude and his unrequited needs set us quarreling.

I could not bear her irresponsibility, her childishness, her insistence on ever going about. She railed at me, calling me miserly and a clod, without the gift to meet people of a better class.

When the time neared for our departure I was impatient to be gone. Then, a few days before we sailed, two events took place that made me very happy. The first was that Elizabeth told me she was pregnant again. I am afraid my happiness was far greater than hers. The second took place aboard the *Dolphin*.

I was in my cabin when a messenger brought a note asking if I was the William Adams who was born in Gillingham and if I had a brother, Thomas.

"If so," it went on, "I am late returned from Holland and would be most desirous of speaking with you." It was signed, Thomas Adams.

For a moment I sat uncomprehending. I reread the note. Suddenly I realized the deep loneliness I felt in the lack of kin. Turning to the messenger, I asked if the man who had given him the note was about.

"Aye, Captain," he said. "He is waiting on the dock. From the look of him I didn't think he was important enough to disturb you. I would not have, save he was so insistent."

"Bring him to my cabin immediately," I ordered. I brought out wine and glasses from my locker, and waited impatiently.

I would never have recognized the man who appeared at my door. We were in no way alike. Whereas I was large of frame and blond, he was but of medium height and dark, with almost the look of a Frenchman.

He came in hesitantly. For a moment there was silence, then, in a surge of emotion, I came forward and took him by the shoulder.

"Thomas," I said. "Is it really you? I am so happy."

He looked at me and tried to talk, but choked and was almost on the point of weeping. He seemed tired and worn and his clothing was rough and in need of repair. I knew hunger when I saw it. I had him sit, poured him wine and gave him biscuit to take the edge off his hunger.

He told me how, after my father had died and I was away, they had gone to Holland. It was a long story of hunger bearable only to those who had religious fervor. Most of his days he had known hunger, cold and want.

I was happy to see him—indeed, my feelings surprised me. My first thought was to take him home, but I saw he was too tired. I therefore sent ashore for hot food, had water brought so that he could bathe, and let him sleep in my own bed.

I watched him for a time as he slept, and thought about the ties of blood and how, though this man was a stranger to me, I felt such warmth and love toward him. He had told me that my mother had died a year before, of colic. Only he and I were left. On my way home I purchased some warm clothing for him, having made note of his size. Elizabeth took the news coolly but I expected no more, since she had never known him.

During the middle of the following day we went to see Diggins, who accepted him with affection. That day being so busy, I had no opportunity to buy him better clothing, but these things were not important. The rough clothing seamen wore was a warm and sensible costume. In my eyes he was as well dressed as any man need be.

Elizabeth and I had had little chance for conversation, having gone out the previous evening. Now, as we entered the house, I noted the disappointment in her eyes as she glanced at Thomas' coarse attire. Evidently she had assumed when I said he had come from Holland that he was a rich merchant.

Dinner did not go well. My brother was uncomfortable having a servant wait on him. Besides, Elizabeth seemed to overdo her lady-like manners and asked him innumerable questions about things she should have known he was ignorant of. She made him appear crude, and in his discomfort I suffered with him. She had made plans for the evening which I refused to consider, so she went angrily off to her room. I knew there would be tears and recriminations later, but I would not subject Thomas to the foppish group Elizabeth favored and emulated, nor would I leave him alone. We had much to talk about.

We sat talking before the fire over a bottle of good wine and some excellent Dutch cheese. Thus I discovered many things in my brother's life that were sad. He was furiously bitter against religion. He drank his wine greedily, with haste, and with no enjoyment of its flavor—as if it was medicine which he took to make him well. His face became flushed when he began to speak.

"William, I'll tell you something true," he said. "When our mother took sick, I hoped she would die. And when she did die, I felt as if I had been released from chains. I know this sounds cruel and heartless, but she took from me every pleasure which a boy should know. Not one day of freedom did I have. Not one day when I was not accused of sin. When she died I got full of wine and cursed all those who believe in that crippled religion. I am afraid I left in ill repute."

He drank again, deeply, and began a rambling talk of how, before he was done, he would know all the sins of the world.

"Thomas," said I, "let us not speak of sin now, but of what you are to do. Were you trained or apprenticed to any trade?"

He had been apprenticed for a time to a blacksmith. But the Puritans moved about so that he had not been able to finish his apprenticeship. He knew a little of a number of things. His speech was almost that of a foreigner, being heavily accented by the guttural Dutch which had become his adopted tongue. With his foreign-sounding speech and no trade he would surely starve in London.

I thought, fleetingly, that perhaps Diggins could find some work for him. But I quickly dismissed that thought, as this would be but an added burden to my friend, for Thomas was well beyond the age of apprenticeship.

So I told him of the voyage, the dangers it entailed, and asked if he would come along with me.

"Of ships I know nothing, William," said he. "Except that I get mightily sick. I thank you, but of what worth would I be to you?"

"Of much worth, Thomas. You are my only kin, and I yours. You shall be supercargo. We have many manifests and much writing. During the months at sea I will teach you some knowledge of ships. You will soon recover from seasickness."

Happiness, release from tension, and the wine he had drunk caused him to weep. I could tell that wine was something that Thomas knew not much of. Eventually he fell asleep in the chair. I carried him to a room, removed his boots, and covered him. I sat looking at him for a time, sorrowing for all the trouble he had known, and thanked God who had brought him to me. I vowed I would try to make it up to him. Then I went in to look at my son, with the same love as I felt for Thomas.

When I came to bed I was happy. Elizabeth, however, was in a petulant mood, saying that the last few days we had were now to be ruined, and that I cared more for any stranger than for her. Further, she complained that no one was interested in inviting a married woman to a ball or party, especially one in the process of making a child.

"And all the time I will be lonely. But this does not matter to you. You care only for yourself and give no thought to me." And so on and on. But her words and complaints could not dim my happiness.

23

For the next nine years, life smoothed out and though there were problems, none were of any great importance. Elizabeth and I, over the years, drew always further apart.

Despite her shame at my being "in trade," it did not diminish her extravagance. Her family never became reconciled to our marriage and I was always treated as some poor relation. This had humor in it as, by then, I was supporting more Howards than I thought existed. I would, no doubt, have revolted against such treatment but for a sense of guilt that always rode me, not only because Elizabeth claimed I had ruined her life, but because of Procopia.

Elizabeth never knew of her but I think she suspected. This might have been why she never came to maturity but behaved always like an irresponsible girl.

With Procopia I found warmth, love, and unceasing effort on her part to make me happy. Never did she give thought to her own comfort or wants. When I brought her a gift she was happy but not once did she ask for anything. Possibly the delight I took in Procopia was because she was completely the opposite of Elizabeth. Should I speak a harsh word to her, she would respond as if I had struck her deservedly and would try to find her error, never blaming me. God knows she never received much from me except shelter and food. Of this I am ashamed. I always intended to provide some investment in Turkey to provide for her in the event something happened to me, but always I put it off.

That next voyage was a happy one. My brother Thomas was with me and I came to know and understand him. He was bitter over the severity of his early years. He took the opposite tack from the Puritan teachings, drinking and roistering even beyond the habit of a thirsty sailor in from the sea. Yet he was shocked when he came to know of Procopia, and on one occasion delivered a long lecture on the sin of it. He was drunk at the time and had about him several fat Turkish women like a sultan in a harem. I had come to bring him back to the ship and soak some wine out of him.

He lectured me all the way back to the ship, even while I removed his boots and clothing and put him to bed. Then he put his arm across my shoulders and spoke a few words that touched my heart. They have remained with me always. Looking soberly up at me, he said:

"No one could tell where my soul might be:
I searched for God and he eluded me;
I sought my brother out and found all three."

Back in England I found a new member to my family. Elizabeth had given birth to a girl, a lovely, dark-eyed child who stole my heart on sight. My son was then a stalwart two. These children were the delight of my life and I had great plans for them.

In Constantinople another joy awaited me. Procopia had given birth to a boy. On my arrival, Ali met me at the ship and I sensed some strain about him.

"The woman. Is she well?"

"Lord of the sea, if she were not, the first words to pass these unworthy lips would have been the news, even though my tongue would shrivel from the thought of bringing you sadness. The woman is well and fat, though not as fat as I would like to see her."

"You are a rascal and a thief, Ali; I know you well. Something troubles you."

Under ordinary circumstances, when accused of thievery, Ali would have protested his honesty vehemently, offering all proof. Now he merely looked down at his feet and said, "The woman has a son, Master."

"A son! God's word, is this bad news?" Then I looked at him. "Unless it is not mine."

"Oh, Master, it is yours. Both his features and tool are of your own magnificence."

As soon as possible I left the ship and with both Ali and the crier running ahead to clear the way, we reached the house in a short time.

I found Procopia on her knees, with her forehead pressed to the floor. I drew her to her feet and into my arms where she wept quietly.

"Foolish woman, why didn't you tell me? You must have been well with child when I left."

"I was in fear. I thought to give away the child before you returned. But I am weak. You are not angry?"

"Angry? Woman, you are mad. Go and bring me my son."

She brought the child. He was as fair as any English baby, though his eyes were serious as if he had inherited some of the wisdom of the East.

And so my life separated into two parts at Gibraltar. On the homeward journey I thought of my children and Elizabeth in England, and looked forward to seeing them. When leaving England, I was always filled with regret. Yet when we passed through into the Mediterranean, on the leg of the outward voyage, I could hardly wait to see Procopia. The greetings of the two women were as different as their worlds.

In England, Elizabeth ever knew the arrival of the ship. She would be down at dockside with a gay entourage and I would be caught up in a whirl of activity of which I had no enjoyment. Guiltily, I could not spoil her foolish pleasure. We had shared passion in the beginning, if nothing else, but as the years passed she seemed to lose her desire and was in absolute terror of conceiving another child.

In Constantinople, I would come ashore from the sea and hurry to my house, with Ali trotting alongside the chair imparting all happenings during my absence, news of the markets, arrivals of caravans, and much valuable information. During the years Ali had lost none of his irritating ways, but had come to love me with the steadfastness of a dog to a master and I loved him in a patient sort of fashion. Once at home, I would dismiss him at the door and enter to find Procopia waiting, all woman, all understanding. Only after I had slaked my passion would we then go to the children. First one, then two, then three—all boys. I made plans for these children as I made plans for the two in England. I intended they should have a good education, a fair start in life.

My youthful dreams of making a great voyage, sailing into the unknown world and acquiring enduring renown were fading. I still read all of the accounts of the new voyages, kept up my mathematics and navigation and my membership in the Royal Society and the Hakluyt, but there seemed little hope that greatness and fame would come my way.

Yet I had no cause to complain. Little by little, I accumulated some store of wealth. Along with the *Dolphin*, I bought an interest in another ship, the *Godspeed*. My good friend, Augustin Spalding, who had been my mate on the *Dolphin*, and a most competent seaman, I made captain of the *Godspeed*. Thomas, by this time, had learned navigation and ship handling, and was my mate on the *Dolphin*. She was a happy ship.

During the fourth year that I was with the honorable company of Barbary merchants, I almost gave up everything to go with Drake in what was to be his final voyage. I was greatly honored that he should ask me and was sorely tempted, as in my ears rang the wild wind of adventure, of privateering and hopes of fame. On the other hand, I had responsibilities—Elizabeth and the children; Diggins; Procopia and the children; and Ali. Most unhappily I had to tell Sir Francis that, though I longed to be in his company and appreciated the honor, I could not. He understood.

So, in the routine of the sea and of a merchant we made our voyages. Not in peace, for there was ever danger both from the sea and the corsairs, as well as the Italians and Spaniards whose hatred had not abated but had increased since the Armada's failure.

After nine years I had begun to be pompous, accustomed now to being treated with great respect, especially in the Eastern ports. I had put on weight and was well satisfied with everything about me.

Then, as if fate decided that I should again share in the misery of the world, on the tenth year I was suddenly brought to my knees by a series of disasters in which Diggins and I suffered greatly.

By then we had bought both the *Dolphin* and the *Godspeed*, working as carriers for the merchants' goods. By this we took a greater share, but also the danger of a greater loss.

I returned to London to find that the house which I had reluctantly purchased for Elizabeth had burned with everything in it. Fortunately no one had been injured. We had bitter words when I found she was lightheartedly going about replacing everything without thought of the cost.

On her insistence that she had a right to another house as fine, I lost my temper, saying to her:

"Both in attire and costly housekeeping you cannot tell how or when to make an end to expense. Woman, sometimes I believe you have a madness for all curiosities and expense in far greater measure than even those of higher birth and calling. Only what is far-fetched and dear-bought is good for my lady. But we will now have an end to it."

She retaliated in anger also, recalling my low birth and charging that her noble lineage entitled her to such things.

"I am a lady," said she, "and I will be a lady. And I do like the humors of fashion. And if I cannot have these things I cannot endure living."

Once, when we were dressing for a ball, in anger I pulled at my ridiculous neckpiece.

"These goddamned ruffs which make a man's head look like a pig's head on a platter! I must be mad to accept such idiocy as this and such foolishness that is in you. Did I know who invented such a fashion, he would not live till tomorrow. When I step outside and the wind blows, the damned thing goes flip-flop like rags flying about. And if the weather is wet it lies upon my shoulders like the dishcloth of a slut. I tell you, my fine lady, I have had enough! I go no more to gawk about with stupid, foppish people, to listen to conversation as barren as a Southwark whore, to stand and mince about and bow and scrape and toady to people who through birth rather than their own worth feel they stand above us."

With this I ripped the ruff from about my neck, stripped down, put on a Turkish gown, and went in to the children. In spite of her lamentations about my cruelty, from then on I went about with her no more except to a theater once or twice.

My rage did not abate as she thought it would. I found a house toward the country where the air, at least, was clean. I took away her access to money, putting an account with a merchant-banker, instructing him to allow her to spend only a given amount and no more. It was cruel, but had it not been for her extravagance and my supporting her family, I would have by then been a rich man. I had finally had enough.

24

I started my next voyage in anger, and it contained ill luck from the first setting of our sail. We had contrary winds from the Channel all the way to the coast of Africa. During a storm, a sea broke in the hatch to our storehold, ruining all the fresh meats and vegetables.

The winds pushed us first one way, then another. Some days we made no latitude at all. In a short time, with our fresh stores spoiled, many of the crew became sick with scurvy and a number of them died.

By the time we reached the Mediterranean, the *Dolphin* was hardly manned for sailing under fair conditions and certainly not able to withstand an attack. We had days of calm, with hot sunshine, and each day brought with it more sickness.

Early one morning, almost in sight of the safety of Cape Bon, we were set upon by corsairs. The flag of the Sublime Porte flew from my masthead, but the corsairs ignored this guarantee of safe conduct. All that day we fought them off, but we had been so battered by the sea and so weakened by sickness, they were able to drive us inshore until we went aground in shallow water.

We were all aware, should they take us, it meant slavery—or worse. There was not one of us who did not do far more than he was able. To this day I carry the scar across my head from the blow that brought me down. Only my mailed cap kept my head from being split in two. The wound was a serious one and I lost consciousness. When I became aware of my surroundings it was to find that those of us left alive were locked in a most evil dungeon that stank of the unspeakable suffering of others before us.

Being proficient in the Arab tongue, I managed to procure some water from the guard to bathe our wounds and relieve our thirst. I demanded an audience with the Bey, but they paid me no heed.

After the fourth day a doctor came to attend to our wounds, putting on soothing ointments. Then we were fed with something more than the vile mess that had been thrown to us each day. All were sick and wounded. My brother had a deep wound in his shoulder. He had caught a fever and was close to death.

On the fifth day I was taken from the dungeon, allowed to bathe, and brought before the Bey. He was an evil-visaged man, dressed in rich robes. Around him was all the pageantry of a king. Two huge Nubians stood at each side of the throne with naked scimitars. The room was large and richly furnished, I doubt not, from the loot of his piracies.

I saluted him in the manner of the East and humbly addressed him.

"Son of the Prophet, it was our mistake not to recognize your ships. We thought they were Christian dogs from Italy, who hate us. I beseech you, in the name of Allah, to spare us. For the damage we did to your ships I will make what recompense I can. Send a letter, Most Benevolent One, to my friends in Constantinople and they will send you whatever monies I have. Though I am not a man of wealth, but only a poor, ignorant Christian sailor, all that I have is yours."

"Christian dog, put not your tongue to the language of the Prophet. Speak the dog's tongue of the Franks, and it shall be told to me."

"Benevolent One, I am a fool and deserve whatever fate is given me. Being in the employ of the Sublime Porte, and carrying his seal, I have become proud over the favors shown me and act as if I am the equal of the sons of the Prophet."

I watched him carefully. I was gambling with our lives. To say a wrong word could seal our fate. He studied me, and I had a fair idea of what he was thinking. Probably a head or two had already fallen because of this blunder. But the damage had been done and I could see him weighing the chance of coming out of it safely and with a profit.

He took my cue, reviling me, saying that it was only the kindness of his heart and love for the Sultan, whose slaves we were, that kept us alive. He then asked an enormous price as ransom, which I protested I could not pay. We then entered into bargaining. These people love to bargain—it is like food and drink to them.

He dispensed with the interpreter and we haggled back and forth, finally settling on a ruinous amount, but at least one that I could pay. I had so many people dependent upon me that I could do no less than I had done. I swore that, should the chance ever come, the head of the Bey would sit upon a pike.

I retained this thought as my sole consolation for the four months we were imprisoned. Almost half of the remaining men died before we were released, but my brother Thomas survived, and for this I was selfishly grateful.

At the end of those interminable four months, a small ship flying the flag of peace came and we were released. Well aware of the treachery of these people, I was afraid that, even with the ransom paid, we might not be freed. We did not feel secure until we were beyond the port of Alexandria and into the Greek Islands.

I had hoped that the *Godspeed*, with Augustin Spalding, might still be in port. She was to have left England two months after our departure. At Constantinople, I was shocked to find she had not arrived at all. This was a grievous blow.

I was ill, but under the love and care of Procopia I soon recovered my health and strength and consoled myself with the thought that I had my life which, after all, was the key to fortune.

I also had my revenge on the Bey and his corsairs. I was called to an audience with the Sultan, himself. After relating the truth to him, a fleet was dispatched to administer his justice. But this did put nothing in my pocket nor did it return the lives of my men.

Taking passage for myself and those few left of the crew on an English ship owned by merchants out of Bristol, we began the long voyage home again. I depended on my Turkish friends to see that Procopia and the children would not suffer want. I entrusted their care to Ali, whose steadfast loyalty to me and mine was a comforting thought. His offer the day before my departure deeply touched me.

"Master," said he, "over the years I have come by a small store of gold. It is yours, Master. I have no need for it and would be most appreciative if you would rid me of the worry of it. Use it as you will, Master." And he generously handed me a small sack, looking embarrassed that I had seen him with his emotions apparent.

The kindness of it, so unexpected and so sincere, brought back my spirits. I believe there were tears in my eyes as I thanked him, most gratefully saying he should keep it, and should Procopia need for anything then he was to help her and I would repay him tenfold. And I left Constantinople feeling all might yet be well again.

Once back in England, however, I found further misfortune. The *Godspeed* had run into a gale not three days from the Lizard. Being damaged Spalding had tried to beat his way back to England, but had been blown ashore on Goodwin Sands. He and most of the crew had managed to reach shore safely. For this small crumb I was grateful.

Elizabeth, however, had dealt me the last, crushing blow. Believing I was lost, she had forged my name to a letter written, I am sure, by the very merchant I had left her account with. On the strength of this letter she had borrowed a great amount of money. All was gone, and in honor I had to pay or name my wife thief.

Shipping was at a standstill. Like a spread of disease after my sailing, great gales had wrecked many merchants' ships. Not only could I not obtain another ship, nor even a berth on one, but my creditors, sensing my dilemma, were clamoring for money.

Thomas gave me whatever money he had but it was not enough. In order to keep out of debtors' prison I had to turn to Diggins. He went deep into debt to keep me free as, in prison, I would have no chance to repay.

Instead of feeling guilty, Elizabeth, with female logic, blamed me. Without credit or funds we were forced to move back with Diggins. She took this as the end of the world. Only the children and I didn't mind.

I did what little work there was at the yard and spent my free time at the inns and merchants' clubs seeking a ship or hoping someone would lend me money. This was foolish. I was too stiff-necked to ask and no one offered. I came to know how many friends I had. There were not many.

I could care for Elizabeth and the children, but the thought of Procopia tore at me like a vulture at my bowels. I obtained a small amount of money and sent it to her with a letter, trying to put into words my love and the assurance that I had not abandoned her. Each time I heard of a ship leaving I would dispatch, at least, a letter to her.

The only times I could forget my troubles were at the meetings of the Hakluyt Society and the Royal Society. I read with interest reports of all the latest voyages, studying the new maps. I attended meetings and contributed some few things I had learned of wind, tides and currents, though my voyages had been in well-tracked waters.

Then there came such a black day I thought I could not bear. A ship came in carrying a letter from Ali, written for him by a scribe. He told me of the plague which had taken many people from the poorer section of Constantinople, among them Procopia and two of my children. Ali had placed my remaining son in the employ of a Turkish merchant who had promised to care for him until I returned. The letter concluded:

"I beseeched Allah, Master, to take me in their stead. But he would not. Master, I will, while there is breath in my body, watch over your remaining child and keep you informed. I would that my tongue were out rather than have to tell you of this tragedy. Forgive your heartbroken servant. Ali."

This news brought me such despair that I could not see nor think. I wandered down to the Thames where, seated on a pier over the river, I wept. I had loved this Greek woman and the children she bore me, but the greater loss was in the love they bore me. To give love is happiness, but to have someone love as Procopia loved me is a gift rarer than anything in the world. It was only on that day that I came to realize truly how much a part of me she had become. It was as if one of my limbs were torn from me. Nothing could have hurt me more.

For a long time I sat there. My heart turned cold after I had wept. I could see no reason for continuing on. I was bitter at life, angry, and could find nothing to warrant prolonging this misery. I looked at the river with longing. It flowed so smoothly that I felt here would be the place to rest. I swam too well to hope that I could control my body from fighting to live; so I looked about for a heavy stone and a length of rope.

I must have been there a long time and was completely absorbed in my search when Thomas found me. He said nothing, nor did I. When I found a rock large enough, I tugged at it and he silently helped me carry it to the pier.

My anger stirred so that I growled for him to leave me be. He did not answer but went away. Soon he returned with another stone and put it beside mine.

"I need only the one," I said.

"But I also need one, William," he answered quietly, and began tying a piece of line around the stone he had brought.

"Damn you, Thomas, this is not your affair nor your loss. My life is ended. My troubles are so great I cannot bear them, but you have no reason."

He looked at me with compassion. "I read the letter, William. I cannot blame you. But remember that I found my brother and you are all I have. Should I lose you, I would not want to live."

He spoke softly and so sincerely I could not doubt him. Later I thought how wise he had been, as this was the only thing that could have stayed me. I buried my face in my hands and he put his arms around me, saying nothing.

Soon my heart eased and my mind cleared. This was no way out, I saw. Silently we walked home and the pain of my loss became endurable. The next morning fate took a turn as if offering a salve for my sore heart and mind.

PART THREE

The Voyage

25

On that day I was sitting in the office talking with Diggins about a projected journey to the King of Naples where we hoped for the building of two ships of war. With great effort I tried to concentrate on the subject, keeping my great sorrow within myself, for Diggins knew nothing of Procopia.

I had questioned the wisdom of his attempting such a long voyage and offered to go in his stead, but Nicholas seemed to look forward to this as adventure. I could not quarrel with his decision. At that point nothing seemed to matter.

A messenger arrived, interrupting our conversation with a letter stating that a Mr. Peter Van der Haag and Hans Vanderuke would be at the Hakluyt Society on Friday evening and wished to discuss a matter of interest to me. Below their signatures was written DUTCH EAST INDIA COMPANY, a name with which I was unfamiliar.

Passing the letter to Nicholas, I asked if he had any idea what this would be about.

He read it through, then said, "I have heard some rumor of a group of merchants who are planning a trading voyage to the Far East. Perhaps there will be some business in it for us. They may need ships and equipment."

Being in such difficult circumstances, my hopes rose at the thought. Before meeting with them on Friday I made notes and took along the projected plans for a new, large ship Nicholas and I wanted to build.

Upon my entry to the Society rooms, I had no difficulty marking the two gentlemen I was to meet. They were typical of the Dutch merchant, large in girth and broad in the beam, and, unless they were exceptions, very shrewd. They were jovial in their greeting and, in a private room, we had a long and heavy dinner and much talk of ships and shipping and of voyages of discovery, a subject close to my heart and one on which I could discourse at length.

I bided my time, waiting patiently for them to disclose whatever was on their minds. The proposition they offered, after much talk, was the position of pilot major and sailing master of a fleet of five ships they were outfitting on the Texal in Holland for a trading journey to the Far East.

Saying how flattered I was, I asked why they had selected me.

"You underestimate yourself, Herr Adams," Mr. Van der Haag said. "Your reputation has been well known to us for a long time. We have read with interest your papers on trade, on sailing routes and the dangers involved. At the beginning, I must admit, we did intend to hire Herr Davis. But as he was already planning a voyage to the Americas, we have turned to you."

He further flattered me by saying they considered me the best pilot available. The very thought of such a voyage thrilled me. I had long ago given up hope of any opportunity such as this.

I explained my position to them, saying that, with Diggins gone, the work of the shipyard was left entirely in my hands. Of course I told them of my responsibility to my family.

"Ja, Herr Adams," Vanderuke said. "We know of your problems. Our company has authorized the payment to you of fifteen English pounds a month and, of course, some bonus at the end of a successful voyage."

Fifteen pounds a month of clear profit, at that time, meant a great deal to me, though a short time before Elizabeth had spent that much on a bauble if it pleased her. But man is always bound by present circumstances. I tried not to appear overly anxious, agreeing to come to Rotterdam at their expense and talk further of terms and conditions.

On a trading adventure such as this I intended to have a share in the trade goods but, knowing the Dutch, I would have to make my conditions slowly, over a period of time. Having been so accustomed to dealing with the Turks, I knew how to bargain and fully expected to contract an agreement more beneficial to me.

We parted company on most friendly terms and I came home feeling more hopeful than I had been for a long time. Brutally I drove all thought of Procopia from me. I kept my mind to the project and fed my heart on happy thoughts of adventure.

For several days, while I was getting my affairs in order, I walked around lighter of heart, allowing the anticipation of this great adventure to take hold of me. As pilot major I would be navigating five ships through seas few men had sailed before—seas unfamiliar to Englishmen.

From the time the offer was first made, I had little doubt I would accept. Fifteen pounds a month for Elizabeth would be comfortable enough living. The bargain I might make for a percentage of the trading profits could make me independent enough to start again on my own and help Nicholas. All this was good and valid reasoning. But, like a boy, I dreamed mostly of the wide and unknown seas, belonging to a ship again, and the freedom and joy a voyage entailed.

I mentioned nothing to Elizabeth. Knowing her so well, I knew she would count the voyage already made and the profits on hand. Making an excuse of business to her, I journeyed to Rotterdam a fortnight later and met again with the Dutch merchants.

I was treated with the utmost esteem, provided with comfortable rooms, and the day after my arrival, was taken to view the ships they had purchased for the voyage. I was greatly disappointed in them, the largest being but one hundred sixty tons burden. This was to be the Admiral's ship, the one I was to sail in. She was named the Liefde—in English, "Loving Charity." By the balky look of her rig I doubted she would have much charity for any seaman. The four other ships were even smaller, the smallest being but seventy-five tons burden. They were broad-beamed and clumsy-looking, like all Dutch ships.

My suggestion of purchasing larger, more seaworthy vessels was met with quick dismissal. These ships, Mr. Vanderuke informed me, were sound and well-fitted for the voyage. I disagreed, though I said nothing, being anxious to gain the voyage.

The following day I met with Admiral Jacob Majure, who was to be in command of the fleet. I knew nothing of him or his knowledge of seamanship. As pilot major, the sailing and navigation would be in my hands, but I would still be under his orders.

Majure was a short, stocky man who kept the bottle close at hand and said very little. We discussed my share in the voyage that night and the following nights. Finally, after much bargaining, we agreed that each month fifteen pounds would be paid to my account in London and that I was to share in the profits of the company to the extent of three per cent of all monies made on the voyage. We signed a contract.

It was with great elation I left Rotterdam to return to London. I was impatient to get back to London and talk with Thomas. Over the years he and I had formed the habit of speaking long and full well together, opening our hearts to each other. Usually his advice was good.

Thomas had gone to the quay with me when I left London. I would have gladly taken him with me but, in truth, I had not the fare. Now I was in great haste to tell him the good news. I had insisted that the Dutchmen let Thomas sail with me as sailing master's mate, and had also obtained for my friend Timothy Shotten the position of assistant pilot and sailing master. Though I had tried very hard, they would not agree to the employment of other English seamen. I would to God that I had been able to select a crew for at least one of those five ships.

In London I went first to the shipyard and told the news to Thomas, who was as happy as I.

"But think of Elizabeth, William," he said. "How will she take this? She is in a very unhappy time, living in the house of Diggins. Will it not seem to her as if, once again, you are deserting her?"

"Has she or I any choice, Thomas? This voyage is my only hope to recoup our fortune. Another thing, this is not just a voyage for trade, but also one which could make my name. You know how important this is to Elizabeth."

For the first time in months, everything went well on the evening of my return. Elizabeth was in a rare good mood and the children happy to see me home. When they were put to bed I sat down and told her of Vanderuke and Van der Haag and the proposed voyage. I did not tell her, then, that I had already committed myself, but dwelt more upon the profits possible, and also on the fame that could come from such a voyage. I know it was this aspect that made her consent so readily. From force of habit she used the familiar words of my wishing to abandon her, but I spoke further of the honor of being selected for such a voyage, saying I would be the first Englishman to lead ships into the eastern seas, unless Davis found a route by northern passage, the route man has sought from the time of Henry Hudson.

To further win her over I told her the wage I would leave for her. This would be enough for a house of her own. She would be her own mistress again.

"Well," said she, "there seems no other way out for us as things are now. How long will such a voyage take?"

"No more than a year, with luck." I explained that the Spaniards were out and back on most voyages in seven or eight months. "Anyway, Elizabeth, this voyage will not begin tomorrow," I continued. "It will not be until mid-spring. You and the children shall journey with me to Rotterdam and stay there until the voyage begins."

After so much trouble and heartbreak, this little ray of hope cheered us both and we drank some wine and became quite merry and loved one another for the first time in months.

Man being always the optimist, I awakened in the morning as if recovered from a long illness. Though the day was gray outside, life carried a brighter face.

Two days later, Nicholas Diggins returned from Naples a sorely disappointed man. The naval advisers of the king had considered our design much too radical. Though we had proved the superiority of English vessels so often, they still felt a ship should be a great, ponderous thing, wallowing in the water like a tub. Upon his arrival, I hurried to tell him the news of my forthcoming voyage. I did not even have the courtesy to ask about the success of his journey, but, directly after the first greeting, spoke of my own affairs. He took my news gladly, with no thought to his own troubles.

"It will be a great voyage, William," he said excitedly, turning to the large globe on the table. He spread out the sailing records and charts of the Spaniard and Portugal voyages.

"We must draw a tentative map of your route, then we will have a meeting of the Society. This exploration will be for England as much as for the Dutch. A successful trading venture will stir our slow countrymen to action. William, I know that England is only waiting for a leader such as Drake was. When he died, our adventuresome spirit seemed to have died with him. This is a wonderful opportunity. You will start us off again as you did with trade to Constantinople."

Rubbing his hands in glee, he spread the large chart flat on the table and, together, with dividers and calipers, we began charting my course.

We had a meeting with the Royal Society. The excitement was such that the next night the members of both the Royal Society and the Hakluyt Society came together as one group. Again, discussion of the impending voyage went far into the night.

Most of the subjects were of things I knew, though here and there I picked up additional information. Still, not enough. The old hatred of Spain and Portugal against England and the Low Countries was still so strong that almost all information of the route of the Spaniards was not available to us. Worst of all, some of the maps and charts Drake had seized when we took the Portugal carrack had been misplaced or lost.

After sorting all the information we had, and I heard no disagreement among the group, it was felt that we must reach the Cape of Good Hope, at the tip of the African continent, before the monsoon season in order to sail through the Ocean of India. If that point was reached too late it meant either sailing for Cape Horn or staying at the African Cape until the monsoon season was over. The Portugals and Spaniards had found this to be untrue, but in England we had no knowledge of it.

At the end of the meeting, my good friends offered to combine the knowledge of all into one treatise which I could study and refer to later on. A few days later, at another meeting, I was surprised by many gifts which would be most important and necessary on the voyage.

Master Hakluyt personally presented me with his new edition of *Principall Navigations*. This copy was no more than the second or third book which had just come from the printers. I was also presented with the *Arte de Navegar*, both in the original Portugal by

Pedro de Medina and the English translation containing additional notes made by my friend John Frampton; also a book by Martin Artes titled *The Sphere and Art of Navigation*. I was given a new half-hour pilot glass, an astrolabe, a cross staff, back staff, quadrant, and a very fine compass.

I promised to all that I would keep an accurate and complete record of the winds and currents and anything of interest that occurred. It was my hope that I could bring back information valuable to our country, so that England might share in the wealth of the world which the Spaniards and Portugals had so long controlled.

There was much talk, congratulations, and, I am afraid, too much bending the elbow. When Nicholas and I went home that night, being sentimental with wine, he told me freely of the deep affection he had always held for me, calling me his son and saying that of all the work he had done in his life he was proudest of me. Though prompted by wine, his words touched me.

I saw him safely to bed, then walked about the streets of London. And these people of the streets that I passed made no attempt to bother me, not only because of my size. But on that night there was such a strength, such a happiness in me, that I could have knocked a dozen men's heads together without shortness of breath.

By the time we were ready to leave for Rotterdam I had discovered I knew ten times more people than I was aware of. I received an invitation from Lord Howard of Effingham to visit him, which I considered a great honor. He ranked, in my opinion, just below Drake.

We spent an afternoon together and I am afraid I talked mostly, telling him of the voyage and what we expected to accomplish. At our parting he gave me a scroll, made up by his own hand, listing all my experience. I was surprised that he had gone to the trouble to have it searched out. He recommended me highly as a kinsman with the right to use his name and position for any aid I might need.

When I thanked him he smiled and said, "It is I who should thank you. The Howards are a fertile breed. Had I fed and cared for as many as you have in the past ten years, I would be in debtors' prison." He added with a wink: "And after all, you are my kinsman, the only one who has never asked a favor."

"You are very kind, my lord."

"And you are a man, William Adams."

Strange how pleasing to the ear kind words are. I valued his respect more than any favor he could have done me.

On my return home I told Elizabeth of his kindness and showed her the scroll. This pleased her so that it made up a great deal for the inconvenience of the voyage to Rotterdam.

26

According to the Dutch merchants, all was to be in readiness for us to leave Holland during the first part of May. This would give us two months. Elizabeth and the children came with me to Rotterdam. They were sick on the crossing. Rotterdam was wet and colder than even the worst days in England.

Elizabeth hated the climate and the people on sight. The children took cold. She refused to stay, so I sent them home in the company of Thomas, promising that as soon as possible I would come home and spend a little time before we sailed.

I counseled young William to guard well his mother and sister. Even now I can feel my sweet daughter's arms around me and taste the salt of her tears. I prayed that God would be kind to them.

Turning my attention to the business at hand, I soon discovered I was party to a dishonest venture. My name was prominently displayed as the pilot of the voyage and many fine things were said about my skill. This did not flatter me, as Admiral Majure and the other captains were described as "the finest sailors ever to command a ship."

The Honorable East India Company was selling shares in the voyage. Obviously they intended to make their profit before the voyage began. It appeared that everyone in Rotterdam was buying stock. Every man with a dream of adventure was being signed on as crew, the only requirement being the ownership of a few shares of stock.

The estuary where the five old ships lay was like a wing of a madhouse. Stores and trade goods would be put aboard a ship one day. People would then flock aboard to see the display, and a lecture would be given on the vast profits to be made. The Dutchmen would force money on the merchants like idiots, insisting on being part of the venture. Then everything would be taken to another ship and the whole farce gone through again.

By the time I was aware of what really was taking place, a conference of the ships' officers was called by Van der Haag and Vanderuke and it was suggested that we give lectures on the voyage. I was singled out to address a large gathering.

Angrily, I said, "Herr Van der Haag, I was not hired to lecture or to sell shares, nor do I intend to do so. I am disturbed by the condition of the ships, the lack of supplies necessary for a long voyage, and the men you are hiring to man the ships. Most of those I have spoken to have never been to sea. In my opinion, the duties of the assembled officers should be that of looking to the condition of their ships, not acting as professors or sales merchants to people who can't understand what they are talking about."

Van der Haag's face grew red, but he controlled his temper. "Herr Adams, I remind you that such a voyage takes money."

"But not all the money in Rotterdam."

"I will not argue. You don't want to help? We have others."

"Helping is not the question. I know the sea and ships. As we stand, we could not sail to the Channel. Ahead of us is a voyage of at least a year's duration. Those of us who are to sail the ships should put our hearts and minds to seeing that all is in readiness. One other thing. On such a lengthy voyage the very best of seamen should be in our crews."

"Enough!" Van der Haag shouted. "What were you hired as, Adams?"

I spelled it out for him. "Pilot major and sailing master of five sail on a trading venture to Far Eastern waters."

"Ja! Which duties do not include telling us how to run our business. You may leave."

I looked around at the assembled officers. Except for Thomas and Timothy Shotten, they were all Dutch, which does not mean they were stupid, but they resented me. I bowed and left. Timothy and Thomas joined me. Feeling helpless, I was in a mood to cast away from the whole venture and go home.

We stopped at a tavern and discussed the situation.

"William," Timothy said, "I know that you feel as I in that these Dutchmen haven't the sense to pour piss out of a boot without advice. Yet look at it this way. We want this voyage. And we shall have it. Let us find, from all this rabble, some few who know ships and bring them with us. By keeping quiet we can gain our ends, which we cannot do by fighting the merchants."

"He's right, Will," Thomas said. "Anger breeds anger. Give us a few good men and we will teach the others."

"Aye," Shotten said. "And those we can't teach and those who are weak, the sea will take in her own time." Brutal as this sounded, it was true.

At this time a big Dutch seaman came over to our table and doffed his hat respectfully.

"Captain Adams, you remember me?"

I recalled his face after a moment. He had been a mainmast hand on the *Rainbow* during the Armada.

"Sweringen." With one hand I gripped his shoulder. "Sit down." I introduced him to Thomas and Shotten. He had been in my sailing crew, and though young, had been a good seaman. "Sit down, Sweringen. What are you doing now?"

"I go with you, Captain. My uncle has shares and he got me a berth."

"Damme, Sweringen, that's good news!"

Not that I remembered him so well, but any who had sailed with the Armada were linked in brotherhood. We drank and talked, and my feeling of depression vanished.

From then on we formed what was almost a secret society, drawing officers and seamen into our group, hiding rope and sail and stores that were meant for display. At first we worried about time. May passed, and by the middle of June I began to believe we would never sail.

Then a rumor sprang up, spreading quickly through the city, that the whole project was a swindle. All of a sudden there was bustling activity and the ships were hurriedly made ready for sea.

Events moved quickly. I now had no chance to say a last good-by to my family. I wrote a long letter telling them not to worry as, with God's help, I would return in due time, bringing wealth enough to live on happily. I wrote to Diggins, trying as best I could to put on paper my love and gratitude to him.

On the twenty-fourth of June, 1598, we moved out in a long line from the Texal. It seemed half the population of Holland was on the shore watching our departure.

Luck was with us for the first few days, and though the ships were so sloppily handled as to be disgraceful, we managed to get down the Channel with all the ships together and beyond the Lizard before we hit a storm coming out of the Bay of Biscay.

Admiral Majure signaled that we would try to hold together, but if separated, to rendezvous at the Cape Verde Islands, off the coast of Africa.

The weather remained bad, with heavy seas, and the overloaded ship was full of complaints and much sickness. The *Liefde* handled no better than a tub, taking much water so that always we were wet.

Our good Admiral Majure stayed mostly to his cabin and close to his bottle and his alter ego, Van Sartoot, which pleased me, as when he emerged there was always a quarrel. He was a gross, blustering man, continuously blaming me and Captain Quackernack for the faults and conditions in the ship which it should have been his duty to correct.

Van Sartoot was the chief merchant. Between us had sprung an instant dislike which was to endure for so long as we knew each other.

Whatever food that was not spoiled when it came aboard, spoiled now. Our water turned bad, so that when we arrived at the Island of St. Iago at Cape Verde on the fifteenth day of September, half of our crew were ill of scurvy, dysentery and fevers.

Though I had never landed at these islands in my various voyages, I had spoken to many who had. I knew they were barren and inhospitable. Admiral Majure, however, had been told otherwise and seemed to look upon these islands as some sort of paradise.

We found the people poor and hostile. We cleaned and filled our water casks. There was little food to be had at any price. Within ten days our five ships were once again assembled and we left St. Iago, sailing outbound, intending to bear in to the coast of Africa and find a more hospitable place to refresh ourselves.

During the time we lay at St. Iago we were all called into a council and both Timothy Shotten and I spoke our minds, insisting we should sail as soon as possible before more of our people died.

Admiral Majure resented our speaking, more than likely because of

Van Sartoot, who acted as his adviser, but who knew less than nothing about ships and the sea.

"We will sail when and where I order, Herr Adams. You Englishmen think you know everything. We Dutch are sailors too." And he thumped his chest belligerently. "I tell you now you are pilot. I am Admiral. You overstepped yourself. From now on you English attend no more meetings. We will give the orders."

I was very angry, but under the law of the sea I could do nothing.

We were not more than thirty leagues south of the Island of St. Iago when our Admiral died of a fit caused, I believe, by too much drink. Captain Quackernack now assumed command. The Dutch captain and I had been friendly, but with the death of Majure, Van Sartoot influenced his allegiance and soon Quackernack was as stubborn against me as the Admiral had been.

We changed our course for Cape Gonzalez. Landing on the shore, we put all of our sick men on the beach for a rest from the sea. This land being also poor and barren, we set sail again in a few days for Annabon Island.

Here we found a village of about eighty houses of blacks. As we tried to land we were met with hostility from these people. Now we were in such desperate straits that we had to get refreshment or die. A council was held aboard the *Liefde* and the gravity of our situation was discussed. By this time ninety-one of the men who had left the Texal had died.

Mustering every man able to bear arms, we took our longboat and pinnaces and stormed the town. The village was taken with the loss of three of our men and a dozen or more wounded by arrows and spears. But we seized food enough of various sorts to satisfy our hunger. It was cruel, but our condition was so desperate that killing their oxen and eating their crops was a matter of our very existence.

The natives had planted corn that was almost ready to harvest. We guarded it night and day, and meanwhile killed and salted down all of the oxen, goats and other animals we could find.

But here new woes beset us. The climate was unhealthy. Fever afflicted the men, leaving them weak and helpless, many more dying.

After harvesting and drying the corn, we left this island near the end of November and set sail for the coast of Brazil, meaning to pass through the Straits of Magellan.

Captain Quackernack and the other captains now took the same position as Admiral Majure had done. They refused to listen to the advice Timothy Shotten and I offered. Knowing full well the distance and dangers involved by going to the Straits of Magellan, we wished to go to the Cape of Good Hope and remain there until the monsoon wind changed again.

The passage we made from Annabon Island to the Straits of Magellan was fraught with trouble and storms. One ship lost her mainmast. We managed with great difficulty to set a new mast.

It was nine months since we departed from Holland. The leg of the voyage from Annabon Island to the Straits had taken five long months. Not half of the voyage had been covered, and we had thought to be on our way home by now. It was the sixth of April, in the year of our Lord 1599, before we reached the Straits of Magellan. We had been suffering from want of food and water. For months we had been rationed with but a pound of corn or bread, half a pound of meat, and a small portion of wine and water each four days. The men had fallen into such hunger that we had to watch continuously else they would cut away the calfskin that covered our lower rigging and chew upon the leather like hungry dogs.

The wind being favorable to us, we passed through the first narrow of the Straits of Magellan, a grim and inhospitable place. On the eighth day after, we passed through the second narrow and came to an island which was covered with large fowl, called penguins. These birds being docile and unable to fly, we were able to fill our boats with them. The meat was stringy with a strong taste of fish. However, we were able to eat them and were refreshed. Having read of everything dealing with these straits, I knew that it was the greatest of luck that the wind should be in our favor and I strongly recommended to Captain Quackernack that we leave immediately and pass through.

But our Admiral insisted that we wait to take in provisions of wood and water for all our fleet. During this time the wind changed, coming in southerly so that we were forced to seek a good harbor where we could anchor our ships with some protection.

April now having ended, winter came upon us, to the amazement of most of the men. They could not understand how winter could be in summer. May, June, July and August passed and we suffered through tremendous storms, with much snow and ice, and cold of such intensity that we could do little but huddle below and wait, day after day, week after week, for the weather to change.

The wind and storms were so severe that our Admiral seemed terrified. Three times the weather cleared enough so I thought we might venture through. Each time he refused to give the order to up sail.

Finally, on the twenty-fourth of August, the weather cleared and we saw many natives on the shore. They were exceptionally tall and looked as if they might attack us. Our Admiral, in greater fear of the natives than the weather, gave orders to leave our anchorage and attempt a passage.

The weather held good until we came to another narrow, when the wind turned contrary, blowing first in one direction then reversing itself. The smallest of our ships swung broadside into the rocky shore, breaking in two. We on the *Liefde*, being in great distress ourselves, were unable to come about. Not one soul among the ship's complement of officers and men were saved.

That night we suffered through severe gales, and when morning came over a dark and still-stormy sea, there were but two ships left.

With the utmost difficulty we finally worked our way into the south sea and were able to make some sea room away from the rocky and barren coast. Here we attempted to sail north, but now a more violent storm came up and we could do nothing but beat before the wind, which drove us south to a latitude of fifty-four degrees. When the storm abated somewhat, we were alone and almost without hope, lost in a barren and lonely sea.

When it was clear enough so that I could make a reckoning, we turned northward again. Within eight or nine days we came upon the other ship. It was a heartening sight, for by then we had come to feel there was nothing left in all the world but our small, fragile ship and the enormous sea. Keeping in close company, we bore north. Nine days later, the weather making up into a gale, we lost our foresail and once again were alone on the sea.

On the twenty-ninth of October we arrived at the place where we had appointed to meet at a latitude of forty-six degrees. Once again we were cheered to see our other ship there ahead of us. She had come in the day before. Being in an exhausted condition, we put our ships at a safe anchorage and, taking all of our sick, we loaded them in our boats and went ashore, unaware of what fate had in store for us. God being kind, we found the people friendly.

They brought us sheep and vegetables, for which we exchanged billhooks and knives. They seemed contented with the goods and were helpful in providing us with herbs and other medicines which they knew of to cure illnesses.

Then, with no warning, on the sixth day they disappeared. We saw them no more though we stayed there twenty-eight days longer.

27

The place where we made our camp and took this most welcome rest from the misery of the sea was on the edge of a rocky coast where, at one place, the land sloped gently down to a beach on which we landed our boats.

After the great tribulation that had followed us almost from leaving the Texal, we thanked God each day that we had managed to survive. Four hundred and ninety-seven men had left the Texal the year before. Now those of us still alive numbered but one hundred and forty-two. The voyage having been so long and the sea so wearing, many of the men could not regain their spirits, though we were now in some comfort ashore.

I had come to know most of these men well as one man can know another on the bosom of the sea. I knew that there would be many more who would die of no further trial than lack of spirit, worry over family and no hope of success, unless something were done for them.

Therefore I, with Timothy Shotten, Captain Quackernack, Thomas and the merchant's agent, Van Sartoot, and several others held a meeting, proposing that each should take upon himself his brother's burden. Such fraternity would be binding on the survivors to lend help to the families of his comrades and shipmates.

Van Sartoot, who was a small-minded man, and Captain Quackernack, who lacked brains and leadership, argued against it, but I convinced them that we must bring everyone together and give them hope, else we might as well stay upon these shores and die. Without spirit, the men could go no further.

Between tending the sick and searching for food we drew up the articles of our fraternity. After much discussion we titled it "The Fraternity of the Free Lion." Then we gathered in a hollow of the land, propping up the sick so all could see and hear.

Thomas offered a prayer. I can still see him now, standing on a slight rise of ground. He was spare and worn, and yet from him came strength and love that soothed us all. Even his words are clear in my mind, as is his image.

"Lord of life and love and beauty. Look down with pity on us poor pilgrims and receive our thanks for bringing us safely through our long travail. Give us strength to continue on, and receive those comrades who have been lost by the way.

"We are gathered here to form a brotherhood, each holding up the other. Guide us, for we desire to devote ourselves to each other, and go on refreshed on the voyage ahead.

"Let no one of us here remain spectators, but enter into a brotherhood, each with the other, and communion with God. May our comradeship inspire us to dwell in harmony each with all the others, holding our brother's trial and sickness as our own.

"And may we find in our hearts the spirit of Jesus, abounding courage, faith and love. Amen."

The chorus of amens stirred the air. Then I read the articles of the guild which most knew by heart, by then. In the articles we swore to share alike in whatever trial or profit was to come. That those who survived to return home would give all the solace and comfort and help in their power to the wives and families of our brothers.

The articles were long and the words weighty, but it was the spirit which brought us up from despair. Each signed his name or made his mark, and then we gathered around to talk and comfort each other.

This guild had better results than even I expected. It gave the men hope and we drew close together in comradeship, and what strength was left in each was added to the whole, giving us the amount of faith necessary to face the remainder of the voyage.

Throughout all the afflictions and hardships, Thomas had stood beside me steadfast and uncomplaining. In him was the gift, which I also held, of an inborn stamina for which there was no explanation. Neither of us had suffered from scurvy or any of the other fevers and ills that had wracked our company and caused so many deaths. Over the months Thomas had grown so much in stature that he had become almost a Christian, as the word should be meant; sharing with all, acting as nurse, comforting others, thinking not of himself. I was very proud of him.

When some health and spirit had returned to our company the strongest divided up each day to forage for food. Some went along the seashore to fish and seek whatever food was available from the sea; others took guns and went over the plain to seek game. We also ate grass and any fresh vegetation we felt was edible. It was very strange how quickly the men recovered from scurvy, either by being on land itself, or by eating the greenstuff.

Game was scarce, but here and there we would come upon a plot of ground which the natives had cultivated at some time or other. There we would dig for the mealy bulbs which the natives called *batata*. When boiled or baked, the batata had a sweet and filling quality which satisfied like bread.

My mind recalls a day when Thomas, Timothy Shotten, the huge Dutchman, Sweringen, and myself were far out on the plain where we had been hunting for a small animal like a deer. These animals were very wary. The mind being most inventive when necessity is the teacher, we discovered these animals were attracted to a piece of rag flapping in the breeze.

Seeing some of these animals far in the distance, we set a rag upon a pole, then hid in a small hollow away from the wind and where we could remain unseen. While we watched, we ate of some dried meat and the sweet batata. After having our refreshment, we relaxed and talked quietly of England and home.

Sweringen spoke mostly of Dutch and English ports. Being a true seaman, his conversation was mainly about women he had known and wine he had drunk. He had an innocence about him and a manner of speaking which made for laughter. I remember Thomas, as he lay back looking at the sky, with his hand pillowing his head, saying to me, "Whatever comes, William, remember this. I am happy to have been on this voyage, hard as it has been. Somehow I feel that great things are going to come so long as we hold steadfast. In later times, when this earth is well known and the tracks to these unknown lands are used as freely as the ships sailing the Mediterranean, we will be remembered. Maybe they will even praise our courage."

I was chewing on a stem of grass and looking at him as he talked. Then Timothy Shotten said:

"It may be true, Thomas, but I pray to God that they find a shorter and easier route than the one we have taken."

Thomas kept looking at the sky. Then, as if he spoke to his own ears, he said, "Man's knowledge being always on the increase, all the world will some day be known."

Turning to Timothy Shotten, I said, "And when the world is known, Thomas and I have a theory that man, ever pushing forward, will some day reach out into the very sky to explore what that holds."

At this Timothy laughed. "William," he said, "it surely will take a great pair of wings for man to go flying off to the moon, especially for you and Sweringen."

Thomas turned on his elbow. "Timothy," said he, "the world is full of knowledge so that I cannot predict what will happen. But I do have confidence in the mind of man. Some day, I think we will come to peace and tolerance and understanding, with food and freedom for all. Then we can go on with unlimited search for knowledge. Should this come, the skies will be opened for us."

Our talk then turned to God, the mysteries of religion and the strangeness of God's ways that so many men have wrongly interpreted. I said little, neither agreeing nor disagreeing, being happy in the day, the sunshine, the protection from the wind, and in the sound of my brother's voice.

Thomas' mind, so distorted in his early years, was now maturing faster than mine. I took delight in watching and listening to him.

Then, a whispered caution came from Sweringen who was on lookout. Preparing our arms, we peered above the edge of the hollow, waiting tensely for the small horned deer to approach.

I remember we were most fortunate that day in killing three of them. Fresh meat was as life itself to us then. We returned triumphantly to camp where we cooked our meat in a great pot, along with all manner of greens, into one great stew.

Though we hunted and fished every day, we found we could hardly keep pace with the amount we ate, even though we rationed ourselves, toward the last. We finished repairing the ships and decided to sail toward a place called Baldivia, where the natives had told us there were many people.

Upon our arrival there we found strong winds, so we left and changed our course for the island of Mocha. Here, again, the wind blew too strong for our ships to anchor. We then came about for the coast, within a league and a half of a land where we saw many people on the shore. Heading in behind a cape, our soundings showed good ground and we anchored in a fair bay in fifteen fathoms of water.

We put our boats over the side and went to the shore to parley with the people, but they were very hostile, shooting a great store of arrows at us, shouting and waving their arms threateningly so that we could not land.

Drawing off from the shore, we brought our ships together and decided that, under our circumstances, we would have to force them into friendship. We moved slowly in until we were within cannon shot of the shore. Some thirty of us landed and drove the natives back from the water.

Most of us were hurt by their arrows. However, the heavy clothing we wore prevented any deep penetration, though I took an arrow in the leg. It went in not more than an inch and I was able to remove it with no trouble.

Coming to a natural defense position on the shore, we made signs of friendship, showing them knives and cloth and other articles, trying to explain by signs that we came to parley, not to injure them.

Finally they understood and brought us wine and the bulblike batata, along with other foods, fruit and meat. In exchange we gave them iron, and cloth, and indicated by signs that we would come again the next day. They, seeming to understand, indicated they would bring further refreshments.

Next day, the ninth of November, 1599, our two captains and all the officers held a conference. Though we had been successful the previous day, it was decided that great caution should be exercised and that, before going ashore, the boats would stay at a safe distance while the natives brought down the victuals.

As the wound I had received was bothering me, my brother Thomas and Timothy Shotten went in the boat with Captain Quackernack. I watched from the ship's rail, hoping all would go well but not trusting the natives, for the Spaniards had done their work well in making them hate all white men.

Our boats lay off shore and parleyed back and forth, but the people would not come down. I then saw the boats draw together for conference, then row into the beach, contrary to the plan agreed upon.

The natives had piled a great mound of foodstuffs a short distance from the beach where four or five thatched huts stood. Twenty-three of our men landed with muskets and marched up the beach. When they had almost reached the mound of foodstuffs, just beyond musket shot of the boats, the ground seemed to spring to life with savages—a thousand or more, it seemed.

Seeing this, I immediately gave order to up our anchor and move into shore. Our guns were loaded and ready but there was such a heaving mass of people I dared not give the order to fire. Soon all our men were slain, the savages dragging them off to a higher point of ground where they hacked them to pieces before our very eyes.

I was in such a rage, I would have sailed the ship up on the beach as, through the glass, I saw Thomas cut down and hacked to bits.

As we came in, Captain Quackernack's boat came alongside and those left came aboard.

"Come about!" he screamed.

"Hold her as she goes. May God damn you, you Dutch bastard, you sent those men to their deaths!"

We came on, and I gave the order to fire the cannon at will. The savages disappeared over a hill. Quackernack, coming up behind me, struck me over the head with a belaying pin and knocked me unconscious.

He was right in his action, but in my grief I would willingly have died with Thomas.

By the time I came to my senses, we had come about and, picking up our boats, had set sail for the island of Mocha. I was in such sorrow that I left the sailing of the ship to the others. My despair was equal to the day I learned the fate of Procopia. Yet sorrow like that cannot last. I was jolted out of it by the tragedy to those on the other ship.

Our companion ship, going faster than the *Liefde*, left us behind and, reaching the island before us, landed without knowing the humor of the people. They were immediately attacked. Seven men, including three of the officers, were slain.

Being in such a weakened condition and with hardly enough men to work one ship, both ships left there and sailed as best we could to Santa Maria Island, which is in the latitude to the southward of the land, thirty-seven degrees and twelve minutes off the coast of Chile. Here we took council.

It was my opinion we should take all things out of one ship and burn the other, but we could come to no agreement on this. So it was decided to distribute evenly those few stores we had left, and take no more chance of landing on this hostile coast. We would sail directly for the islands of Japan where it was said that our cloth was good trading merchandise.

This information was given by one of the seamen, Derrick Gerritson, of the other ship. He claimed to have been in the islands of Japan with the Portugals and said that woolen cloth was of great value to these people. I lacked faith in this Gerritson. I had caught him in many falsehoods. He had told tales of places where I had been and I knew his stories were false. I could tell by his talk he had never been there. I have met many such as he during my lifetime who lie for the momentary pleasure of being the center of attention. Almost always, their lies are discovered. These people usually have the facility of looking extremely sincere. Thus, the majority wished to do as he suggested.

On the twenty-seventh day of November, our two ships set sail and we stood away directly for Japan. I had little hope, as it seemed most unlikely that any of us could survive the voyage across that vast ocean. By now, I did not care too much whether I lived or died, and was willing to do whatever I could to see that the others survived.

The wind and the weather stayed with us so that we made good speed, the only storms being rain squalls which served to replenish our water casks. Our narrow supply of food was added to by trolling for fish. Some days we caught enough for a full meal for all.

On the twenty-third of February, in the year of our Lord, 1600, we had passed the equinoctial line and were twenty-eight degrees to the northward. At this latitude we had a wondrous, awe-inspiring storm. Through all the days I had spent upon the sea, never had I seen fury to equal this. We tried to hold together, but the last sight I caught of our consort was during a tremendous flash of lightning when I saw her in a momentary glimpse, wallowing off our beam. Morning came and we were alone upon the sea. We never saw the ship or our friends again.

There was nothing we could do. Still holding to the hope that she might have weathered the storm and we would meet her in the islands, we proceeded on our former intention, for Japan.

At a height of thirty degrees of latitude we thought to come upon the northernmost cape of the aforementioned islands but we did not find it because of a fault in all the maps and globes. I was later to discover the cape is at thirty-five and one-half degrees. That five and one-half degrees, for men in our condition, was a tremendous difference.

Day by day we weakened; one by one the men sickened and died. On the nineteenth of April we came in sight of land. We had been four months and two days between the coast of Chile and the islands of Japan. The *Liefde* was little more than a wreck. There were not more than six of us who could so much as stand upon our feet. So weak were we, that even in calm weather three of us would have to stand upon the wheel, it supporting us more than we controlling it.

Without charts, without even the ability to lower our sails, we came toward the land, our sails flapping and the ship beyond control. When we were within a league of the land I managed to stagger to my feet and get Sweringen and two others to go forward with me to let go our anchors. We then collapsed upon the deck.

This was the nineteenth day of April, the year of our Lord, 1600, just short of twenty-one months since we had left the Texal. We knew not whether these people would be friendly or whether they would murder us as we lay upon the deck. At that point, it no longer mattered.

PART FOUR

Japan

28

It was three days before I became aware, once again, of my surroundings. At first I thought I was still aboard the worn and stormy wreck, though even in a calm sea the *Liefde* had never been this comfortable. In my semiconscious state I had the feeling of drifting, as though I were reborn. There were many things to contribute to this feeling: the acceptance of death, which would have been inevitable after a few more days at sea; the complete strangeness of my surroundings; and my body, which seemed to have lost all of its aches and pains.

I awakened in a house of a sort I had never before seen. It was light and airy, with no furniture as I had known furniture. No chairs, no bed, no pillow. I lay on a soft mat on the floor. For a pillow, there was a curved wooden block which I had a faint memory of pushing aside, but always gentle hands had lifted my head and replaced it. My mind now partially clearing, I discovered a dozen or so of my companions in this room with me. As I lifted myself weakly to one elbow, a tiny creature, dressed in a long, bright robe, hurried over to my pallet.

I must have stared at her rudely for her eyes lowered and her cheeks flushed. She busied herself with a bowl, then began feeding me a thin broth. My body crying so for the need of liquid, I tried to seize the bowl, but she would not let me. I was in such a weakened condition, she was stronger than I.

When she had given me the portion of broth, she gently pushed my head back on the wooden block and spoke to me in a language completely unfamiliar but with a soft, musical tone. With a tiny hand she closed my eyes, which I understood to mean that I was to sleep. Instead, with the willfulness of the very ill, I shoved the wooden pillow out from under my head and, taking my jacket which was folded by my mat, I made a pad of it and placed that under my head.

She looked at me and I studied her in wonder. Her long, black hair was piled in coils of intricate design on the top of her head. Her almond-shaped eyes were slanted and had no fold in the upper lid. She had a small button-like nose and a tiny mouth that was yet sweetly designed. Sleepily I smiled at her and voiced my thanks. She placed her head three times to the mat, then again her soft hand closed my eyes and I slept.

A noise awoke me after what must have been many hours and I saw two of the native men carrying out the shrouded body of one of my shipmates, I knew not who. I mustered enough strength to sit up. As I did I saw a line of Japanese men enter. Forming into a row, they kneeled and placed their foreheads against the floor as another man entered, dressed in rich robes and wearing two swords.

As I was the only one showing any sign of life, he came to my pallet, knelt before me on a cushion one of the women placed for him, bowed slightly, and gazed at me as if I was a specimen of mankind he had not seen before. I, in turn, regarded him in the same fashion.

His hair was shaven more than halfway to the top of the head with the long hair in back piled high in a bun, upon which sat a little boxlike hat tied by a ribbon under his chin. His robes were of a great richness; I took him to be some important personage in this strange land.

As I attempted to sit up, he motioned me to lie back, which I did, apologizing to him for my weakness. Without turning his eyes from me, he gave an order, whereupon a young man hurried forward. Dropping to his knees about three paces from us, he then approached bowing repeatedly and whispering sibilantly in a most courteous fashion.

The important person spoke to him again. He bowed quickly, then spoke to me in a jumble of words that I made out to be a peculiar combination of Portugal and Spaniard. He explained to me that the person before me was a Daimyo, or king of this land, which he called Bungo. The king desired to know who we were, from whence we came, and for what reason.

I asked first for water, for my mouth was so dry that my tongue lay heavy and thick in my mouth.

At an order, the tiny woman quickly came forward and let me drink from a bowl. Then I began to tell him, omitting details, how we had set sail from a far-off land to seek trade, that we had had many and grievous troubles, losing the greater part of our goods and ships, and that we were most happy to be safe on shore. I thanked them for the kindness they had shown us.

The king bowed his head and sucked in his breath. The interpreter then said that we were welcome and that all were most sorry we had had such tribulations.

I then asked how many of my companions had died since we had been ashore. They told me that three had been too weak to survive, but that the others, with care, would recover. I begged them to wait before burying our dead so that I could say the final words of parting. This they could not do, I was told; due to the warm weather, it was a law of the land that burials follow immediately after death so there would be no danger of contamination.

The king then looked at me in a kindly fashion and addressed me through the interpreter: "All things needful for you will be done. We have sent word of you to countrymen of yours who live at a place called Langasaki. They are coming to lend their help."

I was quite sure they were not countrymen; in all probability they were Portugals or Spaniards, but I hoped, since we were so far from Europe, the old hatreds might be forgotten.

The following day I was able to be up and about for a short time, though my nurse protested strongly against this. Seeing that I was determined, she brought me a robe. It was much too small, but enough to cover my nakedness.

Of the twenty-four men who had survived the long voyage, all in the end had suffered from scurvy except myself and Jan Sweringen.

Of the twenty-one men still living, he was the only one besides myself who was able to sit up, though he was very weak. I spoke a word of comfort to those who were conscious. Both Captain Quackernack and the merchant, Van Sartoot, were in such condition that they were barely conscious. Sweringen, I found, was able to greet me.

"Goot morning, Captain," he said. Then, referring to the women, like a true seaman, he added, "They is nice, Captain. I wake this morning and one had her hand on my forehead. So soft. Joost like a little angel. I try to hold her hand but she run away. You think we be here a while, Captain?"

I told him it was very likely we would be here for some time.

"Goot," he said and lay back again, weakly. "When I get my strength back I find out what they're like under that funny robe they wear. So small they are! They chatter to each other joost like little birds. Soon's I get up I catch a couple and take a taste of them."

Then he looked me over curiously. "You look funny in that robe they give you. They take away your breeches too? I wish they give me back my breeches. I don't like women to see me like this."

I could not help being amused that, weak as he was, Sweringen's first thoughts were of amorous pursuit, but I cautioned him against making any overtures toward the women.

"Mark me, Sweringen. We do not know the customs of these people. Besides, we are their guests. Do nothing until we have some understanding of the rules they have for the women. You know as well as I that each country's customs are different. Should we do something to insult them we have no means to withstand their anger."

"Ah, I was joost talking, Captain. I could do nothing to them if I try. I joost make little joke with them and I think they don't mind. They giggle at me and hide their faces. But I be goot."

I then returned to my pallet. I was served another portion of thin broth, after which I fell asleep. I awakened to find the young man who had acted as interpreter kneeling silently by my pallet, intently studying my face. When he saw I was awake he performed the ritual of the three bows, then told me that he, being a Christian, had attended the burial of my shipmates and had offered a prayer over them for my sake.

I thanked him with all my heart. I felt a great sadness that they, after surviving the long and terrible voyage, had succumbed upon reaching this haven of refuge.

He informed me as though I would be happy at the news, that our Christian brothers would arrive on the morrow. I was afraid there would be more trouble than help in their arrival.

It was all so quiet in this house where we lay. I asked him where we were. He said the king, not knowing what our sickness was, had had us moved to a large house at the outskirts of town and called for volunteers to care for us. There were many women who had come to our aid. He said further that many people in the city were anxious to come look at us, but until we were well we would not be disturbed.

I took an instant liking to this bright, intelligent young man and enjoyed talking to him, but soon my small nurse came and drove him off. Before he left I asked his name.

"My name is Shoki, but in my country, we never say a name without also adding *san*. It is as in your country you would say Señor Adams. You may call me Shoki-san."

I slept and woke intermittently, feeling well enough at last so that I arose and went outside to fulfill nature's demands, taking this burden from my small nurse. She protested loudly at my being up, and tried to lead me back to my pallet. However, I went among my shipmates, giving them a good morning.

I had almost to laugh at Van Sartoot. Though he was still so weak he barely could raise his head to speak, he commanded me to find out if our goods were safe aboard ship. He was still the typical merchant, who, though dying, would try to retain his bag of gold. I suppose in this world men like him are necessary, else there would be neither progress nor trade.

I told him I knew nothing of our goods or the ship, but that we were alive, the people seemed friendly, and thus far we were being treated kindly. In the meantime, I suggested, the thing to do was not to worry, but to get well.

He grumbled, saying it was my duty to look after things. Somehow Van Sartoot had forgotten how, at any suggestion of mine, he had been quick to remind me that I was no more than a pilot and not to interfere with any other person's duties.

My little nurse tugged at my arm and scolded me, then fed me a delicious fish gruel. When I had finished she washed my face and began combing my beard. I was an object of great interest to these people. My beard had been untrimmed for two years; now, when combed and brushed, it fanned out like the mane of a lion.

Soon there was a chattering group of young women around me. They would not look at me directly. When I would catch one's eye she would quickly and demurely duck her head. I enjoyed seeing and listening to them. They were so shy, so pretty and delicate, and so graceful.

Now my body began to recover quickly. It seemed I could not get enough to eat, though I was fed continuously.

The following day, Taiko-san, my little nurse, came in and proudly presented me with a robe she must have had especially made. Delightedly she watched as I donned it. This robe was better than the one I had been given before, which, even though I had lost a great deal of weight, would hardly close in front of me and reached above my knees.

Sweringen was also able to get up and about now. Both of us helped our shipmates however we could. I made several tentative sorties out to the gate which led to the street. There I was under the curious eyes of the people. I, in turn, was equally fascinated by them. They passed back and forth, carrying enormous loads upon their backs, or walked beside small horses hitched to tall, high-wheeled carts. They seemed to be a happy people, more polite than any I had before encountered, always bowing to me when I appeared, smiling and sucking in their breath.

On the seventh day our so-called countrymen came to Bungo. It was as I had feared. The hatreds bred by religious differences and war were as strong here as they had been in Europe. The party consisted of a Jesuit priest and two Portugal traders. They arrived with the Japanese king and his court.

Taiko-san, my little nurse, was happy to think that now we had some friends of our own kind. Attended by Sweringen, I came forward to greet them.

The priest looked at me and asked, in Portugal, "Whence came you?"

"From Holland. We set sail two years ago with five ships. Only one survived the travail of the sea."

"Heretics," one of the traders spat. "It would have been better for you if you kept on sailing. You signed your death warrant when you landed on these islands."

The trader was a squat, fat man with an unctuous look about him. The priest was tall, gaunt and ascetic.

"It is strange," said I, "that these people have showed us no murderous intent."

The priest studied me. "You are not a Holland man," he said.

"No, I am an Englishman."

At the word Englishman, the priest drew back from me as if I was contaminated.

"We have brought the true faith to this land," he said. "We want none such as you to turn their hearts away with your heretical ideas."

"Father," I said, "we come not to preach of any faith, but only to trade. Though I know how strongly the Romish Church feels both against England and Holland, these wars and intolerances are far from us. I give you my word that none of us here wishes to propagate the theories of any religion."

My words were ignored. The trader went into a torrent of abuse against us, his words tumbling over each other. The priest silently moved away to avoid further contact with us.

"You are all devil's breed, and we will see that the Daimyo gives you no easy death," he said vehemently.

The king, kneeling on cushions that had been placed for him, was observing this interchange with interest. From time to time the young Japanese, Shoki-san, would tell him of the words being spoken.

Now the Portugal traders, one speaking the moment the other left off, harangued the Daimyo at great length, charging us with being pirates and murderers, and saying we should be immediately killed for the safety of his kingdom.

His words were so virulent that anger came upon me. I turned to the Japanese king and began to speak in a louder voice than the Portugals. All of a sudden the king ordered us all to be silent. Then, with all his court, he left the room.

The fat Portugal, before leaving, spat at my feet and swore that by tomorrow we would all be dead.

There was a heavy silence after they left. One by one, our little nurses disappeared, and we were alone. My shipmates had not understood the words, but knew the anger.

Quackernack asked, "What iss, Adams?"

"I am afraid, Captain, that these Portugals are no fonder of us here than they were in Europe. I am further afraid they intend to stir these people to hatred against us."

"And what we do?"

"Nothing. Not one of us could lift a sword if we had any. I can see nothing to do but hope and pray. It seems to me that God would not have brought us so far, through so much suffering, only to have us die here for no reason. Captain, we must have faith."

We waited, but our nurses did not return. Soon after, a number of soldiers came and we were taken to a place of confinement that was dark and much less comfortable than our former quarters. Food was set inside the door, consisting of no more than a large pot of soup with two dippers.

From this jail in the center of the village, we could hear the street sounds. There seemed to be a wave of excitement among the crowd. There was shouting and laughter, and once I heard the voice of the priest speaking in their tongue. The guards seemed to have disappeared.

We managed to make a step where I could stand and look out through the bars of the window. I saw streams of people going by, carrying the goods which had been stored so long ago as our cargo.

It was not hard to understand what was happening. The Portugals had done as they said they would do. They had incited the people to ransack our ship. All day long the street was filled with people singing, laughing, trading one thing for another. There was a lot of drinking. We expected at any moment to be dragged outside and slaughtered in the street.

Nothing happened that night, but the next morning a large crowd in an ugly temper gathered before the jail. I heard the Portugal traders haranguing them and was sure that now all was lost. We had no weapons, no strength even to use our fists. Some of the men prayed as the crowd began throwing stones at the jail.

Then, from a distance, I heard the sound of men approaching at a run, the clash of swords on shields, a shouting, "Hai, hai!"

The crowd became silent for a moment, then began milling about. When the soldiers arrived they beat the crowd back with bamboo sticks. Soon the street was quiet for the first time since we had been brought here.

We breathed a deep sigh of relief. Death is ugly no matter how many times you have seen its face. It can be accepted in battle, or when age rides your shoulders, but a mob is a terrifying thing.

Before the day was out, the young Japanese who had acted as interpreter for the king passed through the cordon of soldiers and came to see us. After bowing in the usual ceremonial manner, he told us the events of the day. I requested that the men be quiet until I understood all he had to relate, then repeated the substance of what he had told me.

"He says the priest and the traders, after leaving us yesterday, went to the Daimyo and there they told a fantastic tale of how we were pirates and murderers, nonbelievers in the true faith. The king here has become a Christian and they have great influence. They also told that we were just the first part of a great band of pirates, come to spy upon this land and the defenses. Once we searched out the secrets of defense, others would come in swarms to steal, murder and take the people into slavery. They said that for the safety of the country we should all be put to death as an example to other pirates.

"The Daimyo not only has become Christian, but shares in trade with the Portugals. He has become very rich, so that he listened to them. Had they left well enough alone we would all have been killed. But they were not satisfied with that, but went out and spoke to the people and had them steal everything from our ship. Much wine was drunk and it was then they made speeches and told the people to come and kill us. The priest joined in with this and began to preach openly. This has been forbidden by the great king, and Daimyo became very angry. He is a man of law and order and does not believe in allowing the people to riot in the streets. Therefore, he sent the soldiers to disperse the crowd, arrested the priest and the merchants, and has sent them back to Langasaki.

"Knowing that these events will reach the ear of the Shogun, Iyeyasu, he has dispatched a message to him seeking advice. We are to remain alive until word comes back from Yedo as to what the Shogun wishes to be done with us."

Then I asked, "Who is this Shogun, Iyeyasu?"

"He is the great overlord of all Japan. He is the Shogun. All men must bow to him."

"Then is he king or emperor?"

"No," Shoki-san told me. "The Emperor is the son of Heaven and beyond such affairs. The Shogun rules the country for him."

This confused me considerably, and so, changing the subject, I asked:

"How long a journey is it to this place called Yedo?"

"A great distance," he said. "By fast galley, a ten-day journey."

"Then we have two weeks at least to live. Will they hold us here in this jail?"

"Yes," he said. "But I do not think you will be ill-treated. The Daimyo is now angry with the others, not with you. He has ordered your ship to be brought into safe anchorage. The people have been told to return the goods to the ship."

After relaying this information to my shipmates, I thanked Shoki-san for his kindness.

"It is nothing," he said. Bowing courteously, he got up to leave.

"Will you come back and talk with us again? I would like to know something more of your country and your people."

"I will," he promised. "For you are very interesting foreign devils."

29

We were kept imprisoned but not ill-treated. The days of rest were good for us, repairing the sickness caused by the weary months of ordeal at sea. Had our minds been at rest we would have been almost content. Only Sweringen and myself, however, regained our complete health, the others still moved about with great effort.

On the twentieth day, the Daimyo again visited us. This time he did not enter our quarters. Our jail was not a sweet-smelling place, as scurvy has the smell of death about it that takes time to dispel, and the jail was crowded. Those who were strong enough were brought to the courtyard.

Shoki-san, the interpreter, had taught me the custom of greeting. I bowed thrice to the Daimyo, sucking in my breath in the fashion they used.

I was told that the great Shogun had ordered us to be brought to Yedo, their capital city, to be questioned.

I requested of the Daimyo that only Sweringen and myself make the journey, as the others were in no condition. At first the Daimyo refused. I then asked that he have his physicians examine the men and we would abide by their judgment. This was done, and after each man was examined, it was finally agreed that only the two of us would undertake the journey.

I thanked the Daimyo for his kindness, then requested that the young interpreter, Shoki-san, be allowed to accompany us. The Daimyo consented to this also; then, with much formality, he took his leave.

My shipmates, not understanding the conversation, questioned me anxiously as to what had taken place. I told them what arrangements had been made.

"Then it will all depend on you, Herr Adams," Captain Quackernack said. He was up and about, though still weak.

"Joost keep that Sweringen shut up. Always he talks too much and they hang us for being idiots."

"I don't say anything, Captain," Sweringen said.

"You should not. And you listen to Captain Adams. You spoil anything with your foolish talk and these dwarf people won't have to stick you; I will."

"Ja, Captain."

Presently Shoki-san returned. After much searching he had managed to recover some of our clothing. There was enough to dress both myself and Sweringen, though not in the style to go to court.

The following morning we were taken under guard by two soldiers called *samurai*, or knights of this land, along with a number of attendants. We were mounted on horses. As we passed through the town we were regarded with great curiosity by the inhabitants, who lined the streets.

We turned down the bay. There I could see the *Liefde*, alone and forlorn, swinging at anchor. She looked almost derelict. What the sea and storms had not done to her, the people had finished when she was ransacked. She listed far to port. I feared that if she was not pumped out she would soon be lying on the bottom. But there was nothing I could do about the ship now. Our first problem was to secure our lives.

We followed the coast for a day-and-a-half journey. Neither Sweringen nor myself were horsemen. By noon our bottoms were rubbed sore. Noting from the samurai that these people were contemptuous of signs of weakness, I cautioned Sweringen to bear up without complaint. I had given my word to the samurai not to attempt escape. They had not bound us. Our guards were friendly enough.

Apparently Shoki-san also felt the rubbing of the saddle. We joked about it privately. Despite the discomfort, I enjoyed the look and feel of the country. Never, even in Holland and England, had I seen a country so well-kept, so cultivated, so clean and beautiful. The forests and hillsides had a clean-swept look about them. Everywhere, the people smiled at us, and their curiosity was not such as to give offense.

We were happy when night fell and we came to an inn. It was interesting to me that everyone made ready to bathe while food was being prepared. I was to learn that in this country even the poorest of people take a hot bath each and every day of the year. If they have the means, they bathe both morning and night.

The bathroom we entered was a community affair, cared for by women attendants. There was some discussion among the samurai as to whether we should be allowed to bathe with them. Being of a kindly nature, they invited us. In the bathhouse the women attendants did everything for the travelers, even undressing them, though both Sweringen and I removed our own clothing. The women were very curious about us. We in turn were sensitive about our nakedness and I had to caution Sweringen not to rebel. This was the custom of the country, I told him. We must do as they do. None of the native men seemed to give any thought to their nudity. The women wore only a short dress which was pulled up and fastened in front.

In the center of the large room there was a great tub of steaming water. It was large enough for a dozen people, but this tub was not used merely for the bathing. Each of us had an attendant. The small person who timidly took my hand led me to a small wooden stool, making me understand that I should sit upon it. She wet me down with a pail of water; then with sweet-smelling soap and a brush she scrubbed me from head to foot. I found this very comforting. After the first minute or so I forgot I was being bathed by a woman, and watched the others, who were laughing and talking among themselves. It was not so with Sweringen. First I became aware of a tittering among the women attendants that gradually grew louder.

Glancing across the steamy room, I saw Sweringen crouched with several of the women around him. They held him by the arms, attempting to pull him to his feet. The Japanese, their attention attracted by this, began to laugh among themselves. Finally the two samurai went to him and, taking hold of him, they pulled him upright. He looked across at me in terror, crying, "Honest, Captain, I can't help it! I think of everything, even of dying, and it does no good."

Everyone, including myself, was gazing at him in amazement. I had heard some jesting on the ship about the big Dutchman, but thought it merely exaggeration. Standing there, he had the appearance of a rampant stud. In all of my years I had never seen anything like it nor, evidently, had these people. How word got around I do not know, but soon it seemed as if half of the people of this small village were outside trying to peer into the bathhouse.

Not knowing their morals as yet, I was worried. Turning to Shoki-san, I was somewhat relieved to see him laughing with the others.

"What do they intend to do?" I asked him.

"They will find a woman of the village brave enough for him. The bathhouse women are not pleasure girls, but they have sent word to the pleasure girls in the village for one to challenge this *o-tachi*." O-tachi, he explained, was a great sword.

Sweringen now was becoming angry and showed signs of resisting. I found it necessary to admonish him. He looked at me in anger and said, "Ja, even you are laughing!"

I could see the humor of it. "After all, they are merely admiring you and they have sent out to the village to find a woman for you."

As we were talking, a large bottle of rice wine, called *saki*, was brought in. Sweringen was toasted several times. We proceeded with our bath. After a few drinks of the wine, he joined in the spirit of the thing. He began making bull-like runs at the women. They ran from him, screaming, scattering like a covey of quail.

After bathing we went to the main room of the inn where we ate an enjoyable meal and drank much saki. Women came in and the samurai had Sweringen stand up and prance about like a great stallion. The inn rocked with laughter.

Finally he was challenged by a tiny little creature who came hardly above his elbow. They retired to a room with many witnesses. I, being tired, went to sleep on a pallet.

During the night I heard them staggering back into the main room. Sweringen was very drunk and roaring out some Dutch song as they placed him on the mat next to me. Evidently the small woman had been a match for him. They were all in high good humor. Rather than doing any harm, Sweringen had helped us along toward closer friendliness. I was to find that these people greatly respect a man who can drink much and who exhibits amorous strength.

We made a late start the next morning due to the night's carousing. Sweringen looked tired and suffered from a great hangover but I must admit he was in as good shape as the samurai and the others.

As we mounted our horses and passed through the village Sweringen was looked upon with open admiration and the people cried "Banzai, O-tache!" as we passed by. I didn't share their admiration. I would not care to be burdened by such a tool. I felt no envy, as I had never heard complaint.

By noon we arrived at a large fort upon the brow of a hill overlooking a bay. Here a twelve-oared galley carrying the Emperor's colors lay in readiness for the next leg of our journey. She had but one mast and a clumsy sail of a lateen type.

After some formality with the captain of the fort, we embarked. I was surprised at the speed the heavy boat made through the water. They had an ingenious device for the oars, having the long oars placed on a pin which came up through the thwart, so that the rowers, instead of sitting as in our fashion, rowed standing and facing forward.

Once out of the bay our galley picked up a following breeze and the sail was set. After studying the rigging I spoke to the captain through Shoki-san and got his permission to make a new setting on the sail. Sweringen followed my orders in changing the rigging and it did improve our speed. The captain and I talked of ships. He was a man of good intelligence and asked me many questions. With a piece of charcoal I sketched a picture of our latest ships, showing the sail plan. Thus we passed the time in great enjoyment.

From the color of water I could tell that it was not the blue water of the sea. Questioning, I found we were traveling through an inland sea with the main of the Japanese islands on our left and other islands on our right, some of which lay below the horizon. Some we passed close by.

The captain drew a small map showing the route we would take to the main city of Osaka. From there we would journey overland to the city of Yedo unless the Shogun should be at some other place. In tending to the affairs of the country he moved about a great deal, I gathered.

In spite of the hardships we had undergone it was good to be on the sea again. A small charcoal brazier in the galley served for cooking. The food was fish and rice. I noted that since we had been ashore we had been given no meat. Questioning Shoki-san, I was told that most of the people were of the Buddhist faith and did not eat of beef or pork or other domestic animals. However, the wealthy people did eat game, which I understood to be deer and other wild animals.

I thought longingly of a thick slice of good English beef, then reasoned that we were in no position to quarrel about the food. After so much hunger, all food tasted good.

30

On the second day the weather became rough. The samurai soon began to feel the effects, which amused Sweringen. In retaliation for their humor on his horsemanship he commented on it. Shoki-san had informed me of some aspects of the code of the samurai, the strongest being their refusal to show any signs of weakness, for to do so would cause them to feel shame and thereby "lose face," as they phrased it.

I spoke warningly to Sweringen of this, advising him to ignore the soldiers, for to anger them could cost our lives.

By evening we were tied to a dock beside a castle that guarded the land against invaders from the sea. The city beyond was large. I would have enjoyed the opportunity to visit it and observe the people. We could not, however, as the commander of the fort had us brought inside. The castle was built of smooth stone, cut marvelously large, with very deep trenches all around. Many drawbridges plated with iron surrounded it. The numerous bulwarks and battlements had holes for small shot, arrows, and passages for casting stones down upon assailants. I was amazed to find the walls were at least six or seven yards thick, made of stone and of an excellent quarry. They were cut so exactly that no mortar was necessary.

The castle was manned by a garrison which, by my count, was not less than three thousand soldiers. We were courteously treated and made welcome by the commander. It was our good fortune that, on the day of our arrival, the troops were being changed. Shoki-san told me that these troops were maintained by the Emperor and changed every three years so that they would not become too familiar with the inhabitants of the city and form strong ties.

All the troops were lined up in the huge inner courtyard in military precision. From a distance came the solid sound of marching feet. Through the enormous portcullis the new troops marched forward, five abreast.

The first company consisted of men with shot and heavy slings. They had no muskets. Then followed a company of pikes, and next, two companies of swordsmen and two companies armed with bows and arrows. Behind these came men carrying weapons resembling a Welsh hook, which Shoki-san called "*waggadaches.*" Then the companies were renewed, the men with shot and sling, and so on as formerly. What surprised me was they were without ensigns or colors, nor had they any drums or other musical instruments of war.

The first five of the swordsmen had silver scabbards to their swords. The last five, who were next to the captain, carried scabbards of gold. The companies consisted of diverse numbers, some five hundred, some three hundred, and others one hundred and fifty. In the midst of every company were three richly trapped horses, furnished with saddles well set out, some covered with costly furs, some with velvet or broadcloth. Every horse had three slaves to attend it, with silken halters attached by a line to each slave.

After every troop there followed the captain on horseback. His bed and other necessaries were laid upon his own horse, poised on either side. Over the same was spread a red felt covering, the captain sitting cross-legged on his horse as if between a couple of panniers. Some of these captains were old, and so had a staff affixed to the panel so that the rider might rest himself by leaning back against it as if he were seated in a chair.

As the columns entered the castle they took their positions opposite the companies they were relieving. The captain general of the new companies entered in great state. With him came hunting dogs. Twelve men carried hawks, hooded, perched two each upon a board which the men bore across their shoulders. The captain general was borne in on a palanquin lined with crimson velvet. Six men carried it.

Upon entering, the new captain general emerged from his palanquin. With great dignity he faced the officer he was to relieve, bowed three times and spoke words of greeting. The other did likewise. Then they met, clasping each other's arms, and, stepping back a pace, the new captain general gave a sharp order. Instantaneously a servant stepped forward with a scroll on a velvet cushion, which I took to be the orders from the Emperor to relieve the soldiers at that fort.

That night there was much feasting and wine drinking. Before we left the next morning, we watched them move out in the same form and manner in which the new ones had entered.

It was a fascinating spectacle. I admired the discipline and sturdiness of the troops who, though small of stature, were firmly built and gave the appearance of being able to endure great hardship. All this I entered in my journal.

These people interested me profoundly. I liked their ways, their courtesy, their manner of living. I was particularly impressed, even then, with their cleanliness, both personally and in their houses, no matter how rich or poor they might be. No one ever enters a house wearing the shoes he wore upon the streets. Guests remove their shoes at the door and sandals are provided, a custom of which I thought highly.

Two days further we journeyed and came to a great city named Osaka, larger than the city of London. Above the city stood a castle the like of which I had never seen. It stood like a mountain between the sea and the land.

Shoki-san was happy to inform us that our journey would end here, for the Shogun was at Osaka. This saved us a number of days' uncomfortable travel overland by horse.

Once in the castle we were escorted to a room which, though not lavishly furnished, contained every comfort. Since it was now so late, I thought it would be tomorrow or later when we would be summoned before the Shogun. But we had not much more time than to wash and eat the food brought to us when we were marched across a vast courtyard and into another court like a lovely park. In the center sat a gilded house of wondrous beauty. Its size was enormous. But more spectacular was the way the pillars, the roofs, even the paneling of the walls were embellished with gold. The wealth and beauty of this place would have put the palaces of Europe and England to shame. This magnificent house was so completely balanced, both inside and out, that it gave the illusion of being suspended from the sky instead of set upon the ground.

We followed our escort through corridor after corridor until we arrived, finally, at a door which guards opened to us. Compared to the other rooms we had passed, this one was of no great size. Here we stopped and, following the movements of the guards, we bowed three times to a personage seated in a large chair.

He was dressed in exceedingly rich costume. His golden hat, box-like, was worn upon the top of his coiled hair. I gazed intently at this man who was to hold the fate of my shipmates and myself. He, in turn, studied us.

He was of small stature and sharp-visaged, which is unusual in these people, as most have rounded or flattened noses and oval faces. At first glance he seemed ugly until I saw his eyes. They were very large, black, and of great depth and keen intelligence. Suddenly, I knew not why, I felt confident as to our fate.

After studying me for a long time, his gaze shifted to Sweringen, who stood head down, shuffling his feet back and forth in the loose sandals. His bowed neck made it seem as if he expected a sword to fall at any moment.

I was beckoned forward. It was then I noticed the Portugal man kneeling in the background. He crawled up on his knees until he was alongside the chair of the Shogun. I felt some trepidation when I saw it was the same Portugal trader who had come from Langasaki and incited the people against us. I looked around for Shoki-san but he was nowhere to be seen. Knowing how he had reviled us before the Daimyo of Bungo, I had no doubt what vicious pleasure he would take in turning this king against us. There was pure hatred in his glance. My hands itched to reach for his throat, but I put such thoughts aside. Anger would be of least help in this situation.

The Portugal, on his knees before the Shogun, spoke to him, but the Shogun seemed not to hear. His gaze kept traveling back and forth between us as if, by concentration, he could reach through the barrier of language and find what manner of men we were. Finally he spoke to us questioningly.

The trader began to speak angrily. He was checked by a sharp order. The Portugal turned suddenly to us.

"The great Sei-e-tai Shogun, Tokugawa Iyeyasu, wishes to know from what land you thieves and heretics come."

I did not answer the trader, but spoke directly to the Shogun:

"We come from the land of Holland, though I am an Englishman. Two years ago we left with five ships to trade in the Eastern lands. But great misfortune befell us. Only one ship and twenty-three men survived out of the four hundred and ninety-eight who started the journey. We are not thieves and murderers, but honest men seeking merely to trade with you and your people. This man," I went on, pointing to the trader, "comes from a land whose king made war on us and was defeated. This is one of the reasons he hates us. Another is that he and his kind wish to keep the trade of this land in their own hands." I had spoken slowly, in Portugal. The man on his knees could hardly control himself while I was speaking. After I finished I bowed to Iyeyasu.

The Shogun, Iyeyasu, looked from me to the Portugal, who went into a long tirade, his eyes flashing, arms waving, speaking Portugal when he could not think of the proper word in the Japanese language. The Shogun listened for a while, then turned to look at me. I shrugged my shoulders to indicate our helplessness. A faint smile lifted the corners of his mouth. The Portugal went on and on, his words seemingly endless. Finally the Shogun bid him be silent and his words ceased as if they had been cut with a knife.

Ignoring the crawling man, the Shogun motioned me to come forward. I did so, bowing deeply, and mounted one step to the throne so that my face was almost on a level with his.

Leaning forward he peered intently at my face, then fingered my beard. There was a swift in-drawing of breath from the attendants of the court that sounded to me at the time like the hiss of serpents. Later I learned this was a sign of something akin to applause and that the Shogun had marked me with his favor. I knew nothing of this, thinking he merely wanted to examine my beard because of its luxuriousness and golden color, as most of these people had but scanty whiskers.

At his order maps were brought forth and he asked me to show him the land from whence I had come. The situation now eased as another Japanese entered who could speak Portugal. I indicated where our country was located and told the Shogun that we had long sought out the East Indies and desired friendship with all kings and potentates. In the way of merchandise, I explained, we could offer many commodities which these lands lacked. We, in turn, wished to buy such merchandise from these lands which our country required.

He then asked whether our countries had wars. I replied that our wars of late had been with the Spaniards but we were at peace with all other nations.

"And in what do you believe?" he asked.

Knowing that the Portugals had blackened our character, calling us unbelievers and heretics, I answered him with honesty.

"I believe in God who made heaven and earth, though on some interpretations of God and His works our country has disagreed with the Spaniards and Portugals."

He smiled at this and told me that in his land were many sects, not one of which could agree with the other, though they lived at peace with each other.

He asked me many questions, and I answered as best I could. Then he queried me as to how we came to his country. In the room was a chart of the whole world made up by the Portugals. On this I showed him how we had come and passed through the Strait of Magellan. I could see that he wondered at this and thought perhaps I was lying. He knew the distance well. I assured him I spoke the truth.

At this point he dismissed most of the attendants of his court and we retired to a small room with Sweringen, the interpreter, and one or two others. We remained there until past midnight while he asked me of government, of people, religions, wars, guns and ships. Finally he asked what merchandise our ships contained.

I told him of the goods we had brought, and also told him how the Portugals had incited the people to steal our goods and possessions. Abruptly he made a sign for us to leave. As we bowed before leaving, I asked what our fate would be and if we might be able to engage in trade as the Portugals and Spaniards had.

He replied, but I did not understand what was said nor did the interpreter translate for me. Thereafter we were returned to our jail.

I felt that this king, by his questions, had shown himself to be a wise ruler, but my mind was not wholly relieved. Sweringen, who had remained silent throughout the long hours, now said, "What do you think will happen now, Captain?"

"I do not know," I answered. "Of one thing I am sure, this king is no fool and I think the Portugal did little to further his purpose by trying to turn him against us. In any case we can do nothing but wait."

"Suppose they plan to kill us; what then, Captain?"

I smiled, but not with any feeling of confidence. "Jan, we will do what has to be done. Now that we have regained our strength, we will try to take some of them with us. It is not my intent, after living through so much travail, to be slaughtered like a sheep. If the time does come and we must fight, we will fight hard. But there is little reason to ponder our fate. What comes will come. We have seen the face of death often enough so that we need not fear it."

Sweringen held out his hand and I clasped it in friendship.

"I will do whatever you tell me to, Captain," he said with sincere simplicity.

31

We were treated well. Food was brought three times a day. It was almost always fish, and now and then a few slivers of what I took to be chicken, besides rice wine. My appetite was good but nothing in comparison to that of my shipmate. Sweringen ate as if he had little hope of many more meals.

Two days later the great Shogun Tokugawa Iyeyasu called me again for a conference. This time Shoki-san acted as interpreter. Through his good offices the interview went more smoothly. The Shogun was extremely friendly, asking me a thousand things of the Western nations. I came to have great respect for his scholarly mind and character. In him could be felt the great force with which he had united Japan.

After this second long meeting we were taken from the jail to a much more comfortable residence, situated on a rise of land near the edge of the city. We had the use of most of the house and garden but were guarded by six samurai soldiers.

At my request, Shoki-san had permission to stay with us. I learned much from him as the days passed. The natural facility I had with languages helped and I set my whole mind to concentrating on learning Japanese, which set so stiff on my tongue at the beginning. Yet all languages being to a great extent like music, first you learn the rhythm and sound, then the words. He explained, among other things, that in this land names are reversed, the family name being said before the given name. Tokugawa, for instance, was the family name of the Shogun, and Iyeyasu his given name.

Outside of keeping a journal of my conversations and events, my days were thus occupied with either Shoki-san, the samurai, or the servants who worked in the gardens.

I admired the samurai greatly. I had never seen men who could handle a sword with such ease, as if it was an extension of their hand.

Once, while sitting in the garden, I watched two soldiers as they parried with their swords. These blades were of a metal much better than the finest Toledo steel. Such control had they that neither was so much as scratched, though at times the blades would touch one or the other's body. Noting my interest, and to demonstrate their skill, one samurai took an apple from a basket of fruit and, baring his arm, set the apple upon it. The other, taking a sword with both hands, slashed downward with such force that the blade was but a blur in the sun. The apple was cut in half perfectly yet the skin of the man's forearm remained unbroken. The sword is to these people their proudest possession.

I was determined that, if at all possible, I would discover the secret of how they made such steel. Metal such as this, in England and Europe, would make anyone a rich man.

I learned that these soldiers were in a class apart, being as the knights of old in my own land, though I do believe the samurai code of honor was more strict. They were absolutely without fear and would die unhesitatingly, without flinching. Their great pride was at times carried beyond reason. Should they be insulted or suffer "loss of face" which could not be wiped out in battle, they would commit *seppuku*, a method of suicide in which they stabbed themselves with a short sword in a most unpleasant manner.

Through conversation with Shoki-san, I found that their code of honor was known as "bushido," which meant the "Way of the Horse and the Bow." This code, similar to that of knighthood, differs in that a knight vowed allegiance to God, whereas the samurai vowed allegiance to his lord. Samurai literally means "one who serves." As I came to understand their language I heard many of the heroic legends, which always had as the base the virtues of fidelity and the contempt of death.

For thirty-nine days Sweringen and I were kept here as semi-prisoners. We had no knowledge of what had happened to our shipmates, nor what was to be our fate. But the time was not wasted. I learned much.

From the summit of the hill I could look down upon the lovely carpet of rice fields and watch these people, so patient and hard-working, bending to their toil, yet seemingly lighthearted and happy. Across from where we were, on another hillside, there was a pleasant growth of trees and, situated so that it seemed as if the trees supported it, was a temple. At certain times of the day I could hear the chanting of the priests as they worshiped before their god.

I would watch the heavy-laden carts passing to and fro, hauled by sturdy men or patient oxen. At times groups of samurai would come riding by on their stocky ponies, or a messenger wearing the livery of the Shogun would pass at full tilt and all would give way before him. Wandering monks occasionally rang the bell at the gate to solicit alms. In my faulty tongue I would try to engage them in conversation. But I liked best of all to watch the samurai, so brightly clothed, laughing and proud.

Once in a while some official would come to visit and have a look at the "foreign devils" as we were called, but never a word did we get as to our fate. Sweringen seemed quite content. There was plenty of food and no work. He had managed a connection with one of the serving women, who became exceedingly enamored of him. We spent our evenings drinking wine with our guards. They were kind and did not treat us as enemies.

There was, however, one happening during this time that was sickening. Having a view of the main highway, I watched a group of workmen one day set up twenty large crosses. The following day there came a band of soldiers with prisoners. These prisoners were hung up on the crosses and stab wounds were inflicted in their sides with the point of a pike. These were not severe enough to kill them at once, but serious enough so that after a few hours of suffering they died.

Death was not new to me. I had seen persons hanging in chains outside of London, and barbaric methods of slaughter in Turkey and North Africa. I think what shocked me most was the use of the cross which, to us, is a holy symbol.

I asked Shoki-san what manner of people were these to be treated so. He told me they were Christian criminals, that this was considered an honorable way to die, as it was the way the Christian Lord had died. He told me more of the origin of the Christian faith in Japan. Spanish priests had come to Japan sixty years before, led by Father Xavier, and had been made welcome.

"But in Japan," he said, "no one bothers to tell another person what to believe. Soon the Christian bonzes caused much disturbance by proselytizing, saying all other beliefs and religions were lies. In the province of Bungo, from whence we came, many people became Christians, my father among them. The Daimyo, father of the present Daimyo's father, was sincere in the Christian faith. Believing the Christian bonzes' words, he began killing all the Buddhist bonzes he could find. These priests were hunted and killed like pigs. In time it became so terrible that the great Shogun Hideyoshi passed a law banning all Christian priests from Japan. This law has not been enforced up until now, but the Christian priests are forbidden to teach their religion. We still have our churches, however, but they sermonize in secret."

I thought a great deal about this. As the days passed, the stench of the bodies hanging upon those crosses filled the air. They hung there day after day, and carrion birds came to feed on the flesh. It was a travesty on the gentle religion of Christ.

I was reminded of a scene many years before of a day in my youth in London, when Jamey Bryant and I had gone on a Sunday to Tyburn Hill to see the execution of two criminals. There was a great mob on that day, like a fair. Through the crowd were cake sellers, hot pie merchants. All were laughing and talking as if on a holiday. As the two men who were to be hanged came through the crowd in the executioner's cart, they joked and laughed and accepted the cheers as if they were heroes. I do not know what their crime was. I do remember, though, that when the men were hanged I turned away sick with disgust at the casual way life had been taken. My disgust was also for those two who had been hanged. I do not say that man should die in a panic of fear, but this unknown journey should be met with some dignity at least.

Since those days I have seen many men die, and die bravely, but not with idiot laughter on their faces. It seemed to me we, being Christians, should hold a higher value on a man's life, so how could I condemn these people? For myself, I have never believed taking a life ever stopped anyone from committing a crime. On the same day I had watched those men hung on Tyburn Hill, I saw a pickpocket steal a man's purse. For this crime he could have been hanged and knew it, yet this did not deter him. The incident made me think further and I feel truly that hunger and poverty cause the most crimes, as religion has caused the most wars.

On the thirty-ninth day the Shogun returned to Osaka with a large body of troops he had led against some enemy. I was called into his presence again and was most anxious to learn our fate. I waited a long time in the anteroom of the vast palace. Finally I was summoned to a private audience. Only a secretary and Shoki-san were in attendance.

I could now greet the Shogun in his own language, using the proper terms of formality. He returned my greeting kindly and motioned for me to sit on a cushion before him. By now, having become accustomed to squatting cross-legged, I was able to sit without the discomfort I had first known. My legs, being so long, however, still had a tendency to become cramped if I sat overlong in one position.

Two very pretty serving women came in to attend to the Shogun's wants with wine and food. They poured saki for us and looked always to the comfort of the Shogun, seemingly able to read his mind and yet were not obtrusive.

I noticed he looked very tired. Still, behind his eyes glowed the flame of energy that set him apart from other men. After some words as to our well-being, he said: "The Christian bonzes and the Portugals have presented much evidence against you and your men. They insist you are thieves and robbers and that this is known to all foreign nations. They tell me that should I suffer you to live it will be against my profit and the safety of my country. They claim that you people, under the guise of trade, go nowhere without robbing, murdering and taking slaves. For our safety, they said, all of you should be executed, so that your countrymen would be afraid to come again to this land." He paused, then said, "These people have many friends and many of them have spoken against you."

I told him honestly that all these statements were lies. He had but to examine the contents of our ships and the goods contained therein to discern that we came for the purpose of trade.

He smiled at this and called for saki and we drank. Then he spoke again.

"My answer to those who sought your death was that, up to now, you had done no harm—neither to me nor to any of my lands or people. Therefore it would be against reason and justice to have you put to death. Though your countries have war one with the other, that is not my quarrel."

His words made me very happy. I asked how they had responded to such a statement. He told me they were much out of heart and sorely disappointed.

Now I asked what was uppermost in my mind—the welfare and whereabouts of my companions.

"I have ordered the ship to be taken to the city of Yedo. It, and all your companions, should now be in the harbor of my capital city."

Remembering in what terrible condition the *Liefde* had been the last time I saw her, I expressed doubt she would be able to travel anywhere. But he informed me she had been careened, her bottom cleaned and caulked, and he had sent with her twelve large galleys in the event she needed help.

I was greatly relieved to hear this. He then asked if it was my wish to go to Yedo to see my countrymen. I replied that I wished this with all my heart.

I had his permission to go. He would provide a galley to take us to where the *Liefde* lay.

We sat thus until late in the evening. His mind was of an inquiring bent and he asked me many more questions of the Western lands.

Dismissing me, he thanked me for answering him so patiently, and I took my leave regretfully, as I had come to have a warm admiration for Iyeyasu. As a final word, he said that he would be in his capital city in a short time, having first to journey to the Emperor's court to inform him of the success of his last campaign.

Sweringen and I were no longer prisoners. With Shoki-san and our samurai friends we went about the city the following night and enjoyed a most wondrous drunken celebration.

During the course of the evening, while we were drinking and holding carouse with the girls, the Portugal trader came in.

At sight of him Sweringen cursed and started to his feet. I held him back and called the Portugal to me. He came over with a hangdog look.

"You look unhappy, señor, or is it sadness because we are not nailed to a cross?"

"Señor, I swear your imprisonment was none of my doing. You must understand I am only a servant to the company. They are in fear that the Dutch and English will take all the trade. I did only as I was told."

"A servant such as you are is a very valuable possession. The hatred you showed was a marvelous piece of acting, if, as you say, you merely followed orders."

"I swear, señor!"

One of our samurai, who had been our guard since Bungo and who had been friendly from the beginning, looked up at the Portugal with a scowl.

"I like not this one. He is greasy and has a dog's look. Shall I let my *tachi* taste of him?"

The Portugal turned pale with fright. He knew this was no idle threat.

"For the love of God, no, señor!"

I restrained the samurai, whose name was Itsuke-san, then asked the trader: "What is your name, señor?"

"Alonso Lusiad, señor. Believe me, I am a friend to all. The priest, Padre Madero, whom you saw at Bungo, and the others—they hold hatred for you. Not I."

I shared Sweringen's and Itsuke-san's dislike for the man but thought perhaps there was some truth in what he said. Also, the taste of freedom was too sweet to be marred by violence and hatred. I dismissed him, saying:

"From what I have seen there is trade enough for all. You have tried to do harm to me and my shipmates. I give you this message:

Tell the padre and the others I take a lesson from Christ and forgive you." Then, feeling the utmost magnanimity, I added, "Go and sin no more."

And I turned my attention back to the wine, laughter, and the pretty maid fondling my beard.

The next morning I suffered from the effects of the wine, but within me felt cleansed and happy.

32

The trip was a long one, by boat, of more than a hundred leagues from Osaka to Yedo Bay where Iyeyasu had built his new capital city on the Yedo plain.

I was in a fever of impatience. While our small galley rowed past numerous small islands into the great bay I stood for over an hour, eagerly waiting to catch my first sight of the *Liefde*. When finally we pulled alongside, all those left of my companions were at the rail. We were greeted with loud salutations of joy as we were helped aboard and there were many wet eyes among those who received us. They had thought that Sweringen and I had long since been executed.

The ship was little more than a hulk. Everything had been taken out of her. The clothes on my back were all that I owned. All my instruments and books were gone so that not only had I lost my share of the cargo but also the tools of my trade. This surprised me, as I had understood from the Shogun that both the ship and our goods were secure. However, I was pleased to see my shipmates recovered in health. But they were still worried, not knowing their fate.

Captain Quackernack and Van Sartoot tried to draw me aside for a private conversation, but I insisted that we gather in a circle on the deck where I could tell my tale and ease their minds, for we were all equally involved.

Step by step I told of our journey, of my meetings with the Shogun, and how we spent our days until the Shogun freed us.

"But what of our goods? What recompense will we receive for what has been stolen? There is nothing left. Even the ship is of no value, since all is gone, including the sails and rigging."

I felt sorry for them. My loss, however, had been greater. My instruments, charts, and books could not be replaced. But Van Sartoot complained as if it was I who was to blame for the loss. It irked me. Therefore I replied:

"Herr Sartoot, let's not be impatient. We now hold the most precious possession, which is life. Let's enjoy this freedom. In time, I am sure, the king will treat us with justice. Our most Christian brothers, the Portugals and Spaniards, tried in every way to damage us, but by their very actions they have turned the Shogun's sympathy toward us. We, in turn, must be careful not to show our greed and beseech, rather than demand, the Emperor to have our things returned to us. These are a sensitive people and, from what I have seen, more honest than most. Herr Sartoot, be patient. It is a grand, rich land. I have seen things of unbelievable beauty. One shipload of their lacquer, gold work, and other native goods could bring a fortune."

I then inquired about their treatment. They said they had been given food in abundance, though not of meat. Each day supplies were brought to them—fresh vegetables, fish and wine. I suggested that we be content for these things. This did not sit well with Van Sartoot who seemed to expect me to go like a bailiff and demand immediate recompense.

In the afternoon a large galley came out from the shore and a number of people of high quality, to judge from their attire, came aboard. I now was able to greet them and make them welcome in their own language. I offered them wine and showed them about the ship. They were impressed with the size and thought it a wonderful ship. To me she was no more than a parody of a ship. We were informed that, by order of Iyeyasu, we were to be provided with housing ashore and all things needful to our comfort.

I thanked them formally for their kindness. Then, at the prodding of Van Sartoot, I asked when the great Shogun would return. They answered that he would be back at the capital city in one or two days.

It seemed to me there was little sense in bringing up the subject of the return of our goods. These men were officials of the port city of Yokosuka and our goods and possessions were far off, in the land of Bungo. But at the insistence of the others, I mentioned the fact that we had nothing left.

The governor of the port said he would advance us whatever monies we needed for clothing and necessities, saying also that the Emperor had instructed them to do everything for our comfort. I passed these heartening words on to my shipmates and there was great rejoicing. Even Van Sartoot seemed to shed some of his annoying worry.

Within the week we were settled in comfortable quarters ashore, each with a small apartment. Captain Quackernack, Van Sartoot and I were supplied with a large house and four servants.

About a week later there was great excitement in the city of Yokosuka, as if a riot was taking place. I found it was a celebration in honor of the arrival of the Shogun Iyeyasu. Shortly after, we were all summoned to his presence and received with friendliness by the Shogun and many members of the nobility.

After the ritual of greeting he asked how we had fared. On hearing how all our possessions had been taken, he showed signs of anger and immediately ordered that a number of galleys should proceed at once to the Daimyo of Bungo and there recover our goods.

This being done, he generously told us that anything needful to our well being would be given at once. It was his pleasure, he said, to have us as guests. All that was expected was that we respect the laws of the land and the people.

I promised that we should do so. He then commented on how well I used the language after such a short time. This pleased me much, for though Shoki-san was with me to help when I stumbled over a word, I was quite able to carry on a fair conversation.

Taking advantage of this, I requested that Shoki-san be permitted to stay and act as our teacher rather than be sent back to Bungo. Iyeyasu questioned Shoki-san as to his desire. When Shoki-san indicated that he would be happy to stay, Iyeyasu gave his permission. I think, even then, Shoki-san had some premonition of what the future would hold. With me he would have far greater opportunity than in his own province. Between ourselves, the bond had already been sealed.

With complete freedom to go about as we would, many of my shipmates soon took a woman to live with and spent their days enjoying the hospitality of the people. They drank and caroused in the usual manner of sailors ashore, which offended no one. In fact, their behavior was looked upon with much amusement, and pleasure that the visitors were enjoying themselves.

Now that I had the opportunity I wished, I spent most of my time becoming acquainted with the people and their ways, making journeys with Shoki-san, for whom each day I came to feel a deeper affection. His mind was bright and ready, with a wondrous humor which, as I delved deeper into the language, I enjoyed more and more.

Within the month most of our goods were returned. They were stored ashore under Van Sartoot's supervision. He made a thorough count of everything, protesting loudly to himself and anyone who would listen whenever he discovered something missing.

He besieged me with such insistence that I finally sought an audience with the Shogun. We journeyed to Yedo to place the complaint.

Iyeyasu listened patiently to our demands. Van Sartoot then unfolded a scroll and began to read off a long column of missing articles. After a moment of listening to his droning voice, Iyeyasu waved him aside and asked for an estimate of what our loss amounted to.

With shocked ears I heard Van Sartoot barefacedly claim the loss at fifty thousand reals of hard money.

With not a moment's hesitation, the Shogun ordered his secretary to bring in the money. This was promptly done and delivered into Van Sartoot's hands. He accepted it greedily. He was ordered to distribute the money according to our needs.

On our journey back to Yokosuka, Van Sartoot seemed lost in gloomy thoughts. I asked him why he was so unhappy. Hadn't we received far more money than we had lost?

He made me angry by mumbling that I knew nothing of business —I who had made a profit dealing with the Turks. I knew trade— but also had learned that greed is dangerous. When I asked that he speak up, he burst out:

"We were fools. We should have asked for a hundred thousand!"

I could bear it no more. At these words I hit out instinctively and knocked him from his horse. When he cried for help from the others I cursed him roundly. My dislike for him was too great to hold in any longer. Nor did he get any assistance or sympathy from any one else. He wept, saying we were cruel and inhuman and had no right to strike him. He was a merchant, and a merchant's duty is to make the best bargain. Furthermore, he said, he had done it for all of us.

Since there was no sense in further discussion with him, for I could not change his greed or his way of thinking, I decided to have no more to do with him than was necessary.

We rented a building as a factory, selling our goods and buying only articles of high value such as gold, jewels, fine lacquer and pottery. Van Sartoot did most of the trading; he struck harder bargains than most of us had the stomach for. I protested that selling dear and buying cheap should not be carried to the point of dishonesty. There would be other voyages, and fair dealing would pay far more in the long run. I said he acted as if this was his only opportunity. I brought out the fact that in the ten years I had dealt with the Turks, by fair dealings I was able to do better in trade than my greedy competitors. But Van Sartoot would not listen. And I was so interested in filling my journal with facts about the country, the customs and the people that I had time for little else.

Iyeyasu came again to Yokosuka and asked to see the ship. He seemed greatly impressed by her size. I had never thought it in me to hate a ship, but the *Liefde* was the exception. For two years I had fought her cranky stubbornness, over a voyage of sixteen thousand miles, and cursed each mile of it. I would sooner have sailed a pinnace home.

After touring the ship, Iyeyasu informed us it was his wish to buy her and have his shipwrights take her apart, piece by piece, to learn how she was made. In that way, he said, they could build another like her.

I explained that she was a poorly built ship. Her whole bottom was now rotten. Even when new she had been badly constructed, of small value. Nonetheless he insisted on purchasing her.

When I relayed his desire to the Dutchmen they all protested, to my surprise. They were all fully aware of her condition; she could sail nowhere. But perhaps they felt she was their only link with home.

I spoke to them seriously, saying we really had no choice in the matter. Refusal to sell the ship would merely cause hard feelings and denote our ingratitude. We owed these people much for their kindness and our good treatment, yes, even our lives. I pointed out that a large sampan would take us to Java sooner than this hulk.

Finally they agreed and it was now only a question of price. I realized that Van Sartoot, naturally, wanted to squeeze as much as he could out of the Shogun. Yet he was torn by not knowing how much to ask. Turning to me, he asked how much I thought we should price her.

"Not more than the price of two large sampans," I told him.

He protested and I spoke abruptly to him.

Turning to Iyeyasu, I caught a half smile on his face and was sure he had understood our exchange.

When we left the ship I returned with him to his magnificent residence in Yokosuka. Here, after our affairs were put in order and our goods sold, Iyeyasu asked me to come to Yedo and stay at the Imperial Palace. There I could learn to write the language as well as speak it. In return for this, he said, I could instruct his people about the knowledge and culture of the nations of the West. I agreed, entranced at the prospect.

"Great Shogun," I said, "whatever small knowledge I have of the building of ships, mathematics, navigation, cannon making and gunnery I will be happy to leave behind as a gift for you and your people who have treated us with such kindness and understanding. I thank you for this opportunity and look forward to it with pleasure."

He seemed pleased at my acceptance and spoke courteously, saying that when I was ready, a place would be waiting for me in Yedo and all things for my comfort would be provided.

I looked forward excitedly to going to the capital city. I found I preferred the company of the Japanese to that of my companions, who had no interest in the country itself, some thinking only of barter, and the rest only of drinking and wenching. These occupations I considered unworthy of my time, now that I had so much to learn.

Therefore I put my affairs in order and prepared to leave. As I packed what few possessions I had regained, the most valuable being my books and instruments, Shoki-san came in to announce that the friendly samurai, Takomon no Itsuke, wished to have words with me. I asked Shoki-san to bring him in.

After greeting Itsuke-san, I had saki served and we drank and conversed. I wondered about his purpose in asking for this meeting.

Finally he spoke, saying, "Noble Lord, word has come that my master in far-off Bungo has died. I am now without a Lord to serve. It would honor me to enter your service as samurai."

I remembered the first time I laid eyes on him. At that time, to me, he had a most ugly mien, his eyes somewhat protruding, a sparse beard, his head shaved almost to the back. But by now, my eyes having become accustomed to the features of these people, I could look beneath and see the true dedication, honesty and bravery within him.

I recalled all that Shoki-san had told me of the samurai. I wished Itsuke-san to know how deeply touched I was at his offer, as samurai do not lightly give of their services, and, once given, their code of bushido will let them serve no other master. Furthermore, it added a great deal to a man's prestige to have such a samurai as Itsuke as his sword.

I bowed to Shoki-san, then to Itsuke-san. "Itsuke-san," I replied, "I am honored beyond speech that a warrior such as you offer me the use of your sword. Know you then, for so long as I am in this land you will be welcome to share my rice and sit at my side."

As I finished speaking Itsuke-san drew forth his tachi, the long-handled sword, and presented it to me, holding it by the blade. By luck and Shoki-san's counsel, I knew better than to grasp the tachi with my hand, but leaned forward and kissed the hilt. The bond between us was secured. Thus began a long friendship with Itsuke-san. Later, when other samurai came into my service, Itsuke-san led them. Between us there was a deep friendship.

Instead of completing my packing, the three of us sat and drank, called for more saki, and finally sent for girls of entertainment. We got joyously drunk, carousing through the entire night.

While in other lands this might have lessened my dignity, here it was enhanced. When dawn broke over the east, I was still able to clasp a girl with one arm and drink with the other while Shoki-san slept and Itsuke-san nodded drunkenly over a bottle.

33

Before going to Yedo I gave Captain Quackernack charge of my share of the monies received from the goods and asked him to hold it for me. My intention was that once our business was done, we could buy a sampan or perhaps two, and set sail for the island of Java where we hoped to meet with other Hollanders. My companions gave me a farewell party, bringing along the women they had acquired. It was a fine party. We drank many toasts to the women, the country and our success.

At Yedo we were received by the chamberlain of the palace. He escorted us to a comfortable dwelling within a park, at some distance from the palace. I marveled at the beauty of this place. A few years before, I was told, it had consisted of no more than a fort sitting upon the plain. Now it was a vast city, clean and lovely, where even the poorest had sufficient to eat and drink.

I was provided with many servants and my every need was fulfilled even before I thought of it. I met with Iyeyasu, and from this meeting on, there was to be no formality between us. When I wished to see him I would go to his private quarters where we talked without pomp or ceremony.

The more I came to know this man the more my admiration grew and has remained undimmed throughout the years. We disagreed about some of the things he did, but I have come to believe that he was right.

Each day, after I was settled, there came to our house three instructors who taught me language, history and calligraphy—the calligraphy being both the ancient Chinese characters and the Japanese written language which was simpler, though by Western standards highly complicated.

Shoki-san was of great help to me. At times I would come aground on some word, phrase or character. He was always there to explain, using both the Portugal language and the Japanese. Shoki-san being bright of mind and quick to learn, I taught him English and many other things. He was my first student. In time he learned to speak English well, though there were some letters his tongue could never overcome. Not so, Itsuke-san. I had always to speak to him in the language of Nippon, for his mind was closed to other tongues.

Between Itsuke-san and Shoki-san there was ever an area of conflict for my interest. Itsuke-san's nature was that of a warrior, intolerant of anything not conforming to bushido.

Noting how little knowledge I had of the sword, Itsuke-san wanted me to spend all my time taking instruction in the use of the tachi and the code of the warrior. My use of the sword before this had been as cutlass, to cut down whoever stood before me, as if I were a woodchopper.

Itsuke-san wanted me to be as skillful with the tachi as he was. He could cut through the cloth of my robe without touching the skin. I, however, was a clumsy pupil. Never did I attain more ability than to protect myself.

I sat for long hours with Shoki-san, studying the language, reading books, practicing calligraphy. From outside the door the rumbling voice of Itsuke-san would be heard, giving unnecessary orders to the servants. When I continued with my studies, he would mutter, loud enough for me to hear, about time being wasted and the only thing a man needed to know was how to be a warrior.

Evenings, he would entice me to the houses of pleasure, and procured a retinue to march before and behind me, guarding the palanquin in which he insisted I ride. He would belligerently announce my greatness and peer avidly about for some insult to me. For a time it seemed I was to be forever preventing him from drawing his tachi to avenge some imaginary slight upon my honor.

Like all samurai, he had absolute contempt for money. The money I gave him he might readily hand to the porter at the pleasure house, who did no more than bow as we entered, or he might demand all manner of service without thought of paying.

Itsuke-san had many faults, yet I came to love him as I loved Shoki-san. But it took time before I could make him understand my interest was not only in pleasure houses and drinking rice wine. Gradually, so as not to insult him, I withdrew in the pursuit of study and things that interested me. The world of the West receded. I was happy and unaware of the passage of time. Often, in the evening, I would sit and talk with Iyeyasu. From him I learned about government and how the nation was controlled. In many localities, the vast land was governed by lesser kings called Daimyos, who had sworn their loyalty though still resentful of the Shogun's rule.

It was a complex and intricate form of government. Off the main room was a small chamber where the business of court was conducted. Here reports from the provinces were received, directives sent out, and meetings held with the officials to discuss problems.

There were many government officials: the *kobiishi*, who was lord of the police; the *kaqeushi*, lord of finance. There were the Minister-of-the-Right and the Minister-of-the-Left. All these lords had great staffs of people, clerks and assistants, all well trained in their duties. I was allowed the honor many times of sitting in the room and listening to the business of government being conducted.

Kosuke no Suke was secretary to Iyeyasu. By this position, he wielded great power, a power that could be much abused, as all petitions passed through him to the Shogun. Surprisingly, Suke-san was an honest and devoted servant and an intelligent, gentle person. When I had first become friendly with Iyeyasu, I watched those about him for signs of jealousy. It was obvious there were many who resented me, but not the secretary. In fact, we became friends—insofar as we could be friends, for Kosuke no Suke was a man singularly devoted to his work. I used to marvel at him. He was a small, quiet man, self-effacing to the extent of being almost invisible. Always he sat at the right and a little to the rear of Iyeyasu. When a minister brought up a problem Suke-san would lean forward and with a few whispered words give Iyeyasu the complete details. He had a retentive mind that absorbed information like a sponge. Perhaps in a weak ruler this could be dangerous but Suke-san's only ambition was to serve and love Iyeyasu. He could have been an extremely wealthy man if anyone could have bribed him. Later I came to know his son, Sodo no Kami, who was a counterpart of his father.

Both Kosuke no Suke and Sodo no Kami remained my friends even when I fell on evil days, but at this time I had no other thought than to learn all the complicated workings of the government. I asked many questions. As we grew to know each other better, Iyeyasu would turn to me on occasion for advice. After the business of the court was over, Iyeyasu and I would retire to his private apartments for tea.

It took time for me to come to appreciate the beauty of the tea ceremony. To Western eyes the leisured formality would seem excessive for the mere drinking of a cup of tea. But the tea ceremony is not solely for imbibing tea. It is a strict ritual, each movement endowed with quiet beauty, so that a day would not be complete without its enjoyment. The people of Japan have a wondrous sense of the completeness of life and its grace that Europe could do well to emulate.

The room where we drank our tea was bare of things which might tend to distract the eye. The tea service was brought in by three girls of exceptional loveliness. They would stay for just a moment, then withdraw, leaving behind the scent and picture in the memory like a subdued chord of music.

Then Iyeyasu would pour the water and let the tea slowly steep. The brew, when ready, was served in silence. We would talk delicately of it, willing our bodies to be still and our minds to flower. One or two objects of art which had been placed in the room prior to the tea service would be admired—perhaps a sword made by one of the great swordsmiths of long ago. Its scabbard examined and commented upon, and the long, curved blade withdrawn. Blades were often so fine and highly polished, they shone like a diamond in brilliance, and were so keen that a gossamer handkerchief tossed in the air and floating across the edge would be neatly severed by its own slight weight.

Or the subject might be a painting. Not painting as we knew it, but of utmost simplicity of line and suggestion, holding the profound quality of peace, as if the artist had somehow pushed all that was extraneous aside, placing on the screen nothing more than the very heart and essence of beauty with but a few strokes of a brush.

The highest praise Iyeyasu could give to a picture was to say, "That is a quiet picture, Injin-san."

Injin-san was the name I had come to be known by, *injin-san* being the Japanese word for pilot. In time I was spoken to more formally as Daishi-san—great teacher. I was also given many other high-sounding titles, but among my friends I have always been known as Injin-san.

Most of these times I sat alone with the Shogun. When others were present they never numbered more than two or three selected princes, scholars or artists and I was honored to be in their company, for I was accepted as an equal or more. In a savage land this would have meant little; here, where the people were far more cultured than in Europe, it was a pleasing compliment.

Friendship among men can be closer than any relationship between man and woman. Between man and woman there is always sex, and sex causes conflict, even in the midst of love. Between man and man friendship can be an exalted thing. And so it came to be between Iyeyasu and myself. We would talk of many things, without hurry, listening to each other's thoughts. He opened his heart to me, and I did mine to him, until, in spite of the great differences in culture and background, we became as brothers.

I have long been interested in the history of nations and the actions of man. Over the years I have come to believe that there are climactic times in a nation's history when it seems that God provides men who can rise above the ordinary and solve problems which seem insurmountable. I had seen it happen in my own England during the reign of Elizabeth when there arose men of genius who won out against enormous odds and secured our country. So had it happened in Japan.

Generation after generation these islands had been in a state of civil war. This anarchy had weakened the nation, causing plague and famine until it seemed the land would revert back to its primitive state. Then there arose three men, each in his own way a genius. Nobunaga, Hideyoshi and Iyeyasu. In the beginning when Nobunaga and Hideyoshi had begun their campaigns to unite Japan, Iyeyasu had drawn together many of the great clans of the north and they met on the field of battle. None could win against the others, so they called a truce and the three united and pulled the country together under one strong government.

Nobunaga was murdered by an enemy general and Hideyoshi then became Shogun. When he died Iyeyasu had come to ultimate power. Both Nobunaga and Hideyoshi were rulers primarily due to their great prowess as warriors. Iyeyasu had the quality of a warrior in no lesser degree, but also something of much greater value. In him there was humility, combined with a thirst for knowledge and a dislike of unnecessary pomp and wealth. There burned in Iyeyasu a deep desire for the welfare of his country and people. In addition to all these virtues, he had an insatiable love of beauty, art and poetry. Few such men have ever been known to history.

From time to time some of the court nobles and myself, even Iyeyasu, once in a while, would go out into the city and move among the people, to drink at the inns, watch the dancers and enjoy the women, of whom there were uncounted numbers. But this I did not do too often. My ventures out became fewer until they ceased altogether as I became engrossed in my studies. It was some time, therefore, before I became aware of a feeling of tension in the city. I then learned that a number of barons were in revolt, having taken control of several provinces and defied the authority of the Shogun. Iyeyasu began equipping an army to march against them.

War has never made me happy but I reasoned that during the short time I expected to be in this land, I should witness the manner in which their armies fought. Because I had some knowledge of war, I considered that I might be of some service and repay, in small part, their kindness.

Iyeyasu accepted my services gladly. He was pleased to have at his side someone with whom he could talk more freely than to his own commanders, and we had reached that plane.

More and more now I accompanied him as the units of his army were brought together. We had long discussions as to the methods of battle in Europe compared with those of Japan.

Itsuke-san, now in his natural element, happily explained the customs of war in Japan. Battles here were fought in small units of not more than fifty, with individual soldiers performing great deeds of heroism. The sword, spear, bow and arrow were the chief weapons. The few cannon they had purchased from the Portugals were used for the effect of the loud report rather than the expectation of doing any damage.

I read, and had read to me, many descriptions of past battles. I explained to Iyeyasu as best I could the methods and modes of military usage and battle formation which had been used in the European countries from the Romans down to the present day. I pointed out that the methods of combat his people used had great similarity to those of Europe during feudal times. The use of gun powder had outmoded this type of warfare, I told him.

He pondered this, then asked if I could make cannon. When I answered that I could, he gave me the freedom of his foundries. I had spent time during my apprenticeship in the cannon foundry of Richard Phillips of London and this stood me in good stead. These long guns of Phillips were the best in England, and I had learned a good deal about casting metal. The Japanese metalworkers were very efficient so that, by the end of August, we had cast and made six long cannon.

We had also taken the guns from the *Liefde* and mounted them on carriages. Then, all being in readiness for bloody war, we set out. I have often wished I had not been witness to that battle. Yet I did take part. For a long time after, I would awake to the screams of the warriors, the booming of cannon and the combined noise of over a hundred thousand men locked in mortal struggle.

Good seldom comes from war but in this battle I think good did come to this country. Since then I have seen it molded into peace, good government under the law, and man's natural greed for power curtailed.

Before the battle of Sekigehara, Iyeyasu was not indisputably recognized as Shogun. On the death of Hideyoshi, Iyeyasu had taken the title of Regent, holding back until the whole country would recognize him. But the old jealousies had revived. At last, however, after this battle and after peace was made, he was proclaimed Sei-e-tai Shogun.

As we left Yedo and marched down to meet the enemy on the plains of Sekigehara, we had not more than forty thousand men while the Daimyos arrayed against us had seventy thousand. This was not to be a battle on equal terms; all would depend upon generalship.

Iyeyasu selected a position to meet the enemy, and there we waited. As the long column came into sight and separated into formations that had been in use over the many years, our array must have bewildered them.

Under Iyeyasu there were two great captains, Takeda Shingen and Uysugi Kenshin. The three of us had had many conversations. I had pointed out the wisdom Europe had found in disciplined tactics, and among us we had developed a tactical formation which history later called Yama-Garyu. We used it in this engagement. Instead of an individual unit advancing to meet another small unit of the enemy led by a noted warrior, we employed three massed wings, those on the right and the left consisting of three thousand mounted samurai each. Takeda Shingen had the left wing, Uysugi Kenshin, the right, Iyeyasu held the center. On a rise of the hill we concentrated our pieces of artillery.

From our height where we surveyed the enemy it seemed as if their numbers were limitless. Iyeyasu, however, had learned from spies that some of the units arrayed against him were not wholly decided. Our hope was that they would wait to see how the battle turned before joining either side.

In a compact front we held steady. From the opposite camp the soldiers moved about, laughing, talking and drinking wine. From time to time various warriors would come forward, close to our line, giving their names and challenging our famous samurai to individual combat. It was difficult to restrain our men in the face of such tactics, especially when, after shrieking his name, the opposing warrior would call out the well-known battles he had been in and how many men he had killed.

With my company of gunners I had Takomon no Itsuke. As he listened to the words of the opposing samurai, he stalked about muttering "liar," and making lewd remarks, drawing the tachi halfway from the scabbard, slapping it back angrily, tossing his head and working himself into a fury. I cautioned him several times to remain, and help move the guns into position, and check the powder and shot.

There had been little chance for me to train the gunners but I knew that a shot into that mass of men lined up against us would do heavy damage. The enemy paid no attention to our actions, not yet having learned to fear cannon.

When all was in readiness, I signaled to the Shogun and he gave permission to open fire. It was then that I noticed Itsuke-san had left but I had not the time to think of him.

Our first round of shot did even more damage than I had hoped, causing much slaughter to the center. As we continued to fire, the scene was dimmed by the smoke from our guns and what few shot came from the other side was out of range and did us no hurt at all.

But the enemy were brave. With furious shouts a mass of men detached themselves and came forward to do battle. Still our lines did not move. When the enemy neared, the mounted samurai from the right and left converged like the blades of a double scythe, sweeping completely through, cutting down the men like the wind leveling a field of grain; then coming to the opposite sides, they resumed their positions again.

For a time our line began to surge forward as the warriors became impatient to join, but they held back except for just a few who, in the excitement of battle, could not be controlled.

With the cannon we kept up a steady fire, doing much damage. Then Iyeyasu gave the command to advance. I now had the guns pulled back to the very height of the hill where we could have a clear circle of fire in the event we were in danger of being overrun.

From the summit of the hill I could see the whole battle as it was fought over the entire plain. On the other side enormous numbers still had not joined. These were the Daimyos who waited for the tide of the battle to go one way or the other.

The golden banner of Iyeyasu moved steadily, though slowly, forward and I could see the banner of his second son, Hidetada, at his right and always slightly ahead, in the very thick of battle. Hidetada was out to make a name for himself that day. In truth, he did. Such a name did he make that when a new Shogun was named, it was Hidetada who was to take his father's place above all others.

There have been many times when the wish has passed through my mind that Hidetada had fallen that day at Sekigehara. His fame would then have rested upon glory in battle instead of as Shogun. But history moves relentlessly, and who can say with certainty whether a specific event would have changed things for better or worse?

The left wing now swung wide, until one flank of the enemy was turned. The slaughter of men was terrible. The clash of arms and the screams were one roar of sound. As the armies moved, they left behind them a swathe of fallen men. Over forty thousand men died on the plain of Sekigehara that day.

Through the heat of the day, until late afternoon, the clash of arms continued without a pause. Then the tide of battle began to turn. The first of the hesitant Daimyos came over to our side.

Man is a strange creature and I, knowing the futility of war and being firmly against war and killing, found the blood lust flowing in me until I itched to be down there at Iyeyasu's side. Then my mind would revolt against the sight. But whether I wished to join or no, I had my orders to maintain the position, and so I did.

The enemy, as they were cut down, were driven into ever smaller groups and soon all the hesitant barons had joined our side, helping in the slaughter of their former allies. Sad to relate, these people do not regard death as a thing to be feared. To die in battle entails high honor, so that in all their wars the number of men killed is far in excess of what it would be in the most bloody battlefield of Europe.

One by one small groups, so exhausted they could no longer bend their bows or lift their swords, began to surrender. When the sun came to its setting, the great battle of Sekigehara was over.

As the officers returned to assemble on the hill, Itsuke-san came up, so exhausted that his tachi trailed behind him. There was blood from the tip of his sword, all along his arm and over his body. He looked as though he had bathed in blood. I spoke harshly to him while I bound a cut on his face, then prevailed upon him to rest near me as the hill became a mass of triumphant warriors.

Iyeyasu now brought his banner to the hill where we stood and, one by one, the defeated barons who were still alive were brought in to swear their allegiance to him. Not many of the barons had survived that day. With my whole heart I was glad it was ended.

What surprised me most was that after such a grueling day, fragile Iyeyasu seemed outwardly less tired than the others. His son, Hidetada, now came to receive his father's congratulations and blessing. He, too, was covered with blood from arm to shoulder and waist. He was young, flushed with victory, aware that this day would enshrine his name throughout Japan. Songs and tales would be written and told of the battle of Sekigehara and Hidetada's name would be there with his father's.

Until this time I had not known the boy well. On the few occasions we had met I had felt his coldness toward me and did not press the acquaintance, feeling that time would dispel his antipathy. I had been told that he despised all foreigners. As this is a common feeling among all peoples, especially in my own country, I could not do less than understand.

Hidetada still held his sword in his hand, caressing the blade from time to time as he related various incidents during the battle and told of the men who had been felled before his eyes.

Seeing me in the background, and flushed with his victory, he made a slighting remark about my retreat to the safety of the hill and wanted to know my opinion of Japanese warriors.

Trying not to resent the contemptuous tone, I replied truthfully that, man for man, I had never seen braver soldiers.

Iyeyasu then placed his hand on Hidetada's shoulder and said: "You did more than well today, my son. But never forget that Injin-san was the key that unlocked the door to this battle of Sekigehara."

Hidetada's face flushed. I believe that Iyeyasu's comment at that time changed what had been resentment of me to hatred. It was something I was never able to overcome, though I tried.

Our return to Yedo was triumphal all the way. At the capital city there was rejoicing which continued for days as if the whole country was made drunk by the great victory.

34

Some time later I was visited by Sweringen and some of my ship-mates. Seeing them, I felt ashamed not to have kept in touch. They complained of being without funds. Van Sartoot was holding all of the monies and goods, refusing to give anyone a share. They begged me to return to Yokosuka and help recover their share of the profits, or at least enough to buy wine. I could not refuse.

In Yokosuka I found things in even worse condition than had been told me. The men were almost in a state of mutiny. There had been many arguments and much brawling over this matter. Van Sartoot had gone so far as to hire certain *ronin* to protect him. The ronin were soldiers who held no allegiance to any lord, and were similar to mercenaries.

I called everyone together in meeting. Van Sartoot at first refused to attend. I warned him to come else I would have police bring him to us.

When finally he met with us he was belligerent. He had the strange idea that it was his responsibility to act as banker, holding all money and goods until our return to Holland.

Hearing him out, I read him the articles of the Guild of the Red Lion which all had signed so long ago. In it we had agreed to share all profits equally, leaving to the merchants only that which was considered a fair return on their investment.

Van Sartoot heatedly objected to this, despite the fact that he had signed it. "I, as the merchant's agent," he said, "am responsible and must return all monies to the company of merchants. Only then can the wages and shares to each of us be legally paid."

His words caused an angry stir among the men. I was hard put to keep them from treating him violently though I was angered enough to injure him myself.

"Our good friend Herr Sartoot," I said, "seems of a sudden to be greatly concerned with the well-being of the company and thinks lit-tle of the welfare of his companions, all of whom have suffered greatly for what profit we made. I wonder somewhat at his way of thinking. He claims it is his duty to take all the profits of this voyage back to his masters. I'm afraid we would be hard put to collect a farthing in payment for our heartaches. We all know that the Dutch merchants had their profit before we sailed and Herr Sartoot knows full well, as we all do, of the great distance we stand from our homes and loved ones. We know little of the tribulations God, in His Infinite Wisdom, will set in our path. And of Sartoot himself— does he carry some magic about him that he is so sure of reaching home intact with his masters' money?"

I was interrupted by angry comments from Sweringen and some others, but stopped them, saying:

"Hear me out. To look at Herr Sartoot, you would hardly think him capable of crossing the road without getting himself lost. For myself, I hold with the articles we signed. I say those who want to share now should have their money to do with as they will. Whatever is left, Herr Sartoot can return to the fat Van der Haag. I know some will spend their money in riotous living, wasting it to a great extent. But we, being men, should have the privilege to do with our money as we wish. That is the way my mind lies on this. As this is a free guild, let all have their say. We are banded together, therefore let the majority decide what is best."

The meeting went on for a long time, each man bringing out his anger. In the end Van Sartoot was forced to make settlement. This set ill with him, for I was sure he gambled on the chance that many of us would never reach our homes alive. The death of each man would be so much more profit to him. I even doubted that, should he reach Holland, he would share honestly with his masters.

He blustered and seemed almost on the point of tears, but we had an accounting at last and shared alike.

Captain Quackernack took charge of issuing the money. As each man received his share, he made his mark or signed his name in the account book. Finally it was done.

Most of the men now wanted me to take part of their share and invest it in goods. This I had no wish to do. I did not want the responsibility of purchasing for the others. In the end each went his own way to make his own profit. We also had the money which Iyeyasu had paid for the *Liefde* and which we were to use to purchase another boat. I wanted to spend several more months in this land, even though I dreamed often of returning to England— not only to Nicholas and my family, but to my friends. I knew, after a voyage such as this, there would be Englishmen more than eager to form trading companies which I hoped to head.

I stayed some days in Yokosuka, talking with the men, making tentative plans to return home, and was inwardly relieved to find none of them in a hurry to do so. I had a twinge of conscience at my relief but ignored it. I told them to seek out a large junk or sampan, and when they found one suitable, to inform me and I would come to examine it. Then I returned to Yedo with high heart, wanting to crowd in as much as I could before leaving this Morning Land.

Each evening I diligently recorded everything I learned about this land. I obtained maps which I copied. I had learned a great deal about the natural wealth of the islands, the mines in the north, the timber forests, the rice lands and the fishing grounds—all manner of information which I knew would be of interest to the Society in England. Day by day I added to my knowledge, planning on writing a long and complete paper to present to the Hakluyt Society. I envisioned the meeting at which I would read this paper and the fame it would bring me.

It was at this time an incident occurred which sorrowed me, for it caused Shoki-san and others to lose face, yet in another way it was comic, like some foolish play.

On a trip to Yokosuka, where I went to look over several vessels in the company of Quackernack, Sweringen and others, we met with some Franciscans. These monks had entered Japan for the purpose of spreading their denomination. I have always felt that those who believe in the word of God cannot be bad men. Some, however, do act so strangely they not only hurt themselves but others connected with them and also harm the cause they espouse.

Also, these particular Franciscans had entered Japan against the orders of the Pope, who had given this domain to the Jesuit fathers. I learned they had told the officials they were not here to stay but were with some Philippine vessels lying outside Yedo harbor.

On being approached by these men I thought at first they wished me to serve as pilot, and offered to do so. This they refused and instead tried to convert me to the Papist faith. Having my own beliefs, I argued with them, answering their arguments with quotations from the Bible. In the end they accused me of wrongfully interpreting the Scriptures and called me heretic.

We escaped their preaching at last, after I warned them that if word got about they were trying to make converts, or even preach here, the Shogun would be very angry. My relief at escaping them was short-lived. Soon, one of them came looking for me down at the seashore and began ranting at me.

"O heretic," he said, "I will prove to you the truth of our religion by means of miracles which I can perform."

I noted that this Franciscan father had an odd look to his eyes. Seeing he was a fanatic, I tried to soothe him, gently, saying I did not believe in miracles in these modern times. Then he said that a doubter such as I should see the glory and power of God who, through this vessel—meaning himself—would do miracles in greater matters also.

I tried to dismiss him and go on about my business, but he discoursed so loudly that a large number of Japanese gathered. If he had spoken the Portugal tongue I could have kept the argument between us, but he used the Japanese tongue and brayed like a jackass, refusing to be silent. Finally he challenged me to select a miracle for him to perform.

Again I refused, but at the insistence of Shoki-san and others who believed him, half in anger and half in jest I challenged him to walk upon the sea as St. Peter had done.

Joyfully he accepted this challenge. However, he said it would not be accomplished that day but the following morning. At an appointed time he would be there. I felt certain the matter would be soon forgotten but unfortunately the word was passed throughout the city.

In order to prevent the disillusionment of Shoki-san and the possible danger of this reaching the Shogun, I approached the other Franciscans for aid in preventing the friar from making a fool of himself and belittling the Christian faith. They refused to see me even without knowing the reason for my visit.

My next thought was that perhaps if I did not appear, the friar would not attempt his idiocy. But he came by the house where I stayed and harangued me so from the street that I had no choice but to go with him down to the seashore.

With me went many of my companions including Itsuke-san, Shoki-san, Captain Quackernack, Melchior Van Sartoot and Sweringen, all of them eager to see the miracle. Shoki-san was the only one who believed that a miracle would take place.

Standing upon a rock at the seashore, the Franciscan harangued the crowd, which grew larger every minute. He addressed himself to me, though really speaking to the people. He called me many names, the best of them being heretic and doubter, and announced that I could call upon him to do any miracle.

"You heretic," he said, "would you challenge me to lift that great tree which grows on top of yonder hill and transport it to where it will rest lightly upon the water without sinking? Or would you have me take this great tree from where it sits and transport it to the top of the mountain, high in the distance? Challenge me, O heretic, and I will make the sun stand still in the firmament as it did in the time of Joshua!"

I had to restrain Itsuke-san, for he felt I was being insulted. I explained that this was a man of religion and should never have a hand raised against him whether we differed in belief or no.

Meanwhile the friar talked on and on, making wilder and wilder promises, until finally some of his brothers appeared and wished to take him away. But he would not go, and the crowd insisted on seeing a miracle performed.

The Japanese people, who love games, were betting one with the other, the Buddhists wagering against the Christians that such a miracle would not be possible. Itsuke-san, too, placed a wager with Shoki-san that it would not occur. I felt ashamed to see a friar so foolish.

Finally, when he had talked the full length of his breath, he asked me again to state my wish. The crowd screamed, "Ask it! Ask it!"

With much hesitancy I said that he should walk upon the water as St. Peter did, feeling certain as I said so that he would find some way out. Seeing, however, that he truly meant to go through with this, I hurriedly sent Sweringen to find a small boat and stand by for the eventual disaster.

The friar then took his cross in both hands. It was a large cross, almost half his height, and it must have been a most heavy weight, for when he stepped off the rock and into the chilly water he disappeared from sight immediately.

Sweringen, who had fetched a boat, started rowing hastily toward him. The water at that point must have been exceptionally deep, as the friar was down for some time. Then all at once he popped to the surface like a cork from out a bottle. He opened his mouth to say something, but sank once more. When he came up the next time Sweringen was near enough to grasp the friar by the back of his robe. He hauled him in wet and dripping. Then rescuing the cross, he rowed back to shore.

The crowd was divided in its feelings, one half angry at the friar and the other gleeful, for they had won the money and proved that the Christian bonzes could not do miracles as they claimed. Itsuke-san was jubilant and laughing, while Shoki-san was furiously red in the face. I left them to settle their differences. We led the wet and shivering Franciscan around the edge of the crowd and saw him to his house.

For some reason this event sent the people roistering through the streets. There was fighting and quarreling which lasted through most of the night.

Before returning to Yedo the next day, I stopped by to see the friar. I felt somewhat guilty, though it was not my fault. He was sick in bed and very angry with me. He claimed that the reason the miracle did not occur was due solely to my lack of faith. Truly he was a mad sort of man. I reminded him that it was his challenge and told him emphatically that the age of miracles was long past. This did not soothe his anger and he ranted at me until I left.

The other Franciscans were angry with him too, as the attention of those in authority was turned on them because of the furor he had caused. They were all immediately deported. Afterward I learned that the poor friar was punished severely for the incident by the bishop in Manila.

The story grew in the telling. Later I found that I was blamed for having these priests deported whereas, in fact, I had been no more than an unwilling observer. Such is the way of the world. There are times when we are falsely accused and other times when faults are not discovered. In the end it comes out even.

35

Looking back on those days, I think my fate was of my own making, as it almost always is. Yet I could not have done otherwise. With each passing day my love for this land and its people increased.

My friendship and usefulness to the Shogun was such that he placed ever higher value on my knowledge and help. By my own actions I became too valuable to let go.

One day, in conversation with Iyeyasu, he showed me a sheaf of drawings which the shipyard workers at Yokosuka had made of the *Liefde*. They had taken her apart piece by piece and laid her out like a giant pattern. He was very proud of this and sat awaiting my comments.

When I put them down and turned to him I knew not what to say as he looked at me expectantly, happy as a child with a new toy.

Formally, careful not to hurt his feelings, I said, "O great Sei-e-tai Shogun, the ship which you copy is such a poor thing that from the day I stepped aboard her I was ashamed. This misbegotten vessel on which we wandered over so many miles of sea was never of more value than a crippled wife to a rice farmer. I am a builder of ships and on the long voyage I drew up certain plans which would be so far above this poor, worn-out one as your glory is in comparison to your defeated enemies. If you will, I will build you such a ship that will take the banner of Japan proudly across any sea of the world."

I knew Iyeyasu had been amazed by the size and intricate construction of the *Liefde*. Now he looked at me doubtfully.

"You have told me, Injin-san, that this is not a proud ship but I thought your words but modesty. If you have such plans and if you can build such a ship then it would be our great pleasure to have you do so."

I had my first inkling then that I had set a snare for myself. A ship such as I had in mind would not be easy to build without the construction of a way, of the kind we have in England. So, somewhat shamefacedly I back-tracked, explaining the length of time it would take, and lamely finished by saying: "However, I can build a sloop for you and could draw in complete detail the plans for a ship, teaching your shipbuilders all the arts necessary. From what I have seen of them they are quick to learn."

A day or two later I brought Iyeyasu the plans I had drawn and then found myself torn between an opportunity to build a ship such as this and the time element involved.

I was sorely tempted. Here I would have all the facilities to build a ship such as I never could build in England. All things would be provided and I would not have to stint in its construction, nor be hindered by hidebound traditions. However, a ship is not built in a day, and my conscience ate at me continually for my neglect of my family in England. Not knowing my fate, they probably believed me dead and there was no one to care for them.

But now I found myself provided with a sumptuous home, fit for a nobleman, at Yokosuka, near the royal shipyard. I was treated like a lord. Both Shoki-san and Itsuke-san were proud of our new status. As I began the building of the sloop, some nobles and youths of the court were sent to me by Iyeyasu. I was to teach them the science of mathematics, navigation and gunnery. All this was written in a proclamation wherein Iyeyasu extolled my duties as well as my virtues, saying at the end:

"Your knowledge of our language is almost that of our own people. You shall have your secretary, Shoki-san, to assist you, and all other necessities you desire shall be requested and granted in my name."

And so I not only became a shipbuilder once again, but also a teacher. People began to call me Daishi-san. I must admit I relished it. The nobles and youths sent to me had great intelligence. After my classes I would turn to the drawing board like a drunkard to his bottle. I was greedy, and here, for the first time, I was granted the opportunity to design a ship without thought of cost.

I employed some of my shipmates to help in building the sloop which, though large for a vessel of that country, was to be of but eighty tons burden. At first they thought this sloop was being built so that we could leave Japan in it. When they found this not true, I was questioned at intervals by Captain Quackernack and Van Sartoot and others as to when we would be able to leave. Actually, many of the men were not overly anxious, for they were living a most comfortable existence, having all things sailors dream of— women, wine, plenty of food, and easy employment. A few, however, wanted to return home as soon as possible.

Iyeyasu being busy with the problems of government, I saw him not more than once a month and then only briefly.

There were many difficulties in the building of that sloop. The tools used in this land were crude, unfamiliar to me, though the Japanese could do amazing things with them. I had other tools made, built the way, supervised the selection of the timber and the planking which was to go into her making.

Since those whom I taught were not so enamored with work as I, sometimes in the evenings they would persuade me to go out to the tea houses to be entertained by geisha. These geisha are women most artful in conversation, music and dancing. They know all manner of ways to please a man though they do not serve him sexually. Women for that purpose are found in the many houses of pleasure.

At first the music and singing of these people did not set well on my ear, being high-pitched and lacking in rhythm as we are used to. It seemed at first to be discordant, but soon my ear began to understand the undertones and I came to appreciate the subtle beauty in their music, the pleasure of which grew the more my ear became accustomed to it.

I enjoyed going about the city. I was an object of great interest, due to my size and overabundant beard. But in time it became so that the women vied for my favors. Had I tried to service those willing, without even the payment of a fee, I would have had time for nothing else. All in all, the delights of both Yedo and Yokosuka, the good and intelligent company, the women and wine, were something beyond anything I had ever experienced. My conscience bothered me less and less, and when I thought of home and England I pushed these thoughts to one side and continued with my work.

By now we had been in these islands for two and a half years. One day, Captain Quackernack, Van Sartoot and others of the crew asked that I meet with them. I admit I had neglected my crewmates. They had found a vessel which they considered suitable for a sea voyage, and asked that I examine it. Being with them again had the effect of shaking me out of my dream. I realized it was now five years since I had seen my family. All of a sudden, England and home were in my mind again, strong and fresh, pulling at me.

I found the boat to be a large junk of Chinese make, constructed of teak and in solid condition, though most clumsy in appearance. In my opinion her decks could be raised for greater comfort. With proper sail and handling she looked as if she could make the voyage if God would be kind to us weatherwise.

During the time I taught my pupils, I had continued my studies of Chinese and Japanese maps so that the route to Java was known to me. Merchants recently returned from there had said Dutchmen had a trading post in one of the islands.

We purchased the junk and I told them what was necessary to do while I finished the sloop. Some of my shipmates felt I should put my attention to fitting out the junk. I felt I could not, and explained at length that after all the kindness shown us by the Shogun I could do no less than finish this vessel and teach his people to handle her.

In the meantime I had finished the design for the other, much larger ship, spending many hours translating the English terms of keels, ribs, planks and decks into the Japanese tongue.

Finally, the work almost complete, I traveled to Yedo and informed Iyeyasu that on a certain date we would launch the vessel and complete her as she lay in the water. As he had not yet seen her, he came to Yokosuka several days before she was ready for launching. He was exceedingly pleased at the sight of her, and when she was launched and rode high in the water I could see he was as happy with her as I.

While the sloop was being finished, I began taking out my students, using my shipmates as instructors. In a short time we were able to make various smart voyages around the Bay of Yedo and out into the open sea.

When the crew was finally trained I journeyed to Yedo to persuade the Shogun and some of the nobles to visit the ship and see for themselves how well she handled. I was quite proud of her. She was able, with any serving wind, to outsail even the best galleys.

Our talk then turned to other matters. I told the Shogun of the junk we had purchased, that our preparations were almost complete, and soon we would make our departure.

I could see that my news disturbed him.

"Are you not happy here, Injin-san?" he asked.

"Sire," I said with deep sincerity, "these years I have lived in these islands have given me great pleasure. I have come truly to love your country and your people. Yet I have strong ties in my own land that pull me homeward. My wife and children are dear to my heart, and I have many close friends whom I am anxious to see once again. On my journey home I will prepare a full account of our voyage both for the Royal Society and the Hakluyt Society, whose members are interested in the hidden areas of the world and the voyages to these places. Sire, it has now been five years since I left England. I do know that once back, the things I have to say will raise such interest that our two countries will become well known to each other and we will be able to trade, each with the other, in honesty and fairness, for things both countries need."

He said nothing to this for a while. Then, looking kindly at me, he said: "Injin-san, we have been impressed with your knowledge and great ability since first you appeared before us. You know well that I feel toward you a deep and honorable friendship. Since my youth I have fought many hard battles. With great effort I have been able at last to bring stability to my country. But to grow strong we have great need of knowledge as well as strength in arms. You know so many things that are beneficial to us. I ask you to stay awhile yet as our teacher. For this you will be greatly rewarded. I must request that you stay with us for some time longer."

Looking at him, I tried to hide my emotion. What I felt inside of me must have shown in my eyes, for he turned his face from me. By then I well knew that a request from the Shogun, no matter how politely phrased, was the same as an order. England, being denied to me, suddenly became close and dear and desirable. I pleaded strongly with him.

"Most Honorable Lord," I said. "It is not needful for me to speak to you of my gratitude for all your kindness to myself and my countrymen, but I beg of you to consider my condition. My wife and family, hearing nothing from me for all this long sad length of time, depending on me for those things necessary to their health and happiness, must by now be in desperate straits. As to my little knowledge, there are many men with far greater. Once my tale is told in England of the rich loveliness of this land, I will be assured of the command of other ships. Other men will gladly come with me, bringing both knowledge and goods useful to your country and your people."

He frowned and shook his head. I knew, before he spoke, that my pleas were useless.

"You have told me often, Injin-san, of the great dangers of the long voyage. Only by the kindness of fate did you not meet the fate of your comrades. I will give you money for your family to send home with your countrymen. I am so sorry, my honored friend, but

I am a selfish man when it comes to that which is of benefit to my country. We need you and your knowledge."

"Will you hold my companions then, too?" I asked.

"For so long as you will need their help in building the other ship."

"These are seamen, my Lord, not shipbuilders. Your workmen and shipwrights have great talent."

This he granted me, nodding slowly. "Then if you say that you need them not, they may go when they are ready, with my blessing."

Suddenly he placed his hand upon mine. "This has been a hard thing for me to do, Injin-san," he said, "but you must understand that I cannot do otherwise."

I bowed to him ceremoniously and he bade me good night.

I spent the night brooding over this dilemma and thought also of escape, knowing even as I thought of it that it would be almost impossible. Before we could reach the sea from Yedo Bay the entrance would easily be blocked. I knew also, by then, the efficiency of the police and how few things went on throughout the length and breadth of these islands that Iyeyasu was unaware of.

Before the night was over I had resigned myself, saying that, after all, none of us is really free. Freedom was nothing more than a fantasy of the mind, no more than an illusion, a feeling, of little worth. And so my mind went on. I was saddened. Yet the truth was that deep in my heart I was in love with this Morning Land, feeling more at home here than I ever had in England. Had it not been for Nicholas, Elizabeth and the children, and the hope of honor and praise which I knew I would receive on my return, I doubt that I would have felt any sorrow at all at being forced to stay. My family was beyond my help for the time being. However, with the money I already had, they would be almost wealthy if I could send it safely to them.

I slept, promising myself that I would do whatever I could to contribute something to this country—without bitterness, without feeling I was a prisoner.

The following day, without seeing Iyeyasu again, I returned to Yokosuka. When I broke the news to my comrades our meeting became a stormy one. Many wild plans of escape were made for me. To each plan I said no, I would not endanger their chance to return home. I asked only that each of them vow that somehow the monies and letters I sent would be delivered to England. Finally, when I had argued it all out and they found there was no escaping from my position, we did what all good sailors do—got drunk. Though the Japanese take to the bottle freely, we showed them such drinking as they talked of for years after. . . .

I went on with my work, at the same time seeing that the boat my comrades were to leave in was in the best possible condition.

When the day of parting came we met once more, for the last time. To each man I gave a letter. To Captain Quackernack I gave a large amount of gold and had his vow that he would try, even at the risk of his life, to see that it reached my family in England. To Sweringen and the others I also gave money for the same purpose. Then I said good-by to each man in turn and wished them a safe and sound journey. Sweringen, whom I loved best of all, wept for me and would have stayed with me had I asked him.

As they left the land, many of the men were weeping, not only for me, but for the women, children and friends they were leaving behind. I turned my back as they put up sail. I could not bear to watch any longer.

36

After my shipmates had sailed I felt so alone that I fell into a sort of melancholy, my thoughts ever dwelling on my family and England. Though I tried to be philosophic, I found no solace. I reminded myself that a man seems to have no control over his fate but only the ability to make pleasant the road he must travel. It did not help. I neglected my work and classes.

Iyeyasu had gone with his court from Yedo to visit with the Emperor at Kyoto, leaving me without even the comfort of his friendship. I spent more and more time at the geisha houses, and at the theaters and drinking places where I consumed huge quantities of saki, much to the admiration of my companions.

Takamon no Itsuke and Shoki-san were with me always, though Shoki-san had little stomach for saki. Itsuke-san called him "scribe" and "woman" to make him drink. Then, when Shoki-san became drunk, Itsuke-san would laugh at him and pour saki on his head and I, too, would laugh at him.

During this time my only enjoyment was listening to the two of them argue about history. Neither saw it in the same light and it seemed as if they were speaking of two completely different times and different people. But wasn't it ever thus with history?

Shoki-san looked upon Oda Nobunaga, Toyatome Hideyoshi and Tokugawa Iyeyasu as faultless heroes. Itsuke-san, a samurai, had lived and fought in the service of all three, even going to Korea with Hideyoshi under the banner of his local Daimyo. His version was most amusing and, I doubt not, contained a bit more truth.

I remember one night as we sat drinking, Shoki-san told of how Oda Nobunaga, as a young man, had had a vision of uniting Japan. Thereupon he marched forth like a knight, winning to his side all of the great Daimyos. It was only his untimely death, Shoki-san said, that prevented his dream from coming true.

As he talked Itsuke-san sat drinking, making rude comments. At last unable to stand it, he said:

"Faw! Oda Nobunaga, when a young man, was known as Baku Dono, or Lord Fool. There was no sense in his head at all. One day when he came home from a night of carousing, dirty and covered with the stench of the streets, his guardian protested at this Lord Fool's loss of face. When Oda Nobunaga laughed at him, the guardian knelt before him and committed seppuku. It was only then that Baku Dono changed his course. You, scribbler, make him look as a milksop. He was no castrated court nobleman. He was a man. There's a *haiku* which tells the character of Nobunaga." And he quoted:

> *"Nakanu nara koroshite shimae*
> *Hoto togisu."*

> (If the cuckoo will not sing
> Surely I its neck will wring.)

Then, looking disgustedly at Shoki-san, he continued. "And that's the way he was, soft mouth. If the Daimyos would not come to him, then he would go to them and wring their necks for them."

Shoki-san, though in fear of the wrath and temper of Itsuke-san, could still not resist his own idealized versions of the honorable men. He would be completely carried away as he told his stories.

Once he told of how Hideyoshi, who was born with not even a name, rose to fame under Nobunaga, and when the great Shogun Nobunaga was killed, Toyatome Hideyoshi went on with his inspired, selfless work until all Japan was united. Then he set forth with a huge army to take Korea, which he would have done had he not become sick and died.

"He was a magnificent, noble man," he said, his eyes shining. "Most handsome, tall and strong."

At these words Itsuke-san could not control his laughter and slapped Shoki-san across the back so that he fell asprawl, spilling his saki.

"By the light of Buddha, if this scribbler is not a fool! Let me tell you what Hideyoshi was really like. I have been as close to him as I am to you. In height he would not come to my shoulder. He was fat, with a belly like a rice bag. But he was strong. He had six fingers on his right hand and there was no beard on his face. His eyes stood out from his head in such an ugly fashion it was painful to look at him. Injin-san, you have seen the stone dogs of China?"

I knew he meant the small, ugly dogs with protruding eyes and flattened nose and mouth. When I indicated that I knew, Itsuke-san said:

"That's the way Hideyoshi looked. And do you know what kind of man he was? He was the kind of man who would drink with both hands yet no woman was safe from him. When he became Nobunaga's number one general it was even worse.

"The tea master to Oda Nobunaga, named Rikyu, had a daughter of not more than twelve or thirteen years. One day, when coming through the courtyard, Hideyoshi saw her and with no further ado took her into the garden and ravished her. Rikyu committed seppuku and there was a loud crying out that Hideyoshi should be punished. But his six fingers were Nobunaga's right hand and Hideyoshi could have done anything and probably did. Now, scribbler, these three were men, and they were generals, but that's the way of the world. Soon they will have that scrawny Iyeyasu as a giant of a man and a saint. A man he is, but no giant and no saint."

Such words made Shoki-san furious. But between the two versions, somewhere perhaps was the truth. I mentioned to Itsuke-san that I still could not accustom my mind to the readiness with which people in this land took their own lives.

He grunted in the coarse way he had, and said, "Injin-san, life is short. The world is no more than a dream. Only a fool fears death, for what is there of life? All life dies once, sooner or later. Each man has his time to die and he should make his death glorious and a thing to remember.

"Before we embarked for the war in Korea, Hideyoshi spoke to us, telling of the dangers ahead and the great battles to be fought. A famous samurai named Manamoto no Furi stepped forward and said, 'We have no wish to die peacefully, but desire to die by the side of our king. If we go to the sea, our bodies will sleep in the water. If we go to the hills, over our corpses grass will grow, but our swords will never fail you.' At these words, a great cheer arose from the whole army. Injin-san, many men died in Korea and we did not win, but there was not a man who did not die bravely." Then, turning to Shoki-san, he added, "And that is what a samurai is, scribbler. Listen to me and you will learn."

Finally the time came when I reached the point where I tired of drinking, of women and talk. I turned back to my work.

With the help of some Japanese artists, I made a set of embossed plans of the large ship I had designed. I brought the plans to Iyeyasu on his return to Yedo. He was well pleased. He turned to me after studying them and asked, "Will you build the ship for me, Injin-san?"

"The cost will be great," I warned him.

"That is my problem. You build it and anything you ask will be provided."

"Then the ship will be yours and there will be none better on the sea."

First we had to build a tremendous way on which to house the construction. With Shoki-san at my side things went much easier. The Japanese, quick to learn, showed their genius in shaping the wood. My good master Nicholas Diggins would have been sorely envious could he have seen them. Great timbers of teak and mahogany were brought. The keel was laid and the ship began to take form. While it was abuilding I had also to make use of the foundries for casting the cannon.

With Iyeyasu's permission I brought two of the nation's great sword makers to Yokosuka to learn something of their ways of hardening metal. Though they considered it almost a sacrilege to reveal their secrets to a foreign devil, I learned their method. After several failures we were able to cast guns of fine quality. The Japanese craftsmen designed the cannon so they had more frill work than those turned out by the best men in Europe.

As the work progressed, Shoki-san and others brought rumors that there was strong feeling against the building of this ship.

One day I would hear that the Emperor himself would bless the ship and another day it would come to my ears that the Imperial Court was against the entire project. I knew, of course, that there were many Japanese who felt the old ways were the best and preferred that all foreigners be barred from Japan. I paid no attention to these rumors and went on about the work.

Though I came to know Iyeyasu as a brother, a part of his life was hidden from me. Respecting his feelings, I ignored this door leading to his private life.

Iyeyasu had three wives and many concubines, but few children. There were two sons and four daughters. The daughters, however, had little worth in the scheme of dynasty. Although they were loved, the sons would carry on the name.

Of his two sons, Akihito, the elder, was a scholar and a poet. Iyeyasu respected him and loved him but nevertheless turned to Hidetada, who, for all his faults, seemed more capable of running the government, and perhaps Iyeyasu was right in thinking so. Akihito and I were friends, whereas Hidetada hated me along with all things foreign. Perhaps he even hated me more than the others because of the closeness I shared with his father.

Looking back on the rumors about the Emperor and the ship, I should have realized that Hidetada was more the leader of this group than any other.

Iyeyasu had sent him to study with me. Though he was brilliant of mind he always sneered at the culture and civilization of the West. Yet he learned to speak and write English fluently. One day, when I was lecturing on the beginnings of navigation and how man's knowledge had expanded until he was able to find his way across the widest sea, Hidetada rudely interrupted me.

"Of what good are such things to us?" he demanded. "In this land we have all things necessary for the happiness of our people. I know not of one thing, whether it be religion or your contributions, that have not brought us more trouble than value. There are those of us who know the danger to Japan."

Then, addressing the others—since from the beginning he had treated me as a servant—he reminded them of the year 1596 when a Portugal galleon, the *San Felipe,* was wrecked and the crew was rescued.

He said, "There were some foolish ones who were intrigued with the things and ways of the West, aping the graceless clothing and customs of the men from that ship. Some loyal Japanese, who put their country first, reported to Hideyoshi how the captain of the galleon had bragged that soon Japan would be under the rule of the Portugal king. They told the Shogun Hideyoshi how this captain pointed to all the Portugal and Spaniard possessions on his maps, saying:

" 'Our king sends into the countries we wish to conquer priests who teach the Christian religion. When we have progressed sufficiently the priests stir up trouble with the help of their converts. Our king then sends troops to protect them. Once our guns and troops are in the nation, we have little difficulty in winning our way.'

"Hideyoshi, on hearing this, banished the Christian priests from the land of Nippon. It is true they are still here, but one day they will all be gone."

Turning back to me, he said, "And you, Sir Pilot, I wonder at your true purpose. You seem to be a most shrewd and honest-appearing man. Tell me, does your English king work the same way?"

Fully aware of Hidetada's dislike for me and not wishing to be drawn into argument with him, I made a short denial and went on with my lesson. Perhaps I should have made a greater effort to change his way of thinking. My pride, however, would not allow me to force friendship in the face of animosity.

I was somewhat puzzled at the importance Shoki-san placed upon whether the Emperor approved or disapproved the building of the ship. From what I had seen, I felt he was no more than a shadowy figurehead, and that the power of the land was in the hands of Iyeyasu. I was aware of the journeys Iyeyasu made from time to time to the Imperial City to pay respects. One day when we were in friendly conversation I asked him to explain these things to me.

"Our history," he said, "teaches us that the first Emperor was a direct descendant of Amatarisu, the Sun Goddess. The Emperor at one time was ruler in fact, but the weakness of the Imperial Court eventually brought about the division of government into two parts. There have been Emperors during our history who have had the strength to take over the government, but the strength never seems to be passed on to the next generation.

"During times of peace the Imperial Court always has become so engrossed in petty quarrels of rank and ritual that soon they have no time for anything else, forgetting that the true business of government is the welfare of the people. When the people are forgotten, trouble comes to the country.

"Some day, Injin-san, you will journey to the Imperial Court with me and see what I mean. They issue a solemn edict, lengthy and flowery in language, the content of which does no more than to fix the color of official robes for flower viewing. Or it may be the proper stance, or how to dress the hair, or the correct length of the swords for various occasions—not that any of them could draw without assistance. This nonsense leaves the country without direction, weakens it and finally brings on rebellion.

"Life at court is made up of a round of religious ceremonies; ceremonies of homage to the August Presence of the Emperor; banquets, political tournaments, excursions to a flower garden, or to contemplate the moon on a clear night. These events are accomplished with the utmost attention to ritual. In this we have no quarrel and we pay full homage to the Emperor. But from his hands we have taken the direction of the country. Never again will this country revert to warring factions that bleed the land and the people.

"My good friend, my aim and whole desire is to set up the basis for such a system that our Morning Land will always have a good government."

I made no comment, pondering what he had said. Then he added:

"At the Imperial Court there is a saying, 'Chorei bokai,' which in full meaning is an order issued in the morning and reversed in the evening. There is no harm in the issuance of such edicts so long as it is only on unimportant matters. But laws for the people must be permanent and fair and complete, for the good of the country. It is not that I would scorn beauty. I think, even in our court here, we spend much time in certain ceremonies and in the admiration of things beautiful. I do not scorn beauty at all. But when beauty lies like a captured bird in the hands of a few, and the great masses are forgotten, then even beauty cannot last."

I thought over what he said and replied, "As a man who has lived with the sea, I have had little to do with the court, the nobility, or the sovereign of my own country. But during the time the islands of England, which in some ways are much like your own, were at war with the Spaniards and Portugals, I saw what a vacillating monarch can do to the hopes, energies and pride of a brave people."

And I went on to tell him of the great battle of the Armada and the events leading up to the war. He was deeply interested in my account of the battle. Many times afterward, he would ask me questions or have me retell the story of the defeat of the Armada to the nobles of his court.

I was absorbed in the history of Japan; I wanted to understand its social structure, the contributions of men such as Nobunaga, Hideyoshi and Iyeyasu. Japan, I found, was divided into four classes. At the bottom was the lowly, groaning peasant who even in the best of times, had hardly enough for himself and family to eat. When the crops failed, people starved by the thousands. During the reign of Iyeyasu, he in great measure ameliorated the conditions of the peasant. One of his most admirable qualities was his sympathy toward his countrymen.

Next were the samurai, whose sole function in life was that of soldier. On the same level with the samurai was that minor nobility of the fourth or fifth class who turned to scholarship, arts and the priesthood.

The next level were the third-, second- and first-class Daimyos who, by their allegiance in the various provinces, formed the bulwark behind the Shogun.

The princes of the realm clustered about the court of the Emperor and lived graciously, but were of little importance in the structure of government.

Prior to the reign of the three great leaders, Nobunaga, Hideyoshi and Iyeyasu, there had been times when the priests rose to dominant power, becoming so strong that they invaded the Imperial City under arms. I suppose it was ever thus with mankind. Priests too, whether Buddhists or followers of the gentle Christ, are sometimes perverted by greed. On the whole I found these people to be of fine nature, kind without measure, with an innate love for beauty, and warlike only when they thought their honor or the honor of their lord was endangered.

Most of the people, even Iyeyasu, belonged to the sect of Buddhists called Zen, and took as their lord the gentle saint named Amida. The samurai, when old or disillusioned by war, enter into a religious order where they expiate their sins. I found the study fascinating and continued entering all and sundry information into my journal.

During the time the ship was building I taught many nobles. As I came to know them intimately, my liking for them steadily increased. Not that they were without fault, but they had fewer faults than most. I also became more familiar with priests and Portugal traders who came to Yedo and Yokosuka.

This made me happy for, in a sense, they were people from my part of the world. Hoping that gradually we could overcome the old hatreds, I did my best to overlook the harm they had tried to do us.

I noted a more friendly attitude toward me by the Portugal traders who came to Yedo to seek favors or permits to trade. I chose to ignore the fact that this friendliness grew at the same rate as my influence at the court.

One day Alonso Lusiad, the first trader we met on our arrival in Bungo, arrived with another Portugal by name of Enrico Martinez. They very plainly showed their admiration of the ship I was building. Feeling like a proud parent, I guided them through the ship.

"Madre Dios, Señor Adams," Lusiad remarked approvingly. "She will be the loveliest ship in the world! But the sheer and narrow beam—will she take the sea?"

"I would stake my life on it," I said proudly, happy to have some Europeans to talk to. "If you will do me the honor of dining with me I will give you my reasons for building her so."

They accepted, and I extended hospitality as I would have liked to receive it. They were impressed by the size of my house and the number of my servants.

"It is said you have cast a spell over that *wojin* Iyeyasu. Seeing how you live, I can believe it."

The word "wojin" was distasteful to my ears, meaning, in English, scum. Despite the fact they were guests I lectured them.

"You Portugals have been trading here for many years. But to my mind you have not learned much," I said heatedly. "These people are more cultured in many ways than Europeans. As for myself, I have come to love and respect them. I cast no spell. I give them freely of what little knowledge I possess. In return I am learning much and am treated well."

"But is it not true you are a prisoner?"

I hesitated, then said: "Yes, in a way it is true. But of my own free will. When I have taught them what I know I can leave with honor."

Martinez sneered at this. "They are barbarians and heathens. We would do well to send in an army."

"If these be barbarians then I would like to see a civilized nation. Yours, for instance. You call your country civilized?"

Martinez was becoming as heated as I was. Lusiad changed the subject.

"They say, Captain Adams, that you were with the English against the Armada. I was on the *San Felipe*."

Glad to change the subject, we talked of those far-off days. I learned much of the enemy's troubles, the terrible hardships they underwent and the reason for their mistakes.

All in all we had a good evening, drinking and conversing like comrades. They returned a number of times after that. It was a good omen, I felt. At first they were opposed to teaching the Japanese to build and sail ships, feeling it would hinder trade. But I explained that this would help, not hinder, and emphasized that there was room for all, if we treated one another on a fair and equitable basis.

I felt I had convinced them to my way of thinking.

Looking back, it seems that the ship required but a short time to build. Yet there were great difficulties. I had hoped to launch her within a year, but it took much longer. Sailmakers worked under my direction, making the canvas and cordage; elsewhere, her heavy cables were being woven. Her masts and spars had been cut and trimmed and lay awaiting the day when they would be stepped and fitted and made ready for the sea.

Over the months it seemed that half the people of the country came to view the ship. They came in such numbers that we had to fence off the area in the shipyard to keep the curious from interfering with the work.

After much thought, I had decided to name the ship the *Tokugawa*

Shogun, as a mark of respect and honor to my friend. I had samples brought to me by many calligraphers to ensure that there would be no mistake, because in this language the slightest error of a brush stroke can change the entire meaning. I knew there might be some who would deliberately cause me embarrassment. Two were discovered who deviated from the rest. My caution was justified, for had they been accepted it would have been an insult. To these men I sent Itsuke-san and he beat them both soundly with a bamboo cane.

Standing on the way, the lines and form of her nearing completion, she towered high over the shipyard, an awesome sight to the people. I had already marked the day for the ceremony of her launching.

Then one night she was set afire.

37

I awoke from a sound sleep to a loud shouting in the streets. Shoki-san burst into the room with such excitement that he forgot the ritual of bowing and sucking through his teeth before addressing me.

"Injin-san, the ship, the great *maru* is in flames!"

Grabbing my kimono and not even thinking to bid adieu to the lady who shared my sleeping mat, I ran out of the house, Itsuke-san at my heels, girding his sword as he ran.

At the shipyard the flames were eating away the bracing at the foot of the way and showing red high above the side of the ship. Those who were stationed in the area to put out fires were already at work. This land consists almost wholly of fragile wooden buildings, yet these firemen are adept at quenching fires. The blaze was extinguished soon after my arrival. Then I went forward, burning my feet on the hot ground, and examined the smoking remains.

The ship was blackened. She sagged at the stern, and lay so far over that it appeared as if the whole of the way would soon collapse and the ship come tumbling down.

Calling to the workmen, I had them bring lines and beams which we placed against the side of the ship to prevent her sliding down any farther. We worked arduously throughout the day, carefully removing the burned timbers and slowly raising the ship back into an upright position. The local Daimyo and many of the nobles, as well as a goodly crowd of people, watched us. When I had done as much as possible, the officials came forward to make an examination to determine the cause of the fire.

I knew the fire had not occurred accidentally. Without a doubt it had been set, well and carefully. Only the alertness of the watchman and the speed of the fire quenchers had saved her. Though she was seared and blackened, the flames had not reached within her. After careful examination, I was relieved to see she would not have to be rebuilt.

Before the sun had set the Shogun Iyeyasu and a retinue of high officials came storming into Yokosuka. The crowd moved back, clearing a wide path for him.

Not even dismounting, he rode directly to the ship. On seeing me he harshly demanded why I had not personally informed him of this.

Being tired, my anger rode me so that I replied, with total lack of courtesy, that I had been very busy, too busy saving the ship to take the time to write flowery phrases of the disaster. I regretted the words as soon as they were spoken, for I had no wish to hurt this man who was my friend.

His face flushed with anger. Then he, too, must have realized his anger against me was unreasonable. Turning away, he barked a series of commands to the noble in charge of the troops.

Before the day ended they had gathered together everyone who had any connection with the shipyard. Iyeyasu's method for uncovering the guilty ones was cruel but effective. Each person was questioned in turn, and, according to their answers, separated into groups. None were released. Further elimination was made and those left in the suspicious group were brought to grovel before the Shogun. He, himself, shrewdly interrogated them. They were then put to torture. I could not watch this nor could I interfere.

Within a short time a confession was wrung from two men, who implicated the Spaniard priest Moreno, Alonso Lusiad, Enrico Martinez, and several court nobles, among them Hidetada—although this was never acknowledged.

In the space of a few days, all those arrested were brought to a hearing in Yedo. The traders denied any part in the plot, but Padre

Moreno brazenly admitted it and proudly confessed the guilt of his countrymen.

I thought long and hard about this. In my first heat of anger, I felt that death was no more than they deserved. I had to acknowledge to myself that their visits to my home and the shipyard were not prompted by friendship; that this had been well planned and executed with deliberate malice. But after further consideration, my anger cooled and I came once again to my belief that taking a man's life in punishment never solved anything. I therefore determined to practice what I believed. I petitioned Iyeyasu and received permission to visit the Portugals and bring things for their comfort.

Alonso Lusiad and Enrico Martinez could hardly meet my eyes when I arrived. They wept and pleaded with me piteously. I promised to do what I could for them and comforted them as best I could.

I asked them why they had done this.

"Señor, we have often considered that if Japan has the ships, she will no longer allow traders here, for then she will be capable of going anywhere she wishes. We had to do this. We must protect trade for Portugal. You, Señor Adams, with this ship will ruin all we have built."

I found this a most stupid way of thinking. Trade always grows on itself. But this was no time for recriminations; the damage had been done.

I then approached Padre Moreno. He spat at me, calling me heretic. He had taken part in the plot for the purpose of conversion. He had hoped, I imagine, for he would not speak to me but rather at me, that burning the ship would be misconstrued as an act of God and put fear into the people. He refused any aid from me.

The Japanese nobles involved had different reasons. They were of the group who were opposed to commercial relations with foreign lands. Their fears at least had valid reason.

In later years I had almost definite proof that Iyeyasu's son, Hidetada, headed this treason, cleverly using the weaknesses of the traders and the priests to achieve his ends. I do not know if his father knew. In any case, he was not punished though seven nobles involved committed seppuku.

Sadly I went to Iyeyasu and begged for these men's lives, saying that the ship had not been damaged overmuch and that to banish them from the country would be sufficient to remove the danger of their doing further harm.

Iyeyasu, however, would not listen. His anger was great, nor could I blame him. Despite Hideyoshi's law banishing the priests from this country, Iyeyasu had been patient with them and with the traders as long as they caused no trouble. Now he informed me that the three Christians were to die on the cross, and that he would henceforth banish all Spaniards and Portugals from the land. Those who would not leave would be killed.

"We have taken these people as guests," he said. "We have made them welcome, but they have been only a thorn in our side. The Christian bonzes control the trade for their own ends, therefore all must go."

"I have always felt, Most Noble Lord," I said, "that to take a life is a great responsibility. I beseech you to banish them if you will, but not to kill them."

I could see that it was a great effort for him to keep his anger from turning toward me.

"Seven of my own nobles have taken their own lives over this. The workmen who were involved have been killed. These Christians will know the law of the land. How can I take the lives of my own people and let these foreigners go?"

Knowing it was useless, I persisted. "I believe that any man's life taken by violence weakens all men."

"It is a strange thing for you to say, Injin-san. Can you forget that you were with me at Sekigehara?"

"My philosophy did not spring full-blown," I said. "I have killed men in battle when I felt I was fighting for the right. But do not think the men I have killed rest easy on my conscience."

"In this you are wrong, Injin-san. Laws must be obeyed, else chaos results. They have tried to do my people a great wrong. They have injured you personally. Why plead for these men and not for the lives of my own people? Are they better? Are they more deserving of life?"

This made me think. I suddenly realized that, in spite of the evil they had tried to do me, I still looked upon them as being my own kind. This thought made me ashamed, for I could see the rightness in his view. My attitude seemed to say that his people counted less than others. I said no more, but asked him, before he deported all aliens from the land, to speak again with me when there was not so much anger between us. I had done all I could.

Back at Yokosuka I tried to push the fate of these men out of my mind as I went about the work of rebuilding the way and finishing the ship. It was a long and difficult task but it kept me from brooding. I did not even know the day the execution was to take place.

It was some time afterward that I learned the details. The two Portugal traders died begging for mercy. Padre Moreno went to his death as if by crucifixion he could claim kinship with Christ. Such a man I have never been able to understand. I have tried and wished I could. Never could I see where such behavior enhances the power of the Church. But it seems to be so; and there being many things I do not understand, perhaps I am wrong in this also. Somewhere, in the scheme of things, this may be necessary.

Though I have never given credence to the superstition of sailors regarding signs and portents, still I feared that this might be a bad omen for the ship. I took all precautions to see nothing else would happen to her.

Finally the day came for her launching. The people came from all over the countryside, the country folk in their plain costumes making sharp contrast to the gay colorful dress of the samurai and the nobility from the capital city.

On her bow and stern I had her name engraved in gold, both in Japanese characters and in English lettering. The name *Tokugawa Shogun* stood out proudly. At her bow I had constructed a platform, and since no Christian priest would be allowed to bless her, I explained the ceremony of launching and asked Iyeyasu to select a Buddhist bonze to offer a prayer. On Iyeyasu's arrival it seemed as if half the bonzes of Japan were in his retinue.

I had not told him of the naming of the ship. As he mounted the platform I had one of the workers pull back the banner that covered her bow and, bowing deeply as Iyeyasu mounted the platform, I waved my hand at the ship in a gesture that meant she was his.

He bowed to me. His eyes scanned the length of the ship before they turned to the name on her bow. He then turned to me with a smile.

"You surprise me, Injin-san. I thought you were above flattery."

"Not flattery, Most Noble Lord. I spent many nights thinking of the proper name for her. But in the end all the signs and portents said that this was the name she should carry."

He bowed again, formally. From the base of the platform the crowd stood in thousands.

"We cannot argue of signs and portents," he replied, smiling. "And so it shall be. But tell me, Injin-san, why speak you always of a ship as a female?"

"It has always been so, my Lord. The sea is the mother of us and the ship her daughter. The sea is a man's world. In all history no women have ever sailed ships. A ship, like a woman, is contrary and it takes the hand of a man to soothe her, ride her and hold tight rein when she becomes willful, as the sea stirs her passion."

We continued with the ceremony. The old Buddhist monk, Tenkai, prayed for what seemed hours while his assistants rang bells, lit pots of incense that filled the air with such a heavy, sweet scent it was difficult to breathe.

Finally he finished. I left the platform to supervise the launching. Such a sight had never been seen before in this land. The *Tokugawa Shogun* slid majestically toward the water like a bride to the arms of her husband. As they met there was a cheer from the nobles and populace that almost deafened me. She settled herself as if she had come home.

By her cables we quickly pulled her to the fitting-out dock and, placing a stairway against her side, Iyeyasu and all of his court retinue came aboard.

She was sturdy and well-balanced and I was highly pleased with her. As we went through all sections of her Iyeyasu was admiring and as proud as any man with a new and lovely bride.

"How soon then, Injin-san, will she be complete?"

"In three months, my Lord, no more. Everything is ready, her masts and rigging wait at the dock, the guns nearby. You understand, of course, we will have to test her likes and dislikes, see where she wants her ballast and how much is needed. But within three months she will be ready for the ocean and there will be no place in this world too far for her to sail, so long as the men who sail her come to know and love her well."

Before going ashore we stood together on deck for some time. The sight of the bright color of the people ashore took me back to the time, so long ago, when I had seen the launching of my first ship. Queen Elizabeth, with her court, did not make half so bright an array as this. And remembering back so long ago to that day, my memory also turned to little Harriet Gresham and how bruised my heart had been. I wondered what fate had befallen her and in my heart I wished her well. Thinking also of my good friend Nicholas Diggins, I saluted him in my mind. I knew that if he could have seen the ship he would have been proud of the result of his teaching. I did wish, so strongly, that he could be here. I hoped that after a few voyages Iyeyasu might consent to let me make a voyage to England.

Ah, what a day that would be! I could picture myself coming up the Thames with all banners flying. What a curiosity it would be! The Japanese in their rich costumes lining the decks. . . . It was a happy dream.

38

My worry had been needless for there was no further incident. There came the day of her completion, her masts stepped, sails and rigging fitted. She was a lovely sight, standing tall and proud in the water. There was, however, one flaw which I had no choice but to accept— a large eye painted on each bow. I did not like it, but the Japanese believe a ship without eyes cannot find its way across the sea.

I had an artist paint the eyes. He made them slanting and beautiful so that they were a part of her decoration. In time, I felt them no more disagreeable than a figurehead.

When we had her ready I notified Iyeyasu. Then I found myself in a rather awkward position. The *Tokugawa Shogun*, being so much larger than the sloop I had built previously, now required a crew especially trained for her. Sooner or later I would have to take her out of the roadstead and into the open water. There were those who claimed that, once away from the land, I would steal the ship and escape.

I heard of this first from Shoki-san, who said: "Daishi-san, it has been said by some that you might steal the ship. I have heard that Hidetada speaks thus against you. Last night Itsuke-san took to sword, wounding a samurai who spoke against your honor. He was not the first one to do so. I have heard even Iyeyasu has suspicion of you."

I thanked him for the information and reassured him. Next time I met the Shogun I said to him:

"On my honor, you can rely that I shall do nothing to cause you to lose face. I do want to return to my own land—but when I do it will be with honor, so that when I return here I will be welcome."

He said, simply, with utter confidence: "Daishi-san, if you tell me this I can do no less than trust you as I would the word of a samurai. Go then; and when the day comes when she is ready to sail the sea, so that there will be no doubt of my faith in you, I will go with you."

I ached to take the *Tokugawa Shogun* out into the open sea and try her wings on the wind. The day came at last when I sent word that she was ready, awaiting Iyeyasu's arrival. The crowds that arrived far outnumbered those on the day we named her.

This posed a difficult problem for me. I would need room to work the ship and I could not insult these people by refusing passage, for they are very sensitive. There was also the problem of food. We had but few stores. Not even the cuddy was complete for the cook to perform his duties. In haste I had cooks brought from town with charcoal braziers and many stores. Since Iyeyasu and most of the hierarchy of Japan were with us, and any accident could cause dire trouble, I ordered twelve galleys to stay close by us.

There was one important personage who was conspicuous by his absence but I made no comment, nor did Iyeyasu. I knew Hidetada's feelings very well by then.

Many of our passengers had brought pleasure girls and geisha. Remembering the class distinction, I addressed them all, explaining that this ship was a ship of war and they would have to behave as samurai, taking the perils of the sea like good soldiers. I then turned over to Shoki-san the supervision of the foods and the ladies. This task did not please him.

I had given orders to Itsuke-san to guard Shoki-san from trouble, but once under way Itsuke-san disappeared. I thought he was off drinking, wenching or bragging to the other samurai. This irritated me and I had it in mind to speak to him about it. Later I found the motion of the ship had made him ill and he had found a quiet corner where he could hide his shame. I never mentioned it to him. Sensitive as he was beneath his gross exterior, he might, in his shame, have committed seppuku.

Shoki-san, as always, accepted my orders with but murmured complaint. His was a difficult task and became worse as the day wore on. There is something about the sea and a ship that seems to make women amorous unless they become ill. As wine was imbibed, the ladies kept trying to mingle with the sailors. Shoki-san was kept busy dashing back and forth, capturing one or another and herding them back to the area which I had assigned.

It was a fair and lovely day with but a breath of breeze over the harbor. I had the galleys tow us from the dock and far enough out to where we had sea room. Then, as the sails came up, so beautifully did the ship move through the water, she was like a lovely woman dipping and gliding to music.

I had wanted, for once, to sail her free and wild with whatever wind I could find. Now, I could not afford to run into weather where the nobles would be affected by the seasickness, for, should they suffer from it, they would lose face and it would be bad for them and for me.

The wind held light, though once outside the bay when she met the sea there were some who felt the discomfort. Once away from the land she settled down and sailed as well as any ship I have ever been aboard.

Iyeyasu stood close to me during all the maneuvering. He was enormously pleased, but in no measure comparable to how I felt. A new, well-founded ship has always had the same loveliness to me as a rare and beautiful woman. It is hard to explain this to a landsman. Only those who know and love the sea know that in the surge of the sea, the lift and falling, the murmur of the wind in the rigging, there is a whole song of a ship meeting the sea with the same rhythm as an act of love.

After a few hours of tacking back and forth, testing her all around, I regretfully decided to come about and bring her back in. There was great jollity aboard the ship. There had been much drinking. Poor Shoki-san was in such a state of exhaustion that his kimono hung askew. In attempting to get two women out of the waist of the ship he had lost one of his slippers. For the first time I saw him with the braid of his hair loose and his box-like hat tipped to one side, giving him a somewhat rakish air. When he came to me once with some complaint I teased him, accusing him of being tipsy.

He denied it vehemently, waving his hands and demanding how I thought anyone would have time for a drink with so many foolish women running about and behaving as though their mothers had never taught them morality.

"The geisha and *yoshiwara* are still acting somewhat with the decorum of women," he said. "But the court ladies have no sense of decency. Injin-san, I have had more suggestive advances made to me this day than ever before in my life. I am almost afraid to escort any of them below decks."

I had a carafe of saki brought. We had a drink and I soothed him, promising now that we were ready to start back, his trials would soon be over.

Iyeyasu was amused at this. I was thankful for his presence, as no one would approach the cleared area where we stood without his permission, so that although the ship by now was riotous, I was not bothered and was able to maneuver.

By the time we re-entered the bay and neared the city I was most proud of my crew. When we were once more at the dock I thanked them for the day's work, and gave them permission to join in the party. For this I received three banzais. Iyeyasu complimented them and issued gifts and they loved him for it.

Now we began taking the ship to sea. Within six months we had visited Korea and Formosa. The Japanese showed as sensitive a feel for a ship and the sea as Englishmen. Had events gone as we had planned, Japan would in time have become one of the greatest maritime nations of the world.

I was satisfied with the course of events, feeling that fate, in bringing me to Japan, had given me the opportunity to prove some of my beliefs. By building the *Tokugawa Shogun* I had opened the doors of Japan to the world. By having the Japanese sail her to other lands I was bringing her people in communication with others, and so promoting mutual understanding.

But in any man's life it seems there must be discord. My desires for Japan and the world were being thwarted because of Hidetada. In the last months he had become a thorn in my side. Though he had learned well and was a brilliant student, his dislike for all things foreign to the Japanese had increased, particularly toward myself.

I had made a great mistake in being unwilling to exert myself to make Hidetada like me. My stubbornness cost me dear. Though I found early in life that when I have come to know an enemy, we have reached an area of liking and understanding, between Hidetada and myself there was nothing—never the least understanding—just a wall of dislike, and as the years passed this dislike had hardened into a deep and abiding hatred.

He had absorbed what little knowledge I offered much more quickly than the others. English words did not stumble over his tongue. But I could never reach through his contempt for me and always found myself annoyed at his arrogance, his haughty, regal attitude. Many were the times when I felt a strong temptation to take him in my hands and do him harm.

Hidetada was a small, almost fragile man, like his father, physically. I knew there was courage and strength in him, having seen him perform on the field of Sekigehara.

Though Iyeyasu was aware of the arrogance that lay coiled like a snake inside him, he felt that time would mellow this, for he truly loved Hidetada. I could not, nor ever would, say anything against the boy, knowing how it would hurt my friend. Each time I left Iyeyasu I would promise myself to try harder. But I did not.

Hidetada made but one voyage with us—an unpleasant affair of wind and weather. We went to Formosa. It was an unfortunate choice. The climate was bitterly cold and the merchants and people rude and greedy. If I had been able to take him to a fair and pleasant land like the Philippines or Java, his mind might have changed. But this, too, must have been fate. The voyage so upset him and further solidified his opinions, that never again would he leave the shores of Japan.

After a number of short voyages we sailed to Java to make trade. There I found some Holland men. Through them I sent back letters and money to England, praying to God it should reach its destination as I knew not how my poor wife and family fared.

I found myself becoming rich, not only through the goods I traded but through Iyeyasu. Each time I returned, Iyeyasu would reward me. I was given a much finer house, more servants, and after the second successful trip he gave me gold amounting to almost twenty-five hundred pounds, besides costly ropes of pearls, and jewels from China.

Once, while in conversation, we talked of women as men always will. I mentioned that the women of these islands were of surpassing loveliness, except that my Western eyes found flaws in the smallness of their breasts and shortness of their legs. This was in answer to his query as to the difference I had found in the women of these islands in comparison to those of other lands.

On my return home from the next voyage I was greeted by a girl, long of leg and with tremendous dugs. Where Iyeyasu had found her I do not know but she was pleasing to me. To Japanese eyes she was far from beautiful. Her hair was curly. To the Japanese, only straight black hair was considered beautiful. Altogether I wanted for nothing, my cellar always being stocked with saki, Chinese, Portugal and Spanish wines and brandy.

On the voyages I did almost none of the sailing or navigating. Feeling the crew was more than capable of handling the *Tokugawa Shogun*, I got permission from Iyeyasu to let them make a voyage alone. I thought it might be difficult to persuade him to this, but he agreed readily. A few days later I discovered the reason. Iyeyasu was stepping aside as Shogun. Hidetada was to replace him. This news worried me, not only for myself, but for the country.

When we spoke again I made so bold as to ask him if he thought it wise to turn the country over to so young and inexperienced a person as Hidetada. He smiled and said calmly:

"You are a great though simple man, O Daishi-san. By making my son Shogun, those who hate me strongly will lose the object of their hatred. Yet, until Hidetada proves himself, and until the day comes when Japan is powerful enough to leave in the hands of another I will remain as Shogun in fact. The name and the glory mean little to me. In the wars I made many enemies; to them my name is bitter on the tongue. I do not fear rebellion but if I can destroy the seeds of rebellion by any means, this I shall do."

I was greatly relieved at these words. My life under Iyeyasu was one of ease, prestige and riches. I did not expect the same from Hidetada.

Preparations were now made. I watched with interest and anticipation until the day came when all of the court set out for Kyoto to petition the Emperor to appoint Hidetada Sei-e-tai Shogun.

Under the insistence of Shoki-san I, too, got new costumes befitting a scholar, which was my status. Then we waited for the day of departure. I was most impatient to see the Emperor's court at last.

39

During my travels I have seen much of pomp and ceremony. I had thought the Turks were masters in that sphere, but never did I behold a sight to equal the parade from Yedo to Kyoto.

I had suggested to Iyeyasu that we take the *Tokugawa Shogun* around to Osaka but the Emperor had changed his mind and frowned on such un-Japanese behavior.

There were over forty thousand people who were to make the journey. The snakelike column stretched along the road mile after mile. The head of the column circled the base of their holy mountain Fuji-san while the tail was just leaving the city. I had the privilege of traveling with Iyeyasu. He had refused his palanquin, preferring to ride horseback. Hidetada was obliged by custom to travel by palanquin in regal splendor.

The journey, which would take several days, had all the aspects of a picnic. It was spring. The weather as lovely as a sunny day in England. I wondered how so many people would find lodging in Kyoto, but learned that almost every noble maintained a large house at Kyoto for the visits to the Imperial Court, according to tradition.

The court at Yedo was intricate, complicated and formal. I noted with interest that the people from Yedo were considered almost barbarians by those in Kyoto.

Every movement in the Emperor's court was complicated and stylized to the extent that it amused me, for it reminded me of marionettes. Not that it was without a strange sort of enchantment, like watching play-acting rather than actual people arranging for the Emperor's official appointment of a new barbarian-defeating general.

I had hoped to see the Emperor. I was curious to discover what sort of a being he was. I knew the Japanese looked upon him as a "Living God." I did not see him, but heard from others that he was no more than a poor, unhappy fragile boy, weighed down by elaborate costuming and deluded by the myth of his godliness.

The investing of Hidetada was an elaborate affair. Many costly gifts were exchanged. During the extensive ceremony, Hidetada made the ritualistic gestures and words of obedience to the unseen Emperor's majesty and the symbols of his power. As for myself, I got into a holiday spirit and enjoyed myself hugely. The court etiquette was exquisite, formal, entrancing. Watching the mincing steps of the personages reminded me of broods of peacocks with tail feathers extended, strutting and posturing in absurd convolutions.

The men were so feminine and dainty as to seem almost eunuchs. The nobles and samurai of the Shogun's court appeared even more masculine than they had before. I doubt not that our visit had good results, for much new seed was left in the Kyoto court women. This helped somewhat to tone up the blood of these involved and ingrown creatures, the simpering men behaving like castrated creatures, the women incongruously lusty.

There was deep religious fervor among the women of the court, or so it seemed. They would form long columns of palanquins and journey almost every day to a great monastery close by. Here they confessed their sins and heard the bonzes tell them about hell. I soon learned from the lusty courtiers of our party that the thing to do was to go out along the road with carts of food and wine, attended by servants, and there await the ladies' return. We would then eat with them and enjoy the benefits of their visit to the monastery, which had the effect of instilling in them a great heat of passion. The fornication that went on along the river banks and hillsides was a sight to behold.

The ladies were frightened of me at first, but as the novelty wore off I found myself as a Turk in France, or an Irishman in England. They flocked around me, fluttering their fans and beguiling me with their eyes, like queen doves, lovely and delicate, and so tantalizing that I could not help acting like a cock-of-the-walk. I had the good sense to know it was not so much my charm as the novelty of my appearance. None of them had ever beheld a creature like me.

It was my good fortune at this time to obtain a portrait of me that one of the court artists had painted. It was most amusing to see how I appeared in their eyes. I was a great, staring caricature of a man with eyes the size of saucers, standing among the fragile women

like some giant. The women were incredibly delicate and I seemed
to be bearing the earth down with my weight. The painting was not
something to enchant me with my beauty, but there was great art
in it and no man should quarrel with art.

But in time the strange, delicate beauty which these people had
learned to enjoy, the flower watching, moon gazing, poetry reading,
began to pall. When the ceremony was done I was more than ready
to return to Yedo, to live in a world of reality and go on with my
work.

40

With Hidetada as the head of the government and Iyeyasu staying in
the background, I had not the freedom of the court that I had known
previously. As I gained in renown many people came to me with
problems or petitions which they would ask me to bring directly
to Iyeyasu. On occasion, when I felt the request worthy and sincere,
I would do so. Through this, I could have become very wealthy, since
almost all, in asking the favor, would try to present me with payment either in gold or something else of value. I would not accept
any form of recompense, not only because of moral principles but
because money was not of so much value to me that I would involve
myself in the strings and snares of such conduct. But when I refused
even a token as payment, this, too, was resented and caused anger
in those for whom I had just performed a favor. I know my conduct
was hard to understand, for the customs of these islands did not differ from those of any other place I had been where, in order to have
something done, a bribe was expected. If I tried to explain that I
did the favor because I felt it was worthy, I was thought to have
other, devious motives.

For a month or more I was isolated from the court. When I requested an audience now with Iyeyasu I was told he was away. Even
Kosuke no Suke, Iyeyasu's secretary, acted coolly toward me. I was
aware of mounting tension but I could not understand the reason.

As the days passed, once again I felt lonely. I was determined, at
the first interview with Iyeyasu, to tell him firmly that I could no
longer remain in this land. I had nothing further to offer them. I

had no more to teach. If he refused me, I would do no more but sit and wait until he finally consented to my returning home again.

Day after day passed and even those nobles who had been my friends stopped visiting me so that I was sure the disfavor Hidetada held toward me was being made quite plain.

Even the faithful Shoki-san seemed to withdraw from me. The times he was around, his bright ways and humor no longer pleased me. I spent much time drinking with Itsuke-san. But the mind is a strange thing and the more I dwelled upon my fate, the more I forgot the comfort and beauty of my surroundings. I felt as if I were a slave. Now, in my mind's eye, England had the aura of a bright and shining heaven and I longed desperately to be among my own countrymen.

One day I was requested to appear before the Shogun. I was in my garden, seated in a little arbor by a miniature lake, watching the gardeners at work. I had long since given up trying to help them, as it lowered me in their eyes. Also, the flowers and shrubs that bloomed under their tender care seemed to shrink from me. Yet there was great pleasure in watching the work of gardeners. They have a wondrous touch with living things. There is a tenderness in their hands which seems to make the plants reach out for their love. The gardener near me was planting new shrubs, handling each one as if it were a jewel.

Shoki-san came out, highly excited. Bowing three times before me he said, ceremoniously: "O great Daishi-san, three high nobles have come to call."

The visit of three officials such as these seemed a very bad omen. Straightening my robe, I thanked him and went into the house. I had a premonition of evil. After bowing deeply to each in turn I made apology for my poor house and suggested that they might be more comfortable in a smaller room where we would have tea.

Once seated and while waiting for the tea service to be prepared, Irutusu Minemoto, a lord of the first class, asked me with a polite smile if I had acquired further understanding of the "Nō"— the Nō being a type of theater. Although I had attended several performances, I had become more puzzled at each. One night, while dining with Iyeyasu, Minemoto and other nobles, I expressed my lack of understanding. It was Minemoto who told me:

"To understand the Nō, you must forget the theater and surroundings and look at the Nō." Nō, in English, would mean something like ability or art. "Forget the Nō," he went on, "and look at the actors. Forget, then, the actors and look at the idea. Finally, forget the idea and you will understand the Nō."

The words had spread and become a common saying about the court. Yet, in all truth, I think there was validity in his words because no matter how hard I tried to understand, there was no resemblance to the theater as I had known it in England. It was of such fragile content that the end result was no more than a mood or an illusion.

"I have merely reached the point of forgetting the actors and most times that is not hard at all," I replied.

There was laughter at this and we talked in light and friendly fashion, I speaking somewhat at length about the theater in England as we went through the peaceful ritual of drinking tea.

Afterward there was silence. Then the Daimyo Sufa Kimihara, with whom I had been friends since the battle of Sekigehara, said:

"Injin-san, the most noble Sei-e-tai Shogun Hidetada requests your presence before his honorable person."

Friendly as they had seemed, there was something in their attitude that disturbed me. Many of the Japanese resented my influence with Iyeyasu and I also knew how easily loss of favor could take place in an Oriental court.

Making the customary gesture of sucking in my breath and speaking words of pleasure at having such an honor bestowed upon me, I excused myself to dress. After a bath I put on the black, plain kimono of a scholar, and as I combed out my beard I wondered in what manner Hidetada intended to disgrace me. Then I thought further that I did not overly care. I had reached a phase of life where any change would be better than the state I was in.

When I returned to where the nobles awaited me, my plain black attire was in startling contrast to the flamboyant costumes they wore. This mode of dress was now so familiar to me that if I had seen an Englishman coming from the court, his costume would have seemed strange.

As I entered the room the conversation stopped abruptly. I was all the more aware of an undercurrent of excitement. The Japanese are adept at hiding their feelings but they were not succeeding this time.

As we stepped outside the gate and into our palanquins a full company of samurai in dress armor was lined up in column. We proceeded through the streets to the gates of the Shogun's palace in military fashion and the people on the streets bowed almost to the ground at our passing.

With six of the samurai as guard we took a path around to the side of the castle and went down a narrow hall into a small anteroom. Daimyo Sufa Kimihara and the other two nobles left me, disappearing through a small sliding panel.

Suddenly there was a crash of arms; horns blew, and the door was opened. As I stepped forward into the great hall of the palace I could hardly believe my eyes. The entire vast room was filled with what seemed to be all the nobles and ladies of the Shogun's court. A wide path was opened which led directly to where Hidetada sat upon a throne. To his side and somewhat below was his father. Dropping to my knees as was the custom, I bowed thrice. Hidetada then motioned me to come forward. As I walked down that long hall the nobles and ladies were on their knees, heads bowed. When I reached the dais I bowed low, but not from my knees this time, because for me it was almost always most difficult to make such genuflections. I would have felt the same before my own sovereign.

I looked first into the black, smiling eyes of Iyeyasu, and my heart warmed, for I had truly missed him these past months. Then I turned to Hidetada.

"Welcome to our court, Daishi-san."

" 'Tis a pleasure for which the tongue has not words, to be in your presence again, O most noble Hidetada."

A gong sounded and there was a great rustling as the people rose to their feet. Then there was absolute silence. So still was it that the quiet voice of Hidetada carried to every corner of the huge hall.

"Before us, O great names of Nippon, we have a good and dear friend. He has given freely to us of his skills and has asked no reward. He has ever been ready to help those in need with no thought of himself. When payment for his favor has been offered, he has spurned it as a true samurai would spurn such things. Many of us could take lessons from Daishi-san other than his tales of the courts and customs of Europe. Daishi-san came as a stranger and braved great danger with the courage and humility of a truly great samurai. He has met and overcome all obstacles in his path.

"Those of you who were with us at Sekigehara know that the history of Japan might have taken a different course had it not been for his advice and the thunder of his guns. Loving us, he has obeyed the commands of my father and myself even though his heart yearned for his own land and people. His mind is brilliant, shining like a sword made by the hand of Okazaki Masamuno. His strength is that of the greatest of warriors, his courage beyond question, and his gentleness known to all." He paused for a moment, and there was such a stillness that I felt almost alone. As I listened carefully to the words of Hidetada I knew that these were not his thoughts but words that had been placed there by his father. He spoke again:

"Is not such a man to be rewarded?" His voice filled the whole room and the answer came from a thousand throats. "*Hai! Hai!*" My ears rang as the room sank into silence again.

"Bring then the robes."

Two nobles came forward carrying a costume suspended on a silken cushion between two swords. In the sight of all, they removed my plain black kimono and dressed me in the robes of a noble of the Fourth Class of the Fudai. The Fudai were those nobles who had fought with Iyeyasu. Once the robes were fastened about me, another noble came forward, kneeled before Hidetada, and held toward him a jeweled cushion on which two swords in their slings were resting.

Hidetada took the cushion and held it on his lap, then the Minister of Records began reading from a long scroll, giving my name and title as a Daimyo and awarding me an estate at Hemmi, close by Hammamura, of 250 *koko* of land containing houses, properties and ninety families as my servants.

I knew Hammamura, a lovely hillside above Yedo and one of the most beautiful sites in all the country.

After the proclamation was read Hidetada descended from the dais and, with his own hand, tied the sword sash around my waist. It was a great honor. In England it would have been as if the Queen had made me a lord. For such a stupendous gift I could only bow my head and regret all of the hard things I had been thinking and the ungratefulness of my attitude toward this country that had treated me so well.

And so it was that I became a Japanese nobleman. That night, after all the formalities of the celebration in my honor, Iyeyasu,

Daimyo Sufa Kimihara, and many other nobles gathered together for entertainment that lasted through the night.

Hidetada did not appear. I knew that this had not set well with him. But his father's word was still law in this land and he had done his duty, most gracefully, to me.

Many bottles of saki were drunk, many women came to entertain us through the joyful night. The following day, when I moved my possessions from the house allotted me in Yedo to the estate at Hemmi Hill, I was proud and happy.

In the moonlight I stood looking down over the city. This Morning Land was even more beautiful in my eyes now than it had ever been.

41

Before this, despite the friendship of some nobles, I had been set apart by the Japanese. Now, my position as a Fudai Daimyo of the Fourth Class brought many changes. Instead of wearing the robes of a scholar, I wore the gaudy kimonos of the kind prescribed by court etiquette as befitting my new station in life. I was required to attend court functions and maintain a specific position. There I was to stand, to kneel, and to follow the rigid court formula. I was always causing confusion by forgetting one or another of the intricate details, sometimes even hurting the feelings of other nobles by such oversights. In time I avoided all formal affairs except those which were absolutely essential for me to attend.

My relationship with Iyeyasu did not diminish. In fact, we now drew closer together and he came often to my house on Hemmi Hill. If there was ever any condescension on his part it was that of an older brother to a younger. Iyeyasu's whole thought and desire was to form a system of government in Japan which would knit the country together and eliminate the danger of the great feudal barons' once more dividing the islands into separate kingdoms.

Now that he was freed of the time-consuming rituals of the court, Iyeyasu formulated a system of government, based on careful thought and judgment, which I believe will endure, though history will have to be the judge of that.

He reduced the entire philosophy of government into seventeen basic laws which he named the *"Kinchu Jomoku."*

I watched with interest his methods of protecting the country against warring factions. To the west and south powerful feudal lords were held in subjection only by force of arms. Between these he placed certain of the Fudai Daimyos as buffers.

After the battle of Sekigehara he divided the titles among those who had fought with him, called Fudai, and those who had fought against him or held back. These others, who were not Fudai, were allowed to retain their land and dominions but were placed into another class, not entirely trustworthy.

One of Iyeyasu's basic rules was that once every two years all Daimyos make the journey to Yedo to spend part of the year at his court. They were forced to establish homes at Yedo. When their visit was terminated, part of their families had to remain behind. In this manner all the powerful families had either children or relatives at the court—not prisoners, but just to ensure that before any of them rebelled would they pause to consider the danger to their own people.

The country gradually settled into a quiet, prosperous state. I, too, prospered and was happy. I was put in charge of all trade. The desire to return to England grew dimmer, though I still had twinges of conscience. At regular intervals, each time the *Tokugawa Shogun* sailed from Japan to the Philippines or Java, I always sent a letter with money and the request that word of my life and my condition be told in England.

Receiving word that English merchants came to Java, I wrote to them about my coming to Japan, addressing it to "My Unknown Friends and Countrymen." I told of all the events that had happened to me, ending it as follows:

Thus I am constrained to write, hoping that by one means or other and process of time I shall hear of my wife and children. And so, with patience, I await the good will and pleasure of Mighty God. Therefore I do pray that every one of you, if this letter shall come to your hands, do the best, that my wife and children and my good acquaintances may hear of me. By this means I may, in the process of time before my death, hear news or see some of my friends again. If God in His glory wills it, Amen.

By your unworthy friend and servant to command in what I can.

William Adams.

With each such letter I sent also a letter to my wife, and to her also I related all that had happened and by these writings did still retain some contact. But as the years passed, and though I prayed often, no ships came to Japan other than the Spaniards or Portugals. Though by now all permits of trade passed through my hands, there was still strong hatred against me among these people so that I knew there was little use in sending letters by their hands.

My power, without my seeking it, grew more each day so that I was in some things almost as Iyeyasu's right hand. Such power also brought envy and enemies in the court and among the traders but I always tried to treat each as honestly and fairly as I could. This is never enough but I learned to accept things as they were and hoped that by adhering to my principles, and my actions being consistent, time would prove it was the best method.

42

For the past two years both the *Tokugawa Shogun* and the smaller *Morning Land* had been making regular voyages to the Eastern countries and the Philippines which lay to the eastward of the Japanese islands. These are a rich and prosperous group settled by the Spaniards and called by them "The Green Gems in the Spanish Crown." The trade was good.

Don Roderigo di Vivero y Velasco was governor general of this Spaniard colony. He had treated our ships and people with kindness and generosity. No complaint had come back of unfairness in dealings nor of injustice. I had, by the necessity of trade, knowledge of him through correspondences and trading permits, but I had little thought that fate was to bring us into close companionship.

I may have given the impression that this land of Nippon is some sort of paradise. In truth, this land has many faults. It is an uneasy land. From time to time there comes a great stirring in the earth which throws down buildings and causes much distress among the people. Besides the tremendous earth shakes that occur, the land is sometimes beset by terrible tempests which sweep the coast, destroying the flimsy houses and causing great travail.

One of these tempests, which they call *typhoon*, destroyed the ship and shipwrecked the governor general of the Philippines and his party on the shores of the main island. Don Roderigo had finished his eight-year term of office as governor general. His petition to the Spaniard king for permission to return home being favorable, he had taken his goods, servants and entourage and had set sail for the Spanish Americas in a great galleon. The typhoon had blown him far from his path. They foundered on the shore of the capital island of Honshu. Luckily, their ship had been wrecked on a section of coast where there are many fishermen. These people, holding the inherent kindness of the Japanese, saved most of their lives and possessions. A message came to Yedo to announce the disaster.

The word was brought to me and I immediately sent a message by Itsuke-san to the Daimyo of that province to render all aid and to provide transportation for themselves, their goods and baggage to Yedo where we would make them welcome. They had been fortunate in losing only twenty-eight men of their crew, as this typhoon was most severe.

The refugees were brought to me escorted by Itsuke-san and an honor guard of samurai in full regalia to my house at Hammamura. Later I heard they had made the journey with great trepidation, as the Portugals and priests had informed them I held a hatred against all except my own countrymen. They all felt that Itsuke-san and my samurai were there as jailers.

As the party was very large, being upward of two hundred and eighty rescued, I had the governor, the captain, and those of importance stay in houses at Hammamura. I provided lodgings for the others nearby. To Shoki-san I issued orders that everything needful for their comfort was to be provided and gave them time to rest from their journey before asking them to dine with me.

The several Spaniard women in the group declined that first invitation. Only the governor, the ship's captain and certain officers, with one or two others, came on that first visit.

They were met at the front entrance, where their boots were removed and sandals provided, and brought into the large room where I received them. The two serving girls who ushered them in dropped to their knees and put their foreheads to the floor in the Japanese custom, and remained in that position awaiting my orders.

I rose to greet my guests. Thinking back, I must have looked strange to them, for I had become accustomed to the Japanese dress and to sitting cross-legged on a low seat. I was attired in the ceremonial robes of a Japanese lord. At first sight of me they stopped for a moment, startled, before coming forward. My hair was dressed in a knot on the top of my head, with the flat Japanese headgear, giving somewhat the appearance of a bent spoon. My long, flowing beard and the brightly colored robes with the two swords about my waist would have given anyone pause.

Don Roderigo, a gentleman, controlled his astonishment. They bowed as I came forward, remembering to shake hands in the European manner.

"Welcome to Japan and to my poor house, señors," I said in the Spaniard tongue. "I wish that your visit could have been made under less trying circumstances, but we will do everything in our small power to make you forget the disaster you have been through. As my guests, you must know that this house is as your own and you have but to ask for anything you need."

I sensed their trepidation and hoped my small speech would put them more at ease.

Don Roderigo was the sort of Spaniard I have always admired—proud, and tempered like a sword, yet warm and generous. He looked directly into my eyes as we shook hands, as if to search out my falseness. I smiled at him and turned to shake hands with the others, inviting them to be seated. They were unused to sitting on the low cushions. I remarked that it had taken me a long time to become accustomed to this mode of living. At a nod from me, serving girls came forward with saki and dainty portions of appetizing foods.

After moving to my estate on Hemmi Hill I had started eating meat, which the Japanese looked upon with great distaste. Being an Englishman, I felt in sore need for this in my diet, although when Japanese came to call I saw that they were served the traditional foods. I noticed the eyes of Don Roderigo and the others light up at the beauty of the serving girls, with their high-piled, black, varnished hair and the smooth almond skin. Don Roderigo smiled as he was being served. They dropped their eyes demurely.

Captain of the galleon, Don Alonzo de Cordova, was an older, taciturn man whose worry about the loss of his ship robbed him of any interest in women. As they refreshed themselves, Don Roderigo asked a question regarding the wine. I explained that saki was made of rice, and was subtly potent. Since I also had Spanish wines, I offered them a choice, but they preferred to taste the Japanese drink. Eventually we talked about the storm and of their disaster.

"I have been in many storms during my years at sea, señor," the captain said. His voice was so deep and strong that the serving maids glanced up at him in wonder. "But never in all my years have I seen such a storm as that which took our ship. It was only by God's grace that any of us were saved." He crossed himself.

"Were many of your people lost?" I asked him.

"Twenty-eight," he said, and crossed himself again.

"You have my sympathy. I well know the terrors of the sea."

While the captain was talking, Don Roderigo was looking around at the rich furnishings and, being a man of taste, he was evidently impressed, though they were unlike the heavy furniture with which the Spaniards clutter their houses. This room was light and airy and open to the garden, which seemed to be but a continuation of the room.

Turning to me, he said, "We have heard you are English, señor."

I nodded. "A Kentish man, Your Excellency."

"Your Spanish is that of a native. This is a strange place to find an Englishman—or any European, for that matter. We have heard a great deal of you and something of the strange fortune which brought you to this land."

I recounted the long and sorrowful tale of our journey and what had happened to me since.

"We have been told by certain of our countrymen that you hold an abiding hatred toward the Spanish and Portugals because of some wrong done to you. It has been said also that any Spaniard falling into your hands would be lucky to escape with his life." He paused, and then added with a smile: "It is also said you are in league with the devil and hold some power over the Shogun and his court."

I returned his smile, saying, "If you really believed that I was such a man, speaking to me thus would be a dangerous thing. Set your mind at ease. I hold no hatred, desire, nor intent to harm. I hope your stay will be a long one, long enough to disprove these untruths. My sole purpose is to help you in time of distress as I would wish to be helped, and to provide what hospitality and protection lies in my power to give you. I might add there is a second reason. You being a man of importance, I would like for you to see for yourself the excesses your countrymen practice in this land and among these people. The Portugal traders are almost uncontrollable in their greed, and the priests behave with little sense, balance or reason. The time has come when all Europeans, including the religious orders, are to be banished from these islands. This I have fought against always."

There was a priest among the group. I turned to him, saying, "What struck me most in this country was the refreshing fact that these people have a wondrous freedom, letting each man believe in whatever religion appeals to him. The Jesuit priests did good work, but the Dominicans and Franciscans have caused great trouble by their fanaticism. In some instances they have stirred the people to revolt. They have caused much dissension and for some time have been forbidden to preach. The new Shogun, who has an abiding hatred for all things foreign, intends to banish aliens. This would grieve me. These are kind and civilized people from whom we could learn much. There is much, too, in our Western culture that we could leave here, were the representatives of our religion and trade of the proper sort. Perhaps, by seeing what is going on at first hand, when you reach Spain you will be able to do something to counteract this hatred. There is room for trade between Japan and all the countries of Europe. But let us speak now of other matters. There will be other days and other times to talk of this."

As we ate together we discussed many subjects. They told me of some of the new voyages, new discoveries. I learned of happenings in Europe. It was a most pleasurable evening. We parted in friendly fashion.

"Buenos noches, señores. If there is anything you desire, you have but to ask. In the event there is any fear in your minds, you are in no fashion prisoners. You may go where you like, do as you wish. It would please me if you would inform your seamen that these are kind and generous people but, though small, they are proud and fierce warriors. Being a sailor myself, I understand their needs. I will have my men show them where the houses of pleasure lie, but

Japan

they must not be less courteous to these women than they would be to women of their own country. The laws are very strict here. Your men are guests in this land and as guests they will be forgiven certain breaches of conduct. I cannot protect them, however, if there is any serious breach of the law."

Shaking hands warmly, Don Roderigo said, "Buenos noches, señor, and a thousand thanks. Now that we have met we will rest much easier in our minds."

Because I was busy with affairs of trade and a long conference with Iyeyasu, two days passed before I could meet with them again. As there were two Spaniard ladies in the governor general's party, I had my servants attend them, although they had retainers of their own.

Making sure Don Roderigo's crew and servants were comfortable, I requested the governor general and his company in to dine with me on the third evening. The women were very stiff and formal, still suffering from the ordeal of the shipwreck. They regarded me in my strange costume with suspicion. To allay their fears I showed them the gardens and took them to the small lake in the center of the estate. Even a blind man would have been aware of the beauty of the gardens, the small summer houses, and the delicacy with which each part blended into the other so that the garden in its entirety was like a lovely painting.

By the time we returned to the house the women were much more at ease and even willing to flirt a bit in the Spaniard fashion, to which I responded as any gentleman would.

It was strange how my concept of beauty had changed. At one time I would have thought these Spaniard women lovely. I now found their faces harsh and pointed compared with the delicate features and almond skin of the Japanese women. Like all women, they were interested in the Japanese dress. The intricate *obis* of the women and the brilliant colors of the kimonos entranced them.

I explained that the color of the kimono and the tying of the obi indicated many things: the person's station in life, whether she was married or single; and if single, whether betrothed.

When I had dined with Don Roderigo on that first night I realized I would have to solve the problem of furniture, for the Spaniard ladies, in their voluminous dress, could not be expected to sit upon the low cushions. I therefore had carpenters construct benches and a long table of suitable height for this evening's repast, which puzzled the carpenters. Though covered with rich cloth, the furniture seemed out of place in the room. To me it was very uncomfortable sitting with my feet resting on the floor.

In spite of these conditions, we enjoyed ourselves. The company of the Spaniards was pleasant and stimulating, especially that of Don Roderigo.

We talked politely of many things, the women asking innumerable questions which I did my best to answer. When we parted for the night we were friends, the women bidding me good night with flirtatious glances over their fans.

The following day I sent some of my serving women with a number of rich costumes for the Spaniard ladies and instructed them to explain how they were worn. When I saw them in Japanese dresses the two women, in my eyes, had increased a great deal in beauty.

On the arrival of the Spaniards I had gone through the formality of requesting an audience with Hidetada to present the visitors to the court. Word was sent back from Kosuke no Suke that he would be delighted to receive the strangers and that all the formalities of the court would be observed on this occasion.

In my relations with Iyeyasu and also with Hidetada I had knelt and bowed but not to the extent that the Japanese nobles of the court were forced to kowtow. Being aware what Hidetada meant by "all formalities of the court" and realizing the pride of the Spaniards, I felt that Hidetada was asking too much and trouble might result.

I explained the problem to Iyeyasu. Through his intervention, special formalities were canceled. Hidetada, I knew, would resent this and it would not further my relationship but I had come to realize sadly that no matter what I did, never could we be friends. Before the presentation at court I counseled Don Roderigo, the ladies, and other members of his entourage as to all of the procedures entailed in a meeting with the Shogun. In doing so I also told Don Roderigo something of my relationship with Hidetada and of the barrier between us.

Since there were five priests with the party, I had requested them not to express their beliefs in any way to the people while they remained guests. The invitation from Hidetada omitted them and they were duly incensed at this. There was nothing much I could do, nor was I anxious to exert myself on their behalf. They were likely to say something to further antagonize Hidetada and it was my hope that the charm of Don Roderigo might change Hidetada's attitude.

We entered the royal room of the palace at the appointed hour. In accordance with the intricate pattern, we bowed deeply, then at a signal approached the dais where I presented the guests according to their rank, with some embellishment of their titles and noble lineage.

Hidetada did not once glance at me. Instead of using me as interpreter, he motioned for me to retire to my position in the assemblage and brought forth a Japanese who spoke the Spaniard tongue. The Spaniards offered the gifts they had brought. He accepted them with barely an acknowledgment.

"We were sorry to hear of the loss of your ship," Hidetada said. "And we hope that our foreign servant has seen to your comfort. Had we been advised of your coming, we would have made other arrangements. But there are some who always put themselves forward to take over a burden which were better left to others."

This was a direct insult to me. When the words were translated I could see Don Roderigo flush. He spoke quickly in my defense. Though I admired him for it, the words were wasted.

"Though the loss of our ship was a great tragedy to us," he replied, "we were most fortunate in landing on these beautiful islands. Our good friend Señor Adams has been kinder than our own countrymen could have been. He has made us comfortable, provided us with all the necessities, and has been helpful in informing us of the customs and habits of your wonderful people."

"It would have been more fitting if the customs of our land had been explained to you by a Japanese, not by a foreigner. We tender our regrets."

I knew that this interview had not been of Hidetada's choosing. Had it not been for his father, Don Roderigo and his people would have been at best ignored.

Hidetada spoke a few more stiff sentences of welcome, then expressed the hope that their further voyage would be more fortunate. With that we were dismissed. Outside I found Don Roderigo angry.

Not only did he feel he had been treated with less respect than was his due, but he was in a fury at the insult that had been leveled at me.

I passed it off by saying, "You have lived about the world and you know that there are some people with whom, upon first meeting, a deep friendship is kindled as if you had known them long—it is a sort of kinship. At other times you meet a person and there arises deep enmity, without rhyme or reason—as between me and Hidetada. With his father it is just the opposite. From the first moment we have been friends."

I explained how Hidetada was no more than a figurehead and that, so long as Iyeyasu lived, I would be in a position of honor.

"Tomorrow," I told him, "we will meet with Iyeyasu, the true ruler of Nippon—a man of wisdom, kindness and courage. I know that you will be friends."

The following day Don Roderigo, the captain, and several of their number went with me to Iyeyasu. There was no stiffness between us, no stylized etiquette other than the ordinary courtesy of an introduction. Iyeyasu was at his most charming. His warmth and friendliness soon completely captivated the party. Before the evening ended we were all warmed with wine and good conversation.

We met together a number of other times and had long conversations on the various problems which the priests and the traders had caused in Japan. I showed the Spaniards about the city and the countryside and, with Iyeyasu's permission, I sailed with them on the *Tokugawa Shogun* to the island of Kyushu, to Ferrando, where the Portugals had their trading factories.

I had complete confidence in Don Roderigo's intelligence, so I left him alone to speak freely with his countrymen, knowing that no matter what they said about me, he would find by his own observation that I spoke the truth.

Don Roderigo was enchanted by the land, just as I had been. We made many trips together, visiting temples, castles, and meeting with the Japanese nobility in the various seaport cities. He admired our ship for her sailing qualities, her speed and easy handling and styling. He had hoped that at Ferrando there might be a Portugal ship which he could commandeer for the voyage back to Europe. But no ship was expected for almost a year. When he suggested that he buy the *Tokugawa Shogun* to continue his voyage, I was shocked.

"That, my friend, is impossible. I doubt if there is anything that Iyeyasu values more highly than this ship. It is like his child and it fills him with great pride. I would insult him even by the hint of such a thing."

To cheer him up, I told him not to worry, that I would strive to obtain permission to sail with him and his party to the Philippines, where he could get another ship. And that was how the matter was left for the time being.

43

Iyeyasu, though he still would not consent to my leaving Japan, continued to show his regard and respect for me. During the past year or two I had not brought up the subject. Living so comfortably, there were long intervals when I did not even think of England.

At this time Iyeyasu had set a national celebration in honor of the battle of Sekigehara and the unification of Japan. The entire nation sent representatives to Yedo to attend the celebration. There were many elaborate parties, outdoor theaters, and lavish feasts for the poor.

There were fireworks and a mock battle by the samurai on the field outside of the city. At the Shogun's palace the parties were attended by bright processions of nobles from every province. No single noble family of the realm was omitted, and many from the Emperor's court attended, though the Emperor himself did not appear.

At the end of the last day's celebration a number of us gathered together at Iyeyasu's private estate. As the evening wore on there was a considerable amount of drinking. It became a contest until, one by one, the men either retired with their women or went to sleep.

Finally all that remained were Iyeyasu, Daimyo Sufa Kimihara, Don Roderigo and myself. I was more sober than the others, partly because I had been engaged in translating from the Spaniard to the

Japanese and back again. Finally Sufa-san went to sleep at the table and the three of us sat drinking.

Iyeyasu had come to like the Spaniard a great deal and Don Roderigo returned the feeling. The latter raised his glass in another of the countless toasts of the evening.

"To these jewels of islands and all the lovely ladies they contain."

"Banzai!"

"To the ladies of Spain for being like this hot rice wine, or so Injin-san tells me," Iyeyasu offered.

"Banzai!"

Don Roderigo looked happily at Iyeyasu. "On my return to Spain I will send back to you a dozen of the most beautiful women of the country. No man should go without having a taste of Spanish beauty."

As I translated, Iyeyasu smiled and shook his head. "I thank the noble lord for his thought, but at my age even one would be too many. I accept the thought as the gift and thank you for an undeserved compliment. Even in my youth a dozen would have been too many."

Don Roderigo began to talk of his home and family in Spain. The wine he had drank now made him sad. His family would be waiting in despair, sure that by this time death had overtaken him. "I have been away so long that my heart is heavy."

Iyeyasu laid his hand on Don Roderigo's knee. "You are a friend of my brother and myself and your sadness makes me grieve. Ask a favor of me."

Don Roderigo said nothing. I too sat in silence.

Iyeyasu looked at us. "There is something on your minds—a request that you hesitate to make. Ask it of me."

I searched his face before I dared to speak. "I do have a great boon to ask. If Don Roderigo returns to the Philippines it will add at least another year to his journey. Let me take him aboard the *Tokugawa Shogun* to the Spanish Americas. Grant me this and I will sail her as captain and give you my word to return both the ship and myself in safety."

Iyeyasu's eyes went blank for a moment as if he were greatly pained. He looked at me for a long time before turning his wise and direct gaze to Don Roderigo.

"You have discussed this matter between you."

I nodded. "Don Roderigo offered to buy the ship. I told him what an insult that would be to you. I have explained to him the pride and love you have for this ship, as if for a first-born child. I have no right to ask this of you. But I am imposing on your friendship because of the friendship I feel for Roderigo."

Iyeyasu sat quietly for a time, then motioned to the serving woman to refill his cup. "Everything in nature, just as the birds themselves, are drawn to their homes as the needle of the compass points ever in one direction. Before giving you an answer, my first thought was to ask you if, in reverse circumstances, such a favor would be done for me. But I will not. The ship is yours. Treat her well, for a great deal of Injin-san and myself went into the building of her." Then turning to me, he said, "But I cannot part with you, my friend, as yet."

When I translated, Don Roderigo looked ashamed, and began to speak of how he would return the favor tenfold. Iyeyasu stopped him with a gesture, understanding his words before I could translate.

"The ship is given as a gift, and for this there can be no payment. Now it grows late and I feel my years. Good night and dream well of a pleasant journey."

We bowed deeply before leaving, without another word. Instead of taking our waiting palanquins, we walked through the faintly stirring city in the early dawn, to my house on Hemmi Hill. We walked for a long time before Don Roderigo broke the silence.

"Adams, *mi amigo*, never in my life have I been so impressed by a person. It is not the ship, but the manner with which the gift was made. Truly this man has a great love for you." He shook his head sadly. "It is such a temptation, but I cannot accept it."

"Do not speak madness," I said. "The gift has been made and to refuse would be an insult of great magnitude. Also, look at it sensibly. It is but a ship. I can build another and better one. It is nothing but wood and iron and canvas." Suddenly I was filled with a great longing for England, my wife and children, my friends. "I would to God I could come with you!" I burst out.

He looked at me in surprise. "And why not?"

The wine I had drunk fumed in my brain and I shouted in anger, "Why not? I will tell you why not. Because I am a prisoner! Honored, yes. Comfortable, yes. But in reality no more than a slave. I am trapped here in this land and I can never leave it."

He took my arm in sympathy. "My friend, I did not know how it was. I will help you to escape if this is your wish."

I laughed. "You would not get beyond the entrance to Yedo Bay. Besides, such a move would cost you your life. How could you hide me? I am better known than even the Shogun himself. No. You go your way and may God protect you on your journey. Some day I will have permission to leave, but until then, here I stay. I would ask no one to jeopardize his life or freedom for me. In any case, what cause have I to complain? Are we not all trapped by life, in one way or another?" My words saddened Don Roderigo. I clapped him on the back.

"Forget my complaints. It was but a momentary feeling induced by the saki. I am sure, once back in England, I would never rest from the longing to return to this land. No. All I ask of you is to see that letters and money I give you are delivered to my wife and friends in London. If I could but be sure my wife knew I still lived, it would be enough. And if I could know whether she and the children are alive and in good health, my mind would be more tranquil. Soon, I am certain, I will be given permission to return. If Hidetada had his way he would be more than glad to see me gone. When the day comes, I will send a message to you, and if Englishmen are still unwelcome in Spain perhaps we will meet again in Venice, Rome, or elsewhere."

We had come to my estate by now and the watchman opened the gates. Inside we stopped on the rise of the hill and looked in silence at the morning sky with the sun showing a brilliant halo around the cone of the lovely mountain, Fujisan. Through the garden and over the lake small tendrils of mist clung to the water and encircled the trees. In my eyes there was no place in the world so beautiful.

"Go to sleep now, Don Roderigo. Your days ahead will be busy ones and I am as happy we have found a solution for your problem as if I had found one for my own."

He shook my hand without a word as we parted and I, now feeling a great weariness, sought the solace of sleep which heals by letting us forget, for a time, the afflictions of our lives.

44

Until the day the *Tokugawa Shogun* disappeared over the sea carrying Don Roderigo and his party toward the Spanish Americas, I had hoped that Iyeyasu, knowing of my longing to return to England, would relent and grant me permission to leave. I also wanted to see the colonies of New Spain. But it was not to be so. I had come to know a real fondness for the Spaniard. When he left I was very lonely and life tasted stale again.

I should not have felt so, for there was much to please me. I was a noble, held in high esteem. Itsuke-san had brought seven samurai into my service. When I went about the city in a palanquin, or in the countryside on horseback, I was escorted by my own men and the people bowed low before me.

The ever faithful Shoki-san took good care of the affairs of the estate. He did all my writing, for my calligraphy was still ugly despite my efforts to improve it.

I enjoyed Michiko, the long-legged, full-breasted girl Iyeyasu had presented to me, but she was strong-minded and jealous. She and Takamon no Itsuke fought often, Itsuke-san ever grumbling that he had never seen a woman from the Kanto Plain who was not a shrew. "It is the wind that does it," he would growl. "The wind blows up the kimonos, through their behinds, and emerges from their mouths in a ceaseless stream. Flap, flap, their lips go. But this one must have been caught in a typhoon."

One day I caught Shoki-san casting sheep-eyed glances at Michiko. By that time she had become a problem to me and gratefully I accepted this solution. I managed then to arrange that they be together until Shoki-san was in that state of infatuation wherein he was completely miserable both from love and a sense of guilt.

One day I spoke roughly to him in front of Itsuke-san, asking Shoki-san what manner of friend would steal his master's woman? Itsuke-san growled and made as if to draw his sword.

Seeing the jest had gone too far, as Shoki-san was like to die of fear, I stopped Itsuke-san. Raising Shoki-san to his feet, I embraced him and gave him Michiko, saying he could either marry her or take her as his concubine.

Michiko, having given me up, decided to marry Shoki-san. Thus he had no choice after all. But they seemed happy. I gave him a gift of ten koko of land for his income and he was content now. I was relieved that Michiko no longer would be sneaking over to my mat unasked, or crying outside when I took another woman, or when I came home drunk. This woman in a very un-Japanese fashion had the air of dominance about her and, in truth, Shoki-san needed such a woman. With Shoki-san she had proved productive, giving birth in two years to two sons, on whom I lavished the affection I could not give to my own children so far away.

I now turned to the building of a new ship and lost myself in my work. Some new plans which I had evolved during my journeys were tantalizing my mind. In the trips I had made to the land of Korea I had seen ships that were sheathed in metal. I experimented at great length with models. I had a theory that a ship could be built to carry the weight of metal and still remain seaworthy. I spent much time in trying to work out the theory of weight and displacement. A ship sheathed with metal would be almost invulnerable against cannon shot.

When finally I came to the building of the ship I found myself with problems on all sides. With the *Tokugawa Shogun* I had merely to mention a need to Iyeyasu and it was granted. Now I found all manner of annoyances and harassments: workmen unwilling to work, timbers no longer available, until even through my thick skull it penetrated that Hidetada was not happy with the thought of this new ship.

I could have gone to Iyeyasu and all my problems would have been solved immediately but he, at this time, was busy writing a book of maxims relating to government. Hidetada was becoming ever more the true Shogun.

On the ninth month after the departure of Don Roderigo there was much excitement throughout the city. A tremendously tall Spaniard galleon had come sailing into Yedo Bay, to the harbor at Yokosuka, followed by a small pinnace.

I met the Spaniards as they came ashore and escorted them directly to Yedo, where I presented them to Iyeyasu.

Don Roderigo had sent the ship, laden with all manner of goods made in Europe, many of which were of value in Japan, such as Swiss clocks, music boxes and certain types of woolen cloth. It was a princely gift. Iyeyasu was delighted, remaining in close attendance as the ship was unloaded and the presents were brought to him to inspect. Happy as he was in examining the presents, I knew that it was the beauty and sincerity of the thought behind the gift which counted more than anything the ship contained. The ship itself was given to the Shogun Hidetada by Iyeyasu. To the eye of a landsman she seemed huge, tall and over eight hundred tons burden. But in the *Tokugawa Shogun* the Spaniards had the best of the bargain.

I took the Japanese crew, that were trained to sail the *Tokugawa Shogun*, aboard this ship. They liked her clumsiness little more than I did. I knew myself capable of building a far better ship.

There were also gifts for me, and a long, friendly letter in which Don Roderigo thanked me profusely for my kindness and promised again that my letters and money would be delivered safely to London. He pleased me by saying that the *Tokugawa Shogun* had made a faster voyage than any ship had ever made before. His letter went on to say:

Guillermo, amigo, as you know it has been nine long years since I was last in my country. Since that time the Most Royal King Philip has died and the new King, who was but a boy when I left, is now full grown and that place which was mine at court has been taken by someone closer to him. But once in Spain I promise faithfully that when I speak to my King I shall do the utmost in my power to impress on him the necessity of laws for the governing of the trading factors not only in Japan, but throughout the southern seas. You must understand, of course, the Church is another matter. Under the edict of the Pope, the Society of Jesus called Jesuits were given all the eastern waters and lands as their domain for the spreading of the Word and Teachings of our Glorious Lord, Jesus Christ. The Dominicans and Franciscans penetrating into this area against the will and law of the Pope have caused most of this trouble. The Church, in itself, is well aware of this, but I think you understand that in the Church there is more politics and more devious maneuvering for power than in any kingdom. What I shall do is to go, not only to the King, but to our Cardinal, and give a complete story of what has happened in Japan and the danger involved by such actions. Out of this some good may come, with God's will. I do pray that some day our Lord will grant that we meet again. Until then, God be with you always.

Your sincere friend and devoted
Servant,
Don Roderigo de Vivero y Velasco

Although Iyeyasu presented the Spaniard's ship to Hidetada, the latter felt insulted, for it had been originally sent to Iyeyasu. When Iyeyasu returned to his seclusion, many small annoying things happened to me.

Hidetada, as a loyal son, could express no outward sign of displeasure to me. On the surface, nothing could be traced directly to him, but I suffered many grievances and insults of which I could not complain; however, they were obvious to Shoki-san and to Itsuke-san, who was careful that I should never go about without him.

During this year two attempts were made on my life. Once, coming from a tea house with Itsuke-san, I was set upon by three samurai who behaved as if they were drunk. Only Itsuke-san was with me, and he was also drunk, nevertheless we fought with them, killing one and driving the others off. I received a cut across the shoulder.

Thereafter when I moved about the city or made a journey I took all my samurai in attendance. I would have been happy to give up the position I held, but what Iyeyasu had given to me Hidetada would not, or could not, take away.

My sole hope was that once Iyeyasu completed his book of maxims he would return to take a more active part in the government. Then I might persuade him to let me leave for England.

Not long after the arrival of the Spaniard ship I learned that the captain had been drunkenly boasting that the Spaniards would rule the world. His words were resented by the Japanese and there was a general feeling of hatred for the "foreign devils." They quickly turned against the European customs and dress, whereas just a few years before, it had been all the fashion to ape them. Any Japanese seen in European clothes was now set upon and beaten by students and samurai.

Those Japanese who had journeyed to Spain and Rome returned with unfavorable reports about the customs of Europe. Ever more it was being said that all foreigners should be barred from Japan.

Strict laws were passed and enforced. A number of priests and their Japanese converts were martyred on the cross. Much against my will, Iyeyasu, on some impulse perhaps motivated by the gift of the ship, had me raised in rank to Daimyo of the Third Class. With this rank came additional prestige—also further ill will and jealousy.

Iyeyasu appeared seldom in public. Since all things having to do with the control of trade passed through my hands, and since anti-foreign feeling was so strong, I was constantly being torn on both sides and involved all the more deeply in political intrigue. I longed to leave it all behind, close the doors of my house and retire to my garden. This proved impossible to do.

In 1610 a Dutch ship arrived with more goods. Aboard her was the merchant Van Sartoot. I had made a treaty when the first Dutch ship arrived, between Iyeyasu and the Dutch company. I saw that they were given the same treatment as the Portugals, but no more. Now on learning that Van Sartoot was back I looked forward to seeing him, sure that he would bring news. I should have known better.

Van Sartoot had not changed. His mind was centered on but one thing—trade. In him there was no warmth, no love, no compassion—nothing but greed. I asked him about the journey home.

"It was a long one," he said.

"But tell me of it," I urged. "What of Captain Quackernack, Sweringen—the others?"

"Oh, yes, Quackernack. He was killed."

"Killed? How?"

"Off Java. At Java we found a fleet of seven sail. Many of the crew had died, so Quackernack was given command of a ship. They were attacked by pirates and lost. It was lucky there was little trade goods aboard."

"That is sad. But how many of the crew returned home?"

He shrugged. "I don't know. I left them there and God protected me. Herr Adams, we are being undersold. We must have a trading station at Yedo or at least at Yokosuka."

"So," I said. "You knew you were coming back, yet you brought no news of my family or anyone?"

"Who was to know you were still alive and in such a fine position?" He rubbed his hands. Then, aware of my anger which I could hardly control, he added:

"I tried hard, Adams. I asked, but no one knew anything. I did all in my power. It was useless."

I knew he lied and my hands itched to close about his miserable neck.

"About the trading station, Herr Adams—"

"The Dutch have factors at Hirado, Hyogo and Oda, the same as the Portugals," I told him. "Orders are to grant no more permits."

"Herr Adams, if you will speak for us there would be profit for both."

"Damn you, get out of my sight!" I cursed him roundly, giving vent to what I felt was just anger.

All the letters I had sent to England and the letter and money to my wife—not one word did he bring me in return. And no English ship came. I was sick at heart.

I warned the other Dutchmen to keep Van Sartoot out of my sight else I would kill him. I meant it. I was coming to the point where Hidetada's hatred was understandable.

45

In Nippon, scholars, writers, artists, philosophers, poets, and sometimes actors are held in high esteem. Though I was a teacher with some reputation in the science of mathematics, my teachings were considered mundane, involving trade and commerce, and not the abstractions with which the scholars dealt. Therefore I was not considered truly a scholar.

Our Western philosophy holds little interest for the Japanese scholars. As a whole, they are a most fortunate people, not tortured by a sense of sin or wracked by the problem of good and evil, as in the West. I found not even a trace of that puritanical spirit which has so tormented our own civilization. There is none of that restless spirit of doubt that has perverted the gentle teachings of Christ into disputes of such magnitude that they have cruelly torn apart nation after nation. The more I knew these island people, the more enchanted I was with their ways. They are an impressionable people, not swayed by metaphysics, quick to be deluded by earthly life, readily believing, for the moment, the words of a solemn Buddhist priest as he teaches of life's emptiness. Yet, when they turn away from the priest, his words do not seem to cling to them nor cause them anguish.

In contrast to the West, where it is the habit to complicate religion, the philosophers and priests of Japan have simplified it. The Buddhist god who was first brought to this land was the Hindu God, Amnaratsu. The years shortened this name to Amida. The worship of Amida eventually became more and more realistic, until one of the great religious leaders brought it back close to its original form.

He was a monk named Honen-Shonin who lived several centuries before. He had founded a new Buddhist sect called Nembutsu. Nembutsu eliminated the need for temples and priests. Honen-Shonin taught that man, searching for salvation, could find it by merely repeating Buddha's name. This new version was immediately welcomed by the common people, as the priests were a great burden to them. The Buddhist priests, protecting their own interests, seeing that this could be the downfall of their way of life, protested loudly against his teachings. Honen-Shonin was banished.

But man is a strange creature. The people revered him all the more after his banishment, and his teachings grew. Finally the Emperor had him returned. Instead of going to war to prove one or the other right in their thinking, they reached a compromise. For those who desired temples, temples remained. Those who did not want them merely intoned the name of their lord a certain number of times a day.

Later, a disciple of Honen-Shonin, named Shinran, pushed the Nembutsu teaching to its logical conclusion. Instead of invoking the name of Buddha forever, one sincere invocation of Amida some time during his life was sufficient to ensure a person's salvation. All further praise of God, while desirable, was not necessary. How could one help loving such sensible people?

There are many good points in this Buddhist belief, as I had found in others—the idea that all nature is permeated by one spirit, and the conception of Dharmakaya as the true body of Buddha, not, as the Western religions teach, a manifestation in human form. Nor was his manifestation in paradise in human form, but was the permeation of all nature as one spirit. The idea attracted me in the same measure as the Puritans had galled me with their God of punishment and hate.

Here, artists, poets, philosophers, nobles, common people, find no antithesis between man and nature but seem able to find a conscious and complete identity, as well as kinship with the wonderful tranquillity that lies behind the ever-changing world.

As I became more knowledgeable in the history and religion, I found that gradually I was being accepted into the ranks of the scholars. This did not occur because of my knowledge of the West, but because I was truly interested in their culture.

The finest scholar and poet in Yedo during these years was Daimyo Igichi no Yamamoto. I came to know him and in time we became friends and talked often on many subjects. For me these were stimulating conversations. Yet always, after being in his company, I would find to my discomfort that it was I who had been cast in the role of pedant. I felt somehow I was under examination, as if he searched my mind and found my knowledge limited, with much room for growth.

I had enormous respect for his mind and felt unequal to him. Yet I was flattered that, more and more often, I was invited to attend a select group who met to discuss many topics. It was at one of these discussions at the home of Baron Yamamoto that I met Magome no Yuriko. That day is etched upon my mind like an illuminated, exquisite scroll.

During my life fortune has shown both sides of the coin. This was life's greatest gift to me. Magome no Yuriko gave me wealth beyond measure. In recounting this narrative of my life I have yawed and jibed here and there yet kept on the course. But now I know not how to express in words the beauty that came into my life. If I am halting, forgive me. You who have loved, read between the lines; for this love is too deep for words in any tongue.

At these meetings, after the tea ceremony, one subject would be selected for discussion. This night it was to be the role of Japanese women in history, a subject which had interested me deeply. During certain periods of time, among the nobility, the women of the higher class, given freedom to develop their intellect, had shown great promise. Men had been the great poets and artists, but it was interesting that the women had taken over the role of storytellers in prose. The books of life and love that had survived through the ages had been written, in almost all cases, by women. This should be no surprise. Who better than women knows the secret of life?

Although, among the lower classes, women were considered chattels, among the nobility they had more freedom to express themselves than the women of Europe. Of course, only in exceptional cases was a woman allowed to enter on equal terms into man's discussions about things of greater importance in life.

I had ample time to review the subject to be discussed that evening and looked forward to it with pleasure. To converse with these scholars was always a stimulating experience. There was no parallel in their courtesy among all the races I had ever known. No one would ever speak loudly or arrogantly. When one spoke, others listened in silence and with deep interest, no matter how much they disagreed. This was not at all like discussions among Europeans where each person, hardly listening, waits impatiently for the chance to interrupt, to expound and inject his own words of wisdom.

We gathered in the quiet and simple house of Daimyo Yamamoto. Each guest was greeted with warmth by the honored scholar. He was an old man with a wisp of white beard. Though his face was lined, his eyes were youthfully bright and alert.

After the quiet preliminaries and routine of being served food and drink we relaxed, yet maintaining our dignity, as was proper. Our host, as was his right, opened the discussion with the premise that, potentially, a woman's mind was as good and in some cases better than a man's. If women had been given equal opportunity to enter man's domain of poetry and art, as well as prose, Japanese civilization would be much further advanced than it was now.

The guest on his right took up the argument, declaring that it was not the fault of men that women were not great poets and artists, but of nature, which had given to women the burden of designing a new creature within her own body. This was the supreme reason for her being, he said. The pressure of creation was such that women could never have time for the true concentration necessary to be a great artist, poet or calligraphist.

As the conversation went around, some agreed, some disagreed, but the majority tended to disagree with Daimyo Yamamoto's view.

When each in the circle had expressed his thoughts, the Daimyo signaled, and a girl, tall for a Japanese, entered with an armful of scrolls.

She was beyond doubt the most beautiful woman I had ever seen. During my lifetime I have looked upon many women rightfully termed beautiful, but none to equal this one. She was slim and graceful as a willow, with skin so pure it was almost translucent.

With proper modesty she took a cushion next to, but a little distance behind Baron Yamamoto. Igichi Yamamoto made no move to introduce her. We knew not who she was, though we knew by her kimono and the tie of her obi she was unmarried and of high birth.

With quiet grace she put the scrolls down, unrolled one, and passed it to Daimyo Yamamoto, who looked at it for a moment, then passed it on. The scroll was a brush painting called "Haboku" —in English, "Broken Line."

When it reached me I held it for a long time. The painting was of extreme fragility, so simply done that it had more the quality of sound than of lines. It was a picture of their holy mountain Fuji-san. The mountain rose from the painting in all of its complete and wondrous cone-shaped beauty. I could pay to it that compliment which Iyeyasu would have used: It was a "quiet painting."

As it passed from me I watched the expressions on the faces of the others. There was not one who was not struck and held by the beauty of it. After each had examined it, Igichi Yamamoto asked:

"Do you agree or disagree that this is a work of superior artistry?"

All agreed although one commented that a single brush stroke

The next scroll was passed around. It was a poem. In English it was just a little too bold and energetic.

loses much of the beauty and meaning of the Japanese.

Here's the top peak, the multitude below
Lives, for they can there.
This man decided not to live but know.
Bury this man there.
Here—here's his place where meteors shoot,
Clouds form,
Lightnings are loosed,
Stars come and go. Let joy break the storm.

Peace—Let the dew send.
Lofty designs must close in like effects
Loftily lying.
Leave him—still loftier than the world suspects
Living and dying.

Praise of this poem was instantaneous and warm.

Next we were given samples of the most beautiful calligraphy I had ever seen. The Japanese devote great patience to this work, drawing characters of their language with infinite grace and artistry.

Now I found my mind and my eyes continually turning to the loveliness of the girl, who sat so still and graceful and whose slightest movement was in itself poetry. Her eyes were very large, set wide apart, and so black that great depth lay behind them. Her most unusual feature, and one the Japanese would have termed a flaw, was the fold in the upper lid of her eyes, rarely seen in Japanese women. Her hair, though lacquered and piled in intricate design, gave me the feeling that, if it were let down, it would be somewhat curly. This, too, would set her apart. Japanese think only straight black hair is perfect. Any curliness or lightness of shading is considered a mark of faulty heritage. It is a good thing that men's ideas of beauty vary.

When all the scrolls had been returned, with comments upon their artistry, Baron Yamamoto smiled gently. With great pride he announced that the artist was the girl beside him, his granddaughter Magome no Yuriko.

She bowed gracefully to us and my eyes clung to the pure column of her neck. There were murmurs of surprise and many compliments. The Baron told something of her background.

"As a child," he said, "my granddaughter came to live with me when her parents died. From the beginning she showed an open mind, and such a feeling for beauty, that it has been my great joy to nurture her talent and to watch it grow and open like that of a rare and lovely flower. I have led her gently, allowing her mind to develop, inspiring it to question, search, and try to seek out, at least for the moment, what truth she may discover. When she grew beyond me I sent her to study with the best artists, poets and calligraphers in China for two years. There she gained considerable renown. Had she wished to remain there, a place of honor was offered. But she gratified me profoundly by returning to my poor house to be a comfort to me in my old age.

"I have brought her into our company, not as someone to compliment, but as someone who I feel, though still very young, is our equal. I hope when you come to know her you will agree that this is true, and she has a right to sit with us."

I am sure some of those present felt ill at ease. The thought of a woman joining freely with our group was difficult to accept. Our conversations had been among men, but there was no outward indication of disapproval and our discussion continued.

Yuriko-san joined, in her turn, without giving the appearance of being forward. Her voice, low and melodious, was a joy to hear. She gave no impression of boldness, but spoke with great humility. I felt her words added luster to a group among whom were some of the finest minds in this land.

Listening and gazing at her, I was enthralled, filled with a disturbing excitement which I had felt but few times in my long life. It was an emotion much better suited to a youth than to a man of my years.

At the end of the evening, while bidding good night, I had a moment to speak with her, and though the words were stylized and polite, I was already then deeply in love with her. Yet another part of my mind laughed. Here was I, at the age of fifty-two years, yearning toward her like a youth. She was but twenty and I far beyond the foolishness of love.

She told me she envied those who had been my pupils. I offered to put my small fund of knowledge at her disposal.

I went home filled with a vast excitement, though I knew this emotion was absurd. This was not a woman one would take for pleasure. A wife I already had—at least, as far as I knew. It was now fifteen years since last I had seen Elizabeth. I found, I could no longer even remember what she looked like.

Seven times we spoke together after that. Though five of these occasions were at discussion groups, twice I had come alone. Once for *chanoyu*, the formal tea ceremony, and once for *ainame*, which could be called "together-tasting," a ceremony in which a dish of some special food is prepared, in which the enjoyment of tasting creates a feeling of intimacy between people.

Each time I saw Magome no Yuriko I became more enamored of all the wondrous things about her, only one of which was her beauty. To my mind it seemed that, in her, all the refinements of culture, gentleness, courtesy, sensitivity, along with outward beauty, were the supreme distillation of all the virtues of these people.

By no outward gesture or word did I show my love—love that increased day by day, until there was hardly ever a moment when she was not in my thought and being. Like all lovers, young or old, my hopes rose and fell as regularly as the tides. One day all of the things which scoffed at this love would occupy my mind. I would think of my ties with Elizabeth, of how sooner or later I would leave this land for my own country. That I had no right even to think she might marry a foreigner, for the Japanese frowned on any mixture of blood. Other days I would think of the time when Iyeyasu had suggested that I marry and raise a family, saying that if I would consider becoming a Japanese, my children and their children's children would always be held in honor in this land. My thoughts churned. I could think of a thousand reasons why I had no right to a love such as this. I could also, in another mood, find many reasons why I should have this love.

Then, just as I determined that I would speak and find out if my love might find its ultimate happiness, just as I was about to make formal approach to her grandfather, an event took place that affected all my plans and hopes.

46

It was the year of 1613, thirteen years after I first arrived in this morning Land, when a mesesenger came to Hammamura, to the magnificent house that Iyeyasu had built for me at the time of my second rise in rank.

Shoki-san brought me the exciting news. A huge ship was off Hirado. She was no Portugal, Spaniard or Dutch ship, but of a different nation. Making inquiries, I was sure she was English. The thought of seeing my countrymen once again brought tears of happiness to my eyes.

Immediately I dispatched twelve large galleys to bring the ship's company to Yedo, sending Shoki-san, who was proficient in English, to act as interpreter and to lend what aid he could.

I would have gone personally, being so impatient to see my countrymen, except that Hidetada politely informed me it would be beneath my station as a nobleman of Japan to perform this menial act. Taking this in the fashion expected of Japanese, I apologized for my stupidity and thanked him for his wisdom in pointing out my mistake. Since it was a distance of more than two hundred leagues, I knew it would be ten days, at least, before they arrived. In fact, a month went by before I had word their galleys were entering Yedo Bay.

In honor of their arrival I dressed in ceremonial robes. The costume with the two swords had now become so natural to me that it did not occur to my mind that I would appear odd to my fellow countrymen.

With ill-concealed excitement I waited in the impressive entrance hall for them to be ushered in.

My servants met them at the door with sandals and attempted to remove their boots. The servants were ignored. I heard my visitors talking and laughing, and their boots made a loud, clattering noise on the highly polished floors. The first man to enter was short, with bull-like shoulders and an arrogance as if he was king of the realm.

At first glance there was something familiar about him which stirred my memory. I rose to greet them, and they all stopped to stare at me in wonder as I made the customary ceremonial bow of greeting. Then the short man laughed aloud.

"Damme, they said there was an Englishman here by name of Adams. If you be English, then God's blood, you are the queerest Englishman my eyes ever set gaze upon."

Between us there was that instant spark of hate that occurs at times between strangers. Instinctively, however, I knew this hate was not of this moment but lay far back in my memory. When he spoke his name, I remembered him very well. John Saris, grown heavy now but with the same arrogance I well remembered from our youth. My eyes traveled from his sturdy boots to his costume, which to me seemed hampering and uncomfortable. He stood spraddle-legged, grinning at me. I disguised my feelings with an effort.

"I am William Adams of Kent, former master and pilot in the Queen's service." My mouth faltered somewhat over the strange words. It occurred to me that it had been thirteen years since last I had spoken to an Englishman. He grinned all the more and returned my bow as if it was a huge jest.

"Captain John Saris, His Majesty's ship *Clove*. You remember me, Adams, us being such good friends. I'll be damned if you don't look as if you were made up for a ball. Your master, Drake, would now hardly recognize you as his one-time pogue."

I gazed at him levelly, trying with all my will not to show my anger.

"I remember you well, Captain Saris. As to my costume, I might remind you, Captain, of that old proverb, 'When in Rome do as the Romans do,' and I might also remind you that this is not England. I have found it sensible, when living in another country, to follow the people's customs. Will you introduce your companions?"

"Ah, yes. Forgive me, great lord." And he bowed mockingly. "These men are Master Merchant Cox, Lieutenant Gillie, Lieutenant Gibbons, and Ensign Cockerel."

From force of habit, and without thought, I bowed to each in the manner of the Japanese and waved to them to be seated. The officers, following Captain Saris' lead, treated me as if I was some sort of clown, with the exception of Cox, who looked upon me with friendly and understanding eyes.

For so many years I had been treated with great respect. It sat hard on my stomach to have my own countrymen take a mocking attitude. In courtesy, trying to hide my discomposure, I said:

"For thirteen years I have lived in these islands. During all this time I have waited impatiently for an English ship. I say now that you gentlemen are most welcome. I have had no word from home, except fragments of news brought me by the Dutch. I have had none from either the Spaniards or Portugals."

"Ah, but you are well known in London, Adams," Saris said. "Some of your letters have been printed in Hakluyt's, and the Royal Society builds you up as quite a nabob." He looked around the great room and added, "Damme if it doesn't look as if you have done all right by yourself! Ah yes, as to hearing from home, I have a packet of letters for you."

I half rose from my seat with excitement.

"Gillie," Saris said, "did you bring them along?"

"Why no, sir. I thought you had them."

"Ah, too bad," Saris muttered. His voice did not show regret. "They're safe enough aboard the ship. We will have them sent along."

I felt a surge of anger rise like a flame within me. Such needless disregard I was sure had been deliberate. To gain control of myself I rang a small bell and the serving girls brought in wine and refreshment. Captain Saris and his mates looked at the girls with lustful eyes.

Ordinarily I would have been in sympathy. Now, in my fury, when the girls glanced in my direction to see if I wished them to stay, I waved them out. I drank deeply of wine to calm myself, then said, my voice calm belying my inner turmoil:

"Gentlemen, I hope your mission in Japan is one for which I have waited so long, and that the English will open trade factors here."

The master merchant, Cox, spoke quickly, before Saris could anger me further. "I have come, my lord, with letters and commissions from King James to present to the King of Japan. It is our hope, with your help, to obtain a charter and establish trade with the Japanese."

"Good," I said. "As for the charter, I am sure we will have no problem. I will see that a fair trade agreement is drawn up. The Spaniards and Portugals have been here many years, but having caused dissent, are somewhat in disfavor now with the court. The Dutch, for the present, are more esteemed. With English trade we should be able to open broad areas which the other merchants of the Western world have not touched."

Saris, during this interchange, thoughtfully studied me as if I was an odd specimen the like of which he had never encountered.

"God's blood, man, you speak as if you run the stinking country. Of course it doesn't surprise me, remembering how well you suckholed around Drake. Just what is your position here, Adams?" he demanded.

"That would be hard to define, Captain. There are many things I do. But suffice it for your purpose, all shipping and trade comes under my authority."

"Good and well, man—good and well! Couldn't ask for a better place for an Englishman! If you are what you say you are, we will have these stinking garlic eaters run out of the country, along with the Dutchmen with their fat guts. England, by God, will come into

her own and the rest can pick dung with the chickens." He drank
deeply from the carafe of saki, ignoring the cup.

He had obviously been drinking before. In disgust and anger
I said, "No, Captain. King James and England will have their trade
agreement, and a fair one it will be. Agreements have been signed
also with other nations. They will not be broken, nor will those
people be treated unfairly."

Saris shifted uncomfortably on the low cushion and looked at me
angrily. "Damme! Listen to the man! And you claim yourself an
Englishman? You sound more like a mealy-mouthed Dock Street
preacher to me."

His tone was loud; then there was quiet for a moment, until I
could bear it no longer.

"Captain," I said, "I have waited many long years for an English
ship. And when it does come it seems they sent in charge England's
biggest fool. By what idiocy were you put in command of this
expedition? Without knowing anything about me you come tramp-
ing into my house in your dirty boots, arrogant and insulting, with
not even the decency of bringing my letters. I knew you once, a long
time ago. You were a damned fool then and it seems the years have
not changed you. Let me tell you this once, and only once. In this
land there are few other men holding more power than myself. With
a gesture of my hand or a nod of my head I could have you stripped
and whipped through the streets. Aye, even nailed to a cross if that
were my wish."

Saris started to scramble to his feet, reaching for his sword at the
same time, but Cox pulled him down. I rose to my feet. One by
one, they followed suit. "It is not my habit to give way to anger,
but God knows, enough provocation has been given me here today.
Perhaps a day of rest from your long journey will make you more
mannerly. Tomorrow we will meet again."

Ringing the bell, I said, "My servants will show you to your quarters. One more thing—" In Japanese I ordered the servant to bring
a brush and paper. Saris stood there, spraddle-legged, glowering, but
to him I said nothing until the writing materials were brought.

"Captain Saris, you will write a note and I will send a messenger
to the ship for my mail and anything else you gentlemen need."

For a moment he looked as if he might refuse. Then, with ill grace
and much grumbling at the unfamiliarity of the brush, he wrote a

short note and handed it to me. I bade them good night and busied myself with orders for two fast galleons to return at once to Hirado. Then I had a girl come in to play and sing to me while I drank, to ease the pain of my anger.

Never could I abide a boorish and ill-tempered man, which Saris had always been. He could lay claim to many other faults besides. My hope was that Cox might have authority over Saris in the negotiations. Perhaps I had waited too long and dreamed too often of the time when my countrymen would come to Japan. This day bore out what I have always believed. A man's nationality is no indication that he is either good or bad. In my conversations with Iyeyasu and others, I may have tried to make it seem that Englishmen were better than any other people. Truly, Saris, without any effort, could easily make a liar out of me. Knowing that to brood on the day's events would be useless, I went on with my work, leaving for the morrow the hope that things would turn out better.

47

I remained awake all that night, sitting in the garden, thinking. It has always seemed to me that when a man waits and hopes for an event, when it comes, it never measures up to the dream.

I had entertained the hope that, in my own small way, mine would be the hand to make the tie between the two island kingdoms. This blundering man, Saris, would now probably increase Hidetada's distaste for foreigners. I felt that after all these years of anticipation nothing would come of my hopes and plans.

During the days that followed, while I impatiently awaited the return of the galley bringing my first link to England, I busied myself going through the intricate steps in preparation of a permit for the English to open a factory.

The Portugals and the Dutch had set up their main trading centers at Hirado and I had helped in any way I could to expand their permits to other areas. Hirado, being the outermost point of the islands, seemed to me to be a poor place for a trading center. It was my intent to get permission for the English to set up a factory at either

Yokosuka or Yedo. I considered both these places far better for trade. My relationship with Master Merchant Cox was friendly. He tried to smooth the natural ill-feeling which existed between Saris and myself. In spite of Saris I provided my countrymen with all comforts, food, drink and women. I delegated Shoki-san as host and four samurai to escort them in their nightly tours about the city, to avoid any difficulties with the anti-foreign factions. I did not send Itsuke-san, for he had taken an instant dislike, nay, hatred to Saris.

The day after their arrival, Cox had attempted to apologize for the behavior of Saris and the others, using the excuse they had been drinking. I accepted this excuse, but I could hardly tolerate Saris, drunk or sober.

Iyeyasu was now in semi-seclusion. I did not make the previous error of taking my countrymen to him. I first presented token gifts to Kosuke no Suke, with the request for a formal interview to present my countrymen to the Shogun Hidetada.

Knowing only that these were my own countrymen, my Japanese friends went to great lengths to entertain Saris and his companions. I could not interfere. A magnificent celebration was prepared in their honor, to take place after their presentation to the Shogun.

While waiting for an answer, I carefully tried to explain the procedures and rituals of the court, the stylized formalities they would, of necessity, have to adhere to on meeting the Shogun. I explained the customs of the country and how all, including the nobles, were required to kowtow before the Shogun. I hoped in our case these extremes would not be necessary. However, they would have to kneel on being presented, just as they would do on being presented to King James at his court.

Even at this Saris scoffed, saying he did not intend to bend his knee; no, not even his waist, to some foreign savage.

At these words my temper broke. "The more fool you, Saris. In this land Hidetada is more a king by tenfold than James is in England. I must remind you that you are acting as an emissary from our King and are here to seek favors. Hidetada has never held any love for foreigners, including myself, and his dislike grows each day. If you, by your arrogant stupidity, ruin these negotiations, it shall be on your own head and England will lose by it."

Many sharp words passed between us, he accusing me of being

no Englishman but a tool of these savages. I answered in kind, so that for a time it seemed we would come to blows or worse, until Cox intervened.

I was filled with utter disgust. I knew that should he present himself in such a fashion, Hidetada would do no less than banish them all from the country, and probably a great deal more.

When the day came for us to be presented I had resigned myself, expecting almost anything—anything but what took place. Saris and the officers, resplendent in their dress uniforms, made a fine appearance. Saris, with his dark hair and eyes and his short, heavy body, had more the look of a Spaniard or a Portugal. His behavior and that of his officers was perfectly correct. With not the slightest hesitation, he knelt before Hidetada, and the other officers followed his example as if they had been well rehearsed for the ceremony. All went smoothly. Gifts were exchanged and we were summoned to a private conference with Hidetada and the princes of the state. Soon Hidetada and Captain Saris entered into animated conversation.

Though it was not common knowledge, Hidetada spoke English as well as the Portugals' and Spaniards' tongues. With me he would not speak English and always used an interpreter with the Portugals and Spaniards, but this day he spoke English with Captain Saris. I watched them as I moved about. It was amazing. They seemed to have taken an immediate liking to each other. Hidetada, when he so desired, could be the most charming of men. I thought perhaps they had recognized kindred souls in each other, both being proud and arrogant men.

Now, summoned to join them, I was irritated to find them baiting me, though in the most polite terms. I realized that Hidetada had instinctively sensed the antagonism between Saris and myself and was exploiting it. No man likes to be cast down or to be made the butt of humor. Had it not been that I was so anxious to see trade come about between England and Japan, I would not have accepted their behavior.

Saris was a foolish, vain man. Hidetada twisted him as he willed by casting me down and building up Saris with soft words and praise. Using our dislike as a lever, Hidetada skillfully widened the bridge beween us.

I had drawn up a fair and sensible trade agreement with Cox. I had proved to him that to set up a factory at Hirado would be foolish. Should we do so, we would be trading against the established factories of the Dutch and the Portugals. The center of wealth was here at Yedo or at Osaka. From what I had learned of the seas and currents, it was actually easier and clearer sailing from Java to Yedo Bay than from Java to Hirado.

I did not know it then but even at that time Hidetada determined to rid Japan completely of foreigners. Yet he knew that should he refuse a trading concession to the English, Iyeyasu would countermand that order out of respect for me. Therefore Hidetada carefully turned Captain Saris against the idea of a factory at Yokosuka, implying that I was in the employ of both the Dutch and the Portugals and my allegiance was to them.

Later it developed that he had told Saris that the Portugals, who had been there for so many years, had tried various trading centers but had settled at Hirado, and that he was most anxious to see the English settle there. Since he was angered at the Portugals, he would grant more favors to the English than to the others. Shrewdly Hidetada played on the vanity of Saris, subtly suggesting that Saris could do more than I.

The truth was that the Portugals had petitioned me many times for permission to set up a factory close to Yedo. Hidetada, maneuvering all in the manner of chessmen, had refused with an unremitting flow of excuses.

That night there was a very ugly scene between Captain Saris and myself. In my anger I would have killed him had I not been restrained. Loudly and arrogantly he accused me of treachery against my own countrymen.

"You are no Englishman!" he shouted during the heat of the argument. "I know, from excellent authority, that the Portugals and Dutch pay you for all trading privileges. You bastard, you think more of money than your own countrymen!"

As proof he brought up the story of how I had caroused with Don Roderigo and granted favors to him, going so far as to persuade Iyeyasu to give him the *Tokugawa Shogun*, falsely using my friendship to gain it—that even now the Spaniards were using the ship in trade between the Philippines and the Spanish Americas.

I believe even Cox's faith was shaken in me, at first. Patiently I tried to explain Hidetada's plan. I knew it was his intention to isolate all trade at the very end of the islands so that when the time came, all foreigners could be quickly pushed into the sea.

The argument waxed hotter, becoming more belligerent until my anger burst forth and I slapped Saris hard across the face and sent him reeling the length of the room.

When he came to his feet he drew his sword. In my anger, I welcomed it. Cox and the others flung themselves between us but this would not have stopped me, except at that moment Itsuke-san with my seven samurai entered with drawn swords. I wanted Saris all to myself. But the diversion they caused by my having to tell them I needed no help gave us time to avert bloodshed.

In the days that followed, Hidetada held several conferences with Saris. Only through Cox did I learn an agreement was to be signed between Hidetada and Saris as King James' representative. I was not even allowed to attend the ceremony of the signing.

The English were granted a factory at Hirado where they had to vie with the Portugals and the Dutch in an area where competition kept the price of goods so low as to make trade hardly worth while.

Inwardly furious, I said nothing further of this matter, merely informing Cox that, as soon as I had my affairs in order and the galleons returned with my packet of mail, I would go with them to Hirado.

I determined to make the best of a bad situation and help them in setting up their trading station. I hoped to be able to remedy the situation at a later time. The only satisfaction I could find in the whole mess was that, in time, Saris would receive his rightful condemnation.

48

Ten days went by slowly until the messenger arrived with my letters. For a long time I sat without opening the packet, my memory going back to England, my wife and children, my friends. Fifteen years is a long time in the span of life allotted to man and I had no idea what news lay in my hands.

Summoning my courage, I broke the wrapping. I found three

books: *Hakluyt's Voyages*; next, a bound book of newspapers; and a Bible. There was a letter from my old friend, Augustine Spalding, who had sailed with me to the coast of Barbary; a letter from my merchant friend, Thomas Smith of London; and one from John Stokle. And that was all! No letter from my wife nor from anyone else. . . . Later, I found a message from Hakluyt, enclosed in his book.

I opened the letter from Augustine Spalding first. He began with a prayer to God that this letter might reach me, as, knowing the trials and tribulations besetting a long voyage, it might be that I had as yet received none of the many letters previously sent to me. He went on to say that my name now was well known in London, as a number of my letters had reached home, and each time a Dutch ship had gone out, my friends had sent letters with them.

From personal knowledge he knew that, from time to time, Elizabeth had received some of the money I had sent. But on leaving England he had not been able to locate her or the children and knew not where they had gone, for they were not to be found in London. He told me many of the things that had happened. My good friend Nicholas Diggins was dead; and so also was Martin Beckett, and a list of many others. He told me of the Barbary merchants and how they fared; and most sadly of all, he told me he had found no trace of my remaining son from Procopia, nor of Ali.

He recounted, at great length, the voyage of my good friend Davis and his exploration of the northern coast of the Americas, where he had found but a barren land inhabited by savages, but no passage to the eastern oceans, and of how he had been killed by pirates off the coast of China.

He did say that it had been his wish to make the voyage to Japan but his merchant investors had sent him to Batam. London was awaiting the return of the *Clove* before the merchants would bestir themselves to enter into a trading venture.

I read the letter through hurriedly for news, then reread it slowly and put it aside, feeling very depressed.

Thomas Smith, whose letter I next opened, had received two letters of mine and sent me receipts for monies which he had delivered to my wife. But he, too, said that he had searched for her, knowing how anxiously I awaited a letter by her own hand. Up until the *Clove* had sailed he had been unable to find her. He said my letters had caused much stir and talk of Japan in the counting houses and the inns where merchants and mariners gathered. He, in company with other merchants, was fitting out a ship which should arrive within a year. It struck me with grim humor when, in his letter, he beseeched me to use whatever influence I had to see that trade would flourish.

The letter from John Stokle also gave me news of many who had died, and told that Nicholas Diggins, in his will, had left all his properties and holdings to me, and that he was attending to the affairs of the shipyard and all other properties for me.

I was filled with a deep loneliness and made up my mind that I would dispose of all that had been given me, changing it into goods and money, and return to England. I was sure Iyeyasu would grant me leave. If, God willing, we should have a fair voyage, I would arrive in England a wealthy man. Yet even in my loneliness and despair, the thought of returning did not stir me as once it had. If only I had had some word from Elizabeth! Without her and the children I would return almost a stranger. Knowing the plagues that beset London and that no one had been able to find her, I had little hope my family was yet alive. Yet I felt I had to return to satisfy my own heart. Should it not be right, I could always come back to this land which I loved.

The following day I ordered the galleys made ready and, with permission from the Shogun, we left for Hirado to see to the unloading of the *Clove* and the setting up of a factory.

These activities took my mind to some extent from my own problems, but on the journey of more than two hundred leagues from Yedo to Hirado I thought much of my future. Once I had decided to return to England, my unhappiness deepened rather than lifted.

Since the arrival of my countrymen I had not seen Magome no Yuriko. My heart yearned for her. Often she sent some remembrance—a poem, a flower arrangement, a book, or some other sensitive token.

I had thought the arrival of the English would break the tie between us but she was ever in my heart. To return to Elizabeth would be to return to a stranger—not only because of the years, but each of us had changed. I knew how much I had altered, and I could not even picture her face in my mind. My children now would be grown, and would meet a father more Japanese in his thinking than English. Yet moral laws and duties are not easily discarded. Before this I had the excuse that I was helpless, a prisoner. I had felt that, could I but get permission, I would return home gladly. Now, sure that Iyeyasu would grant this permission, I had no further excuse to linger.

Each day the hatred between myself and Saris deepened, and for this there was no cure. The other officers followed their captain's example, treating me coolly, with very little show of respect. Only Cox and his two assistants, Tempest Peacock and Richard Cock, were in any way friendly. They treated me respectfully but I felt it was only because they were wise enough to know this project would be a dismal failure without my good will.

At Hirado there was enough work for me obtaining the proper warehouse and permits from the Daimyo for the English to trade.

Peacock and Richard Cock were to stay in Japan to run the factory until the arrival of the next English ship. In the meantime they wanted to dispose of as much of their goods as possible and buy others before the *Clove* sailed. They expected me to do all the work on this. Finally I informed Cox and Saris that I would need some time to dispose of my holdings should I receive permission to leave this land. During this time, I felt, they could handle their own affairs.

Saris said nothing to this, but before I left for Yedo, Cox, Peacock, and Richard Cock dined with me. They told me that Saris, while drinking, had spoken gleefully of what he would do to me during the long year aboard ship on the return voyage to England.

"He holds a fair hatred toward you, Captain Adams," Cox said.

I looked from him to Richard Cock and Tempest Peacock. I did not trust Cox completely but I had come to know and like Peacock. He was a slim, handsome man, sensitive of feature and feeling, and interested in this land and the people, which was perhaps what drew me to him. I liked Richard Cock and felt he was a rare breed, an honest merchant—but no more.

Peacock said, "William, it will be a miracle if you arrive in England alive. It is not for me to remind you that the *Clove* is a King's ship and Saris, as captain, is the law, even to taking your life."

Cock said, "What Tempest says is so. It would be most foolhardy for you to place yourself in that position."

I drank a cup of saki and pondered their words. They were right.

Sooner or later Saris could and would provoke me into a quarrel.

Cock said, "Within the year, Captain Adams, there will be another English ship."

"A year is a long time."

"But not too long if it means your life," Cox said.

"I must think on it. There will be time between here and Yedo. Saris is fortunate. Were I another man and did I not place more value on the relations between Japan and England, his bones would lie here."

After we parted for the night I was surprised to find my unhappiness diminishing. Now I had an excuse to stay and I let my anger at Saris grow to ease my conscience.

On my return to Yedo I had made up my mind not to return on the *Clove*. I had been home but two days and was in the garden when Baron Yamamoto and Magome Yuriko came to pay me a visit. Each time I had thought of her I had tried to banish her image out of my mind. Now, seeing her again, I knew she was the reason I could not leave.

There was sadness in her gestures and eyes as she spoke of my leaving. After the tea ceremony we walked down by the small lake talking of minor things that had no bearing on what we both were thinking.

Finally she said, "Daishi-san, the people will mourn your leaving. Do you think you might return some day?"

"And will you mourn my leaving?" I asked her.

She looked away, then turned toward me, her lovely eyes filled with tears. "I will mourn most of all," she replied.

I had never more than touched her hand and now I wanted her more than I had ever wanted any woman before. With difficulty I restrained my feelings. I told her that, should I leave, I would mourn her also, but as yet I had not received permission. Should Iyeyasu refuse me, then I could speak to her with an open heart. That same day I sent a message to Iyeyasu asking if he could spare a few moments from his work. The servant returned with word of an appointment for the morrow.

Since Iyeyasu had been working on his maxims I had seen little of him and, for the past six months, not at all. His greeting was as warm and friendly as always. It seemed to me that age was now approaching him swiftly. He looked old, worn and tired. We strolled through his garden, crossed a small bridge to a quiet spot that contained all of the beauty of what seemed centuries of loving care, although the garden had not been there for the length of a generation.

Sitting together in close comradeship, we were silent as we absorbed the beauty of our surroundings. Finally Iyeyasu broke the silence and there was sadness in his voice.

"It is strange that when your messenger arrived yesterday I had just finished a letter to you. Often I have thought of how many times you've requested permission to leave Nippon and been refused. You have been patient and understanding, Injin-san. The thought of losing you saddens me, for you are my good and trusted friend. So, it is with sorrow, mixed with happiness for you, that I grant permission for you to return to your own land. All of us have been selfish in keeping you here for so many years. But when you return to your country, I hope you will think often of us, and feel that your time here was not ill spent."

I thanked him, and told him of the sorrow I would feel at leaving. Shrewdly he caught the deep unhappiness which I tried to hide. He asked me if I was not pleased at his granting my request.

"It is my duty to return to England," I replied. "But, somehow, it will be for me a journey to a strange land. I doubt much if my family still lives. Of those who were my friends, almost all have died. I thank you for the kindness you have shown me, but, in any event, I will not be leaving until the next English ship arrives."

"But the ship of the English king—is it not to return to your homeland?"

"Yes, my Lord," I said. "It returns, but I cannot return on this ship. The captain is my enemy and the laws of the sea would place me in his power. I would be completely at his mercy throughout the voyage. I doubt if I would live to see England. It is a shameful thing, my Lord, but I cannot trust my own countryman."

Iyeyasu's face was alight. "I am glad to hear that you will not leave soon. My book of maxims is finished and we can now renew our former companionship. Know, my friend, that you may leave us when you will, but what would please me most would be for you to stay. I think, Injin-san, you are an Englishman no longer. It would make me extremely happy if you remained, to wed, and raise a family—so that Japan will never lose you, even by your death. I know you have left your seed in this land, but these children you have made with loose women are not the same. If you would do this, I will make sure your family holds high honor in Japan as long as my family rules."

I sat silent a while, then said: "If the English ship had not come I would have married."

I told him my feelings toward Magome no Yuriko and, in speaking of her, I knew he could see my heart was lost. And now I asked if I might see the maxims. Like all artists, he was pleased to show his work. I marveled at the beauty of his calligraphy as I read the scrolls. He had laid down a hundred rules of good government. They were wise, for he knew his people well. With these rules his family would stay in power as long as the blood held true. It was my belief that his words would live to become a part of Japan's history, a guide for future rulers.

"There have never been, to my small knowledge, any rules of government written by a man who has ruled," I said. "From what little I know of history, I can find no flaw, except that no man can foretell what the future holds nor can these precepts be protected as to the quality of your descendants. If they follow these rules, though, I think that even a weak ruler could not go wrong. Have you shown them to Hidetada?"

He shook his head. "No, I am not yet an ancestor. I still live. Time alone—after my death—will lend value to these thoughts. Hidetada is my son and must follow his own way. When I am gone let this be a guidepost for him and his son and his son's son."

Then, his black eyes twinkling, he unfolded another scroll and handed it to me. "If, as you say, the words I have written hold truth and wisdom, then you shall share the honor. If they prove not true, and contain falseness, you will share the blame."

The scroll he gave me was a dedication to me with these words:

To my wise adviser, teacher and friend, the English pilot, William Adams, better known to my people as Injin-san, who has taught us so many wise and learned things. To him we give our thanks and this recognition for his great help.

I had never expected such recognition or honor and felt it was undeserved, but it was in keeping with the heart of Iyeyasu, his kindness and generosity that I should be thus honored.

When I left his house that day my heart was lightened by the thought that my problems were not so deep and devious as I had believed. Iyeyasu always had this effect on me.

49

Some time later I received complaints that Saris, with other officers of the *Clove*, who were carousing in the company of Japanese nobles and samurai around Hirado, were abusing the Portugals and the Dutch. Threats were being made that all but the English would be driven from this land.

I paid little attention at first. However, as further instances of strife were being reported, I began to worry. There was the looting and burning of a Dutch storehouse. I was told of assaults on Spaniard priests. The trading center at Nagasaki had been burned and looted. It began to seem as if this was a well-planned conspiracy of certain Japanese and English, led by Captain Saris.

Over the years, in the interests of trade, it had been necessary for me to develop an organization which encompassed many men, some of whom were in my sole employ, and others as a source of information. Therefore I sent a messenger to Arizo no Hakada, the head of the department I had set up to see that neither the Japanese nor the traders robbed each other. Before the arrival of the English, during the past year or two things had been going smoothly and my attention to these details had declined.

Arizo no Hakada was a ronin, a soldier without a lord to serve, when he came into my employ. Over the years he had served me well at Hirado. He seemed evasive when he arrived at my summons. I wondered at this, as he had ever been faithful to me.

I questioned him sternly and he confessed that the *Azuku*, a branch of the Shogun's police, were involved, though not openly, in each instance against the Portugals and Spaniards. He had started an investigation and the azuku had ordered him not to interfere in any way.

"Why didn't you come to me?" I asked. "You well know that trade is our department. Under the orders of Iyeyasu, no one is allowed to interfere except upon my orders."

He knelt before me, not speaking. I waited for his answer.

"Most Honorable Lord," he said finally, "when I came into your service I swore allegiance. But on your part it has seemed you are no longer interested in such problems. It has been said that the English captain brought word from your own country that you are a man of no standing, a peasant, and Hidetada has turned against you, favoring the English captain. I waited for some word from you, but heard none. I am your servant, Most Noble Lord, but the azuku are the arm of the Shogun. There are but a few of us against so many, and you said nothing."

I confessed my neglect, then said, "Still, Hakada-san, I am responsible for trade and you have not kept me informed. Is it not true that I have always been fair and just? Have I not protected any man who has given me his allegiance?"

"It is true, noble lord. Ask, and I am ready to give my life."

"Is there anything else I should know of these happenings?"

"Yes, Daishi-san. Everyone at Hirado speaks that the great Sei-e-tai Shogun, Hidetada, has decided to drive all foreigners from our country except the Englishmen. These foreigners are not to be allowed to take their goods, wives or any possessions with them."

He told me more. Thinking back over the events of the past few years I could see that this was not a thing of the moment. I should have known that Hidetada would do this. The first event had been the impossibility of completing the ship to replace the *Tokugawa Shogun*. The second was the seemingly accidental burning of the galleon Don Roderigo had sent.

After Hakada-san left, I sat awhile in thought. It was ironic that, for all the years I had worked to develop trade under a fair and just policy, protecting the rights of all so my own countrymen would benefit, now these countrymen of mine were the very ones trying to destroy everything.

I had to admit there was reason for Hidetada's dislike, and the behavior of the English could now be added to the actions of all the rest. However, since I had been entrusted with this responsibility,

I petitioned for an audience with Hidetada. But Kosuke no Suke made excuse after excuse each day so that, finally, I gave up. I determined to discuss it with Iyeyasu.

Iyeyasu of late had seemed more rested. I thought it was relief from the strain of finishing his book. The true reason, however, was the smell of battle. Iyeyasu was being faced with a danger to his government.

When Shogun Toyotome Hideyoshi died, he placed his eldest son, Hideyori, under the care of Iyeyasu and four other powerful Daimyos. They were entrusted to care for Hideyori until he came to manhood and then he would rightfully be made Shogun. Iyeyasu had intended to honor this charge and had even given one of his daughters in marriage to Hideyori. But Hideyori was weak. Further, the four Daimyos had taken part in the rebellion at Sekigehara and Iyeyasu had no trust in them. Now, after spending so many years in the building of the country, Iyeyasu had no intention of turning over the shogunate to one who could be led so easily.

Hideyori had been raised in the great castle at Osaka that Hideyoshi had built. Now, many of the barons who had been against Iyeyasu were banding together once again in support of Hideyori's claim that he, by right, should be Shogun.

"The years press on me, Injin-san, but before I die," Iyeyasu said, "I must destroy this menace which threatens the future of my country. I do not say Hideyori does not have some claim. But he is not capable; and to allow this claim to exist will cause a division, like a festering sore to poison this land. The only way to peace is to place the power in the hands of my own family and to keep it there.

"I have many enemies, including the powerful Daimyos Morri, Shimadzu and Uszugi. They signed allegiance to me after the battle of Sekigehara. You were there and saw them. Now, once more, they are working against me, using Hideyori's claim to be Shogun as their reason to destroy my house. Should I allow this to be done, this land which now knows peace and prosperity will be as before, divided into dozens of warring clans.

"Daishi-san, I have tried to settle this problem. I am still trying. I think Hideyori would see the wisdom of my plan, but he is surrounded by these greedy and jealous advisers who feed his vanity by flattering him and are merely using him. I have ordered him to leave Osaka and come to live with me in Yedo where he will be honored next to my own son. Should he refuse, then I must prepare once again for war."

I commented that war, like anger, never seemed to solve anything.

"My dear friend, I have never had any love for war. I agree that it always seems a stupid way of settling a problem. But in the history of mankind it seems that sooner or later war is always the answer. Even now some of the great families are refusing to follow my edicts. More and more, in some provinces, they treat the agents of the *Bukufu* with contempt, and refuse to pay their tax. Some of my officials have even been killed. I am afraid that once again we may have to make use of your cannon."

I made no reply, but in my mind I knew that never again would I have any part, nor lend any assistance in any way, to war. I resolved to make some excuse when the time came.

I had been aware for some time of the trouble brewing, but had not thought it inevitable as now it seemed to be. As delicately as I could I changed the subject and brought up the problem close to my mind.

Iyeyasu heard me out as I told him of the treatment of the foreigners, the killing of priests, and the violations of the treaties we had signed. Since I had been given the responsibility for trade, I felt I should bring these matters to his attention.

"In affairs such as these, Hidetada is now Shogun," Iyeyasu answered. "If he feels the foreigners should leave our land, then that will be his decision. In a matter such as the revolt which we have brewing to the south, that is my problem, for I must leave as a legacy a strong and closely knit government. Trade and similar problems are minor matters and I will leave them to the Shogun. Hidetada is now a man. He can now make his own decisions and mistakes. In truth, Injin-san, I cannot but feel that it would be no great loss to Japan to be rid of the foreigners. Once I thought otherwise. But truly these are worthless men."

"But there are treaties we have signed," I reminded him.

Iyeyasu looked at me and patiently said, "Those treaties have been broken time and again by the actions of the foreign ones. We are within our rights to cancel their trading licenses. They have the right, in their own countries, to run their affairs. Their wrong and evil actions have been many. I know the boasting of how Spain always first sends their holy men and merchants to gain a foothold, then on some excuse invade and conquer the land. Those of our own people who have traveled to Europe, visiting Rome and the other grand cities, have returned disillusioned and full of impatience at what you call your Western culture. I know now we are different people and have little to gain from you either in religion or trade. In this Hidetada is right. Possibly, had it not been for the Romish bonzes, we could have found some peaceful means of living together. Since their arrival they have abused every one of our laws of religious freedom. We welcomed them in the beginning, yet they preach a doctrine which, under our laws, is the same as treason. I did not deport them because of your pleas on their behalf, although I should have."

Kindly and gently he placed his hand on mine. "Forget these things, Injin-san. They are not important. Be what your talents intended for you—a philosopher, a teacher, enjoying the things which are important to the mind. Become one of us. Take to yourself a wife and forget the world of the West. Injin-san, I have met many from the Western world but never anyone such as you. I thought, on meeting you, that there were others like you and if so, then the West had something to offer us. But that is not so. In your own land you would be a stranger, lost and alone."

Inwardly I had known that Iyeyasu would feel this way and somehow I, too, had come to believe that he was right. Through the years I had done my utmost to warn the merchants and the priests of the ultimate result their actions would bring. At that moment I think an end had come to my dream of a close commerce and travel and understanding between East and West.

I spoke no more of it but went on to other subjects more pleasant and more in keeping with our ties of friendship.

When I returned to my house I had decided that I would take Magome no Yuriko to wife. With her I would find happiness, enjoy the fruits of my labors and the honors which had been bestowed upon me. I was done with being a buffer between the East and West. I would leave the men to the inevitable outcome of their greed.

50

Several days later, I arranged a meeting with Daimyo Yamamoto. We spoke of many things before I summoned the courage to tell him what was in my heart—my love for Yuriko-san.

"You honor my house greatly, Daishi-san," he replied, "and the thought pleases me. But you must understand that to Yuriko-san I have given every freedom, including the choice in marriage. You must speak directly to her. If her heart lies toward you then I will be happy. There is no one whom I would welcome to my family more than your honorable person."

Each morning I would awaken with the intention of speaking of my love to Yuriko-san. Yet my courage would fail during the day and I would live another day in misery. It was foolish cowardice and she wondered at my hesitation. It was finally Yuriko-san who arranged for us to be alone. The occasion was an *ikebana,* a viewing of blossoms. In her grandfather's garden some new and rare blooms had come into flower.

I remember not what words I used in telling her of the love in my heart, but it was done, and of all the good things that have come to pass during my life this has been the very best.

Once the marriage was agreed upon I saw her seldom, for the custom calls for bride and groom to remain apart until the day of the ceremony, though it was against my power to stay away. Then one day all contact with Yuriko-san and Daimyo Yamamoto was cut off from me. My messengers were turned back by samurai who were stationed at the gates of the house.

I sought the reason. It was not hard to find. Hidetada, hearing of my impending marriage, had quickly arranged a marriage between Yuriko-san and a Daimyo of a distant province. He, as Shogun, had the power to do this. Had I been born Japanese I would have accepted this loss of my love without question. But being born an Englishman, I could not accept it.

In a towering rage I called Takamon no Itsuke and ordered him to gather together our samurai and all the ronin he could find.

His frog-like face lit with pleasure at my order. "We go to fight, my Lord?"

"Yes," I answered. "Fight we will." And I told him of what they had done to Yuriko-san and ended by saying, "Itsuke-san, I will not willingly lose this woman who means far more to me than life."

Shoki-san, realizing what the consequences might be, gathered numerous friends to come and plead with me. I was persuaded at last that by such angry action I would surely not have Yuriko-san but would, instead, lose both my life and Yuriko-san. They suggested I go directly to Iyeyasu.

Though it was against my principles, I had no choice but to do so. In all the years we had known each other I had never asked a favor for myself, with the exception of my request to return to my homeland. Now I beseeched Iyeyasu to speak to Hidetada and countermand his order.

Hidetada had carefully explained to Iyeyasu that this marriage was necessary for the well-being of the state. Falsely he had told Iyeyasu that the Daimyo Ara no Irutsu would not be content without having Magome no Yuriko for wife. Being so smitten, he might rebel, to join forces with the other Daimyos. All this he had reported to Iyeyasu in such fashion that Iyeyasu believed him.

I could not convince him of the truth. I had never before spoken ill of Hidetada to Iyeyasu and he was surprised and angry at my hatred. I demeaned myself to the point of begging him to grant me this woman, even to pointing out that never had I asked anything but this for myself. He consented, although contemptuously. I was filled with shame at having to do this, but my love having come to full flower, I could not bear the thought of losing Yuriko.

Where I had lived in peace before, I was now beset by danger. Three times before our marriage I was set upon. Three of my samurai were killed defending me. Itsuke-san was wounded in one of the encounters. My luck and the constant guard of Itsuke-san held. Magome no Yuriko came at last to my house as my bride.

Amidst all the trouble and heartache that I have suffered in this world, one touch of her hand, a glance from her, have been enough to compensate for everything.

My life seemed to begin again as if I were twenty. The years we have had together I have been young and so full of love for her that neither music, nor poetry, nor all the words of the world could describe my happiness.

For a month we lived apart from the world, finding in each other and our house on Hemmi Hill at Hammamura all happiness. Knowing peace and contentment and joy so profound as to defy description. Her beauty, her every movement, her sensitivity and response to my love, the meeting of our minds and bodies—all were perfect.

Then we became aware of small bedevilments. I had never looked upon the hundred or more families who belonged to me and farmed my land as slaves, but rather as friends and neighbors. I had never taken my rightful share of the rice and produce from my lands. I had no need for this, for Iyeyasu had given me a yearly stipend of cash which was more than ample for my needs.

Now the Bukufu claimed I owed tremendous quantities of rice for back taxes. Shoki-san had warned me many times. Had I listened to him and taken my rightful share of the crops, no worry would have attended me. The deliveries of monies which had been made regularly to me by a messenger of the Master of the Mint now ceased. I was obliged to borrow in order to pay what was owed.

I knew the reason, yet I could not protest to Iyeyasu at this treatment. For Yuriko, yes, because she was all the world to me. But to go and beg for money went beyond my pride as a man. Yet somehow I had to find means of paying my debt.

As if in answer to a wish, a letter came from Cox asking me to come to Hirado to discuss the possibility of my entering the employ of the English East India Company of Merchants. While I had been responsible for trade I would never have entertained the thought of employ, but now that I had removed myself from it, I felt I could honorably accept.

Taking Yuriko with me, I traveled by horse to Osaka and from there we took a galley to Hirado. It was a joyous trip of sunny days and clear skies, my love beside me, so that I wished the voyage would never end.

At Hirado I found the *Clove* ready to sail for England. They were to leave Tempest Peacock, Richard Cock and William Eaton as factors. The three merchants were respectful as they offered me employment, assuring me that my knowledge of the country and conditions would be invaluable to them. Their attitude pleased me. Then Captain Saris, who had been silent during the discussion, now began to haggle on the amount of money to be paid. I wanted one hundred pounds paid to my wife, Elizabeth, if she was still living, on their arrival in England. I would work for the company at the rate of fifteen pounds a month, which, I pointed out, was much less than the Portugals and Dutch had offered me to enter their employ.

Saris insulted me by saying they would pay me eighty pounds a year, but only on condition I enter their employ on a yearly basis. This money, except for small loans, would be paid to my account in England.

Angrily I refused, as Saris knew I would. He had not the authority to bargain but could not resist baiting me. Richard Cock and Tempest Peacock were embarrassed. I turned to go, advising them to speak of this among themselves and to make me an offer in the morning. I would then either accept or reject it, but I wanted Saris kept out of my sight. I was angry, yet uncertain if word had not already reached Hirado of the extent of my disrepute at court and of my lack of funds.

The following morning they offered me one hundred and twenty pounds a year, payable to me monthly in Japan. I accepted it as if the money was unimportant, with the excuse that it was my desire to see trade progress. I felt shame within me, for now it was important that I should have this income and trade no longer held any interest for me.

According to my rank, it was necessary that I maintain a certain style of living. I owed allegiance to the samurai who had sworn allegiance to me. As they are soldiers and nothing else, it was my duty to provide for their living, which was a great expense. I could relinquish none of this, therefore I had to provide.

Since Shoki-san was more diligent in business, I left him in charge of my estates. He took care that the taxes were paid and that the income which was rightfully due me from my farms would be received.

I had assumed that my business with the English factory would be to act as an intermediary. But before the sailing of the Clove, Captain Saris ordered that I remain at Hirado. Again he accused me of working for the Dutch and the Portugals, saying:

"We know you have been in their employ. Now that you are in the employ of our company, you are to work no more for these Portugals against your own countrymen."

His words angered me anew. I had never taken any money, nor even gifts, from either Dutch or the Portugals, although I had done them many favors. He made reference to Don Roderigo and the gifts as evidence. Words passed once again between us. From then on I absolutely refused to have anything further to do with Saris. I entrusted the monies and letters for Spalding in Batam, for my wife and friends in England, to the care of Merchant Cox.

The goods now left at the English factory were of small value. The cloth was low in price since so much had been brought in. Of spices the Japanese used but little. I therefore suggested to Masters Cock, Peacock and Eaton that we buy a large junk and trade to the islands of Ryukyu, and even as far as the Indies, bringing back sandalwood, deerskins and other articles of value. They agreed to this and we set about purchasing and refitting a large vessel for the voyage.

Of late, Hidetada had passed a law that all vessels must have a permit to leave the country. The penalty was death for those who left without permission. I had to go to Yedo to obtain this permit, which they called a *goshun*.

In spite of the fact that the style of living at Hirado was less than that which I had become accustomed to, Yuriko and I had been happy there. Also, shortly after our arrival in Hirado, Yuriko had found herself with child, which brought happiness to both of us. I thought it would be better for her to be among friends and near her beloved grandfather when our child was born, and I hoped that by rushing the work to completion we could make the voyage to Ryukyu and Siam, returning on the monsoon, before the baby arrived.

Should our voyage be successful we would have no more worries about our means of livelihood, as I intended to take a share in the venture. I thought of my other children whom I had not seen for so many years and vowed that Yuriko and our children would have their father and a full and happy life.

It is strange how fate controls a man's life, giving him on the one hand great happiness and canceling it out on the other as a form of payment for the happiness.

I was to find trial and tribulation my lot for the ensuing years.

51

There would be little interest in dwelling on the problems I encountered at the court trying to obtain a goshun to make the long voyage to Siam.

Hidetada, who well knew that only as a final resort would I appeal to Iyeyasu, kept me waiting until my patience was worn thin. Finally he issued the goshun with very ill grace. His delaying tactics, however, had caused me to lose the favorable weather so that I was forced to sail from Hirado at the time of the monsoon.

Though we had paid the exorbitant price of two thousand taels for the junk, and had spent twenty-four hundred taels in fitting her out, she was still a poor vessel, clumsy and ill-handling. I thought yearningly of the *Tokugawa Shogun*. I found some humor in the fact that Cock, Peacock and Eaton had christened her the *Sea Adventure*.

Due to delay we were not able to weigh anchor until November twenty-eighth. I had aboard, besides Mr. Eaton, several Japanese merchants who had joined us in the venture with merchandise of their own to barter.

We were no sooner outside the harbor of Hirado than we met a heavy gale and were forced to seek shelter at Kawaguchi. Here we lay until December seventeenth—much too late for us to attempt the voyage. I prayed that God might smile upon our venture even then, and when the weather had cleared we put out to sea.

On the second day, a gale came up and raised terrible seas. The wind was of such force that we could do little more than try to run before it. The high poop kept us from being broached. But now our proud ship, the *Sea Adventure*, sprang a leak. Trying to hold the water with our pump, we continued on toward Ryukyu, for the inhospitality of the people prevented us from risking refitting on the China shore.

On the twenty-second we were abeam of the island of O Shima. This being a rocky shore, we sailed on, arriving at Naha of the great Ryukyu on the twenty-seventh. After much negotiation we received permission from the king of this island to land our stores and goods but had great difficulty procuring supplies for refitting the junk.

It was as if a pall hung over me. Where before I had a talent in dealing with people, I now met with such backing and evasiveness from the officials that there seemed to be no end to it. Many anxious and weary days passed. When we finally did get assistance to careen the junk, bad material was supplied for caulking the ship. I knew it would not hold. The crew, as if sensing my loss of honor and power, became unmanageable. Holding a meeting amongst themselves, they demanded their wages be paid in advance. This, I absolutely refused, but the merchants begged me to comply saying that we would lose our crew and the prospects of a successful voyage.

Now the governor of Ryukyu, seeing how long we were delayed, became anxious to have us leave, as the officials from China were due to arrive. The Chinese controlled these islands, and the people feared that trouble would result from our being there.

I answered that I was fully aware of their problems, and as for me, I would gladly go, but as I had one hundred twenty-six persons dependent upon me for their lives and goods, I prayed them to give us more time. They agreed to this, but when the ship was finally righted and put into the water and our goods and stores aboard once more, the weather continued so wild and stormy we dared not put back to sea.

The mixture of diverse people in our crew caused great dissent. Even Mr. Eaton and one of the other merchants fell out in a violent quarrel. The other merchants and seamen were split by the argument. It was only by much persuasion and the luck of God that no blood was shed.

By March fifteenth the troubles and the enforced idleness had become unbearably irksome to me. I had thought by now to be seeing home again when actually the voyage had hardly begun.

The seamen, having taken up with women ashore, now did not want to sail, even though against my better judgment I had paid them their wages. I had to appeal to the authorities to compel the men to come back aboard. By then they had spent all their money and we could not sail until I advanced enough to pay the debts they had contracted ashore.

Besides all this—as if it were not bad enough—I was further tormented by news brought by a junk from Satsuma. Iyeyasu, it was told, had fought a battle with Hideyori and numerous Daimyos who had persuaded the latter to revolt. The battle took place at Osaka, and the news was that Iyeyasu, though not defeated, had not won. Now many more Daimyos had joined against him and he was about to lose the country he had worked so hard to forge into a nation.

Though I had vowed I would take no part in any further war, I felt as if I had deserted my friend in his time of need. Right or wrong, my place was with Iyeyasu.

Feeling it would be impossible to continue to Siam with the lack of discipline among the crew, I bought a cargo of wheat and a quantity of ambergris and other products, including batatas, that I thought would be of value since they were unknown in Japan.

We arrived back at Kawaguchi harbor on the tenth of June, 1615. Our voyage was a failure. We had spent much more than the value of our cargo and all the monies I had advanced to the crew were lost.

By good fortune, Shoki-san was at Hirado, having come down from Osaka to seek word of us and to leave letters at the factory for me. Upon hearing that our junk had come into Kawaguchi, Shoki-san made haste to meet me. The sight of his familiar and smiling countenance gave me pleasure.

We sat far into the night and he told me of the events that had happened since I left. The first and most important was that Yuriko had given birth to a boy, having an easy time insofar as any such time can be easy for a woman. Both she and the baby were in good health and anxiously awaiting my return. My estate, he said, was also doing well. The crops had been better than usual. At least there was no failure in that direction.

One of my first questions to Shoki-san had been of Iyeyasu. He told me that Iyeyasu had defeated the factions around Hideyori though he gave me no details, at first.

Now as we sat during the night, Shoki-san told me of the terrible events.

"When the forces of our Lord Shogun besieged the castle of Osaka, things went badly, my Lord. I and Itsuke-san, being sure it would be your wish to lend all aid to our lord, gathered together twenty-six samurai and, arriving in Osaka, we offered our services in your name.

"The castle was besieged for many days with violent battles being fought back and forth on the surrounding plain. But with those huge walls and the deep moat we could not make any breech. On the field of battle our warriors were successful. When he saw that neither side could win, our Lord Iyeyasu proposed a truce."

At this Shoki-san fell silent for a time as if what he was about to relate came with difficulty to his tongue. Presently he continued.

"My Lord Iyeyasu met with Hideyori and the Daimyos who had sworn their allegiance upon the field outside of the great castle. Iyeyasu chose me as secretary and I attended the conference among the nobles. I heard this myself, Daishi-san: Iyeyasu proposed a fair treaty, speaking to Hideyori as if he were his son. He said: 'Your father, the noble lord Hideyoshi, who was my friend, would be deeply saddened at what has taken place between us. I, who ever felt as a father to you, gave you my beloved daughter as wife. It pains me to see our land in the throes of a civil war.'

"Hideyori said: 'Most Honorable Lord and friend of my father, I feel that this war is more your fault than mine. You promised my father that I would be raised to take my place rightfully as Shogun. You have isolated me in this castle, trying to win from me all those who were friends of my father's. You have set your son Hidetada in my place. Now you seek to destroy me.'

"Iyeyasu replied, 'My son, to be a ruler, first the ruler must look toward what is best for his country. For the most part, these Daimyos who have gathered around you are not interested in seeing our land strong and united. They but use you as an excuse to break the power that Nobunaga, your father and myself fought so long to secure. I have attempted to meet with you many times. But always you have been surrounded by those who advise you falsely. So I say now, let us make a treaty between us. I will set you up alongside my son Hidetada, and before I die, I will call together a council of all the nobles and they will decide which of you shall hold the title given by the Emperor of Sei-e-tai Shogun.'

"Those about Hideyori warned him against accepting such an offer but he had faith in Iyeyasu and after several days an agreement was reached. In the agreement, my Lord Iyeyasu asked that certain breeches be made in the castle and the moat filled in so that some other baron should not seize it. You know, Lord Daishi-san, that castle cannot be taken even by the bravest of warriors."

Again Shoki-san paused. He refilled his cup with saki and drank deeply, then put his head in his hands as if seeking courage to go on with his tale. I waited patiently until he resumed.

"Once the agreement was reached, Iyeyasu retreated with his forces from the castle. I thought then peace was made. But instead, calling forth thousands upon thousands of workers, he began filling the moat, sending men to tear down the walls of the castle, tumbling the great stones into the moat and covering them with earth. This work went on night and day and with such speed that Hideyori became deeply concerned and sought audience with Iyeyasu. Lord Iyeyasu did not see him, pleading illness. By now the forces inside the castle were disorganized, many of the warriors having left for their own provinces.

"One morning, without warning to Hideyori, Iyeyasu gathered together all his army and led the attack with such fury that before the afternoon the castle was taken.

"My Lord Daishi-san, men died by the thousands. Those around Hideyori fought well but were driven back until only a few hundred were left in that magnificent inner hall of the castle. Seeing there was no hope, Hideyori gathered his family and friends about him and, rather than face the disgrace of defeat, he ordered the castle to be put to the torch. He and those about him, including his wives and children, committed seppuku."

I was shocked by this account. Now I could understand Shoki-san's horror at the dishonorable manner in which Iyeyasu had won the battle.

Perhaps time will tell if, by his action, he secured the land to peace and a strong government. This I do not know, for the affairs of man ever seem to breed war and more war. My feelings were mixed. I felt shame and sorrow. I knew Iyeyasu's heart so well and realized how much suffering this must cause him. But Iyeyasu was a man of strong will and in his mind felt this was the way it had to be done. Nothing, no one, could have stopped him.

I was only thankful that I had had no part in this. I wondered how I would feel toward him when we met again. Would the shame of his treachery show in his face? Could I keep my feelings from showing in mine? I did not know.

Rather than think about it I sat with Shoki-san through the night in sorrowful companionship, drinking saki until it brought the numbing of our senses and sleep.

52

My heart longing for Yuriko and my eyes hungering for the sight of my newborn son, with all speed I finished my business and made preparation to have the junk refitted for sea during my absence. I promised my countrymen at the English factory to return as soon as possible with another goshun. God willing, our next voyage would be more successful. Taking a twenty-four-oared galley, we made the journey to Osaka in record time and took to horse. I would not have gone out of my way to see the destruction Iyeyasu had wrought, but since the castle lay directly on our route I could not avoid it.

Hideyoshi had been a wonderful builder. When he erected the castle at Osaka materials for its construction had been brought from thirty provinces. One hundred boats a day, it was said, had plied the three rivers surrounding the castle, carrying huge granite blocks for the outer walls and tremendous timbers for the inner structures. Sixty thousand men had been employed in the work. The moat surrounding the castle had been twenty feet deep and the enormous walls measured more than ten miles in circumference. The inner building reached upward for nine levels.

I remembered the first time I had seen the castle I was amazed by its size, which was far beyond anything I had ever beheld. The mines of Sado and Kai had produced the gold for the decoration within. The roofs were covered with richly gilded tiles. The inside ceiling, pillars, door frames and metalwork all were plated with gold.

The bedroom of Hideyoshi where Hideyori had died was fifty-four feet square. The low bed had been eight feet long and five feet wide; the bedding, poppy-colored with gold ornaments at the head. Now the castle stood, a fire-blackened ruin, the monstrous walls broached in many places, and the air of desolation was deepened by the smell of death that hung over it like a pall.

Though we were tired from our sea voyage, I could not rest at Osaka near the scene of that awful devastation. Shoki-san seemed as depressed by it as I. We therefore took to horse and rode through the night until we were in fair, green country, where the heavy smell of death no longer sickened me.

I had sent ahead a messenger to announce our coming. The following evening, as we approached my estate, all my samurai and servants were lined along the road holding torches. My samurai rode forward in full regalia, led by Itsuke-san, who gave me formal welcome due a great lord.

I felt as I had in the old days. These people were my own people, my friends. As I passed between the long line of torch bearers they roared "Banzai!" and followed behind us, some running ahead with torches to light our way right up to the door where I spoke a word of thanks.

As the serving women removed my boots, I breathed deeply of the cool and sweet cleanness of my house. There was my lovely Yuriko, slim as always, with her head pressed to the floor in the traditional Japanese attitude of welcome.

I raised her, and her dear face which I loved so well had become even more beautiful with motherhood. At home at last I realized how tired I was. I felt as one who has crossed the parched desert and suddenly found a sweet spring to quench his thirst. In a moment she took my hand and led me inside where a lamp burned and a maid stood quietly by the baby's couch. She pulled back the cover and I had my first look at my son.

He opened his eyes sleepily and gazed up at me, though probably without seeing me. I picked him up. He was so small. His hair was brown and curly. There was but a slight slanting look to his eyes. He looked like neither the one nor the other of us, but as if our blood and heritage had truly mingled.

I pressed my lips to the soft cheek and his tiny hand came up and tangled in my beard. Gently I put him down.

"We must find a name for him," I said. And she, taking my hand, answered, "He is your son. It is the privilege of the father to name his son."

Looking down at him I said, "Being of two nations, he should have two names. I will let you select his Japanese name and I shall find one to fit the English tongue."

"Will you name him William-san?" she asked.

"The name Will is a good enough name but I would not care to decide right now," I said.

The next day, in my study, feeling much rested, I found the name. I picked up the Bible that had been sent me. Opening it, I came to the story of Joseph, and somehow, in this strange land, it seemed there was a similarity between young Joseph and my son. I decided Joseph should be his English name—Joseph William Adams.

He was a happy baby. The days I spent at home before once again seeing to my affairs were among the most contented I have ever known. The sea had worn me overly much. I felt as if the years had begun to press upon me. Now I became young again, even if only for a short time, as if the youth and beauty of Yuriko and the new life of my son had relieved me of some of the burdensome years.

All too soon I had to enter the world of the court. My first duty would be to see my honored friend, Iyeyasu, who, according to rumor, was now declining rapidly. I feared there would be constraint between us, but whether or no, I had to and wanted to see Iyeyasu.

53

Sodo no Kami greeted me on my arrival. He was most apologetic.

"My Lord, Daishi-san," he said, "the Sei-e-tai Shogun Iyeyasu sleeps, and though he will be angry at me for not wakening him before your arrival, he sleeps so little nowadays that I have not the heart to disturb him."

I answered, "I understand, Kami-san. It has come to my ears that Iyeyasu has not been well and I would be the last to disturb his sleep. There is no loss. I am not pressed for time. It will give us a chance to talk once more. I have been away for so long I know little of what has happened."

We sat and talked quietly as friends. He congratulated me on the birth of my son. He told me then of various occurrences, one of which was the arrival of some Franciscan friars at Yokosuka. This had caused much disturbance. This was also upsetting news to me. It might even be the final straw for Hidetada.

After we had talked for some time a servant entered and announced that Iyeyasu was awake and waiting for me. When we entered I was struck with dismay at the age which had settled over him like a mantle. Sodo no Kami, with his head pressed against the floor, did not stir while Iyeyasu abused him for not announcing me, complaining like a querulous old man. I had never seen him act thus toward even the lowliest. He could be stern. I had been witness often as he signed the death warrant of a person or persons, but never in an angry or a petulant fashion.

When he had finished, Sodo no Kami retreated from the room, still on his hands and knees. Then Iyeyasu greeted me with a spark of the old warmth. After the customary polite phrases of greeting, tea was brought and we drank it slowly and peacefully, with just some small comment on the beauty of the day.

Then, abruptly turning to me, he asked: "Do you come as my conscience, Injin-san? I can see in your eyes you believe I have done a wrong and terrible thing."

"I have never questioned your wisdom, Lord Iyeyasu, and in this I have no right to judge."

His hands, which had become scrawny and mottled, clasped themselves together and no other gesture could more eloquently have expressed his anguish.

"My own daughter I gave to Hideyori as wife. I treated him as I would my second son. But you know, Injin-san, that to maintain the country in peace there can be only one ruler. Had I accepted his claim against that of my own son, those Daimyos who had fought by my side would have turned against me, and those who gathered about Hideyori were never friends of my family. He had not the strength to rule. This I know, because I watched him grow from a boy. He was too easily swayed by those about him. I had to do what I did." His voice then changed from sadness to shrill anger. "And the Romish priests—they gathered about him. They promised him miracles from their Christian God, and assured him that, with their God on his side, he could not lose. The day we took the castle my one great regret was that none of those priests lived so that I could have had my revenge on them for the havoc they caused. Injin-san, I have been weak in letting them stay in this land, but my son does not have the same weakness. With all our warnings they persist in coming. Now we will see the end of it."

His words caused a chill in my heart. Ever before he had been the balance between Hidetada's fanatic seclusion and the opposite extreme. Now that barrier was down. But I let him speak without interruption, feeling that if the anger was released it would be better for him, and for us also.

After a time he calmed himself and asked me about my affairs. I told him of our ill fortune. He shook his head in wonder at me. "I think, my friend, you grow senile, like me. I give you land and a fortune. You take a wife. Then, all of a sudden, you go wandering. What do you seek? What are you looking for, Injin-san?"

I was tempted to tell him my trouble, but the temptation was momentary. He had given me so much and I wanted no anger to trouble him so I let him think it a foolish whim of mine. Changing the subject I made some comment about my son, but he seemed not to hear, lost in thought. Then he placed his worn hand on mine and said:

"Good friend, time wears on me, but I have left instructions with my son that as long as you live in this land you will be honored under my name. In this, Hidetada will obey me."

We then talked of my son and he was happy at my good fortune, forgetting his fleeting anger at my choice of Yuriko-san. He asked that I bring the boy to him so that he could see him and give him his blessing. I replied that he could name the day, or send a message and I, like any proud father, would be more than willing to show off my son. We made some small jests about fathers. Then, seeing he was very tired, I made my excuse to leave. He urged me to stay, saying that to sit and talk with me always relieved his mind, for, like a brother, I understood him. So I stayed with him until his head was nodding on his chest. Then, calling Sodo no Kami, I bade him carry his master to bed and I sadly said farewell.

Instead of going directly to my home I went by the Shogun's palace and was received by Kozuke no Suke. I arranged with Suke-san to present my petition for a new goshun to Hidetada. Then we sorrowfully spoke of how Iyeyasu had aged, but also of his greatness which would live, growing as the years passed, until he became a legend.

Parting with words of friendship, with my retainers, I journeyed directly home rather than spending the night at some inn. Early the next morning I received a summons from Hidetada to report to him immediately.

The message being urgent, I did not delay. Hastily bidding Yuriko *sayonara*, I summoned Itsuke-san and my servants and proceeded with all haste to the palace, where I was kept waiting through the long day. I was then instructed to return the following morning. I did not know the reason for this insulting behavior, but in dealing with Hidetada I had been forced to learn patience.

It was not until midday that I was finally called into Hidetada's presence. Without preliminary courteous phrases, he began to berate me, saying that I had traded with the Spaniards, having them in my house, and accusing me of being responsible for the arrival of the group of Franciscan monks who were at Yokosuka.

When he had finished his tirade, I politely replied that I was innocent of the accusation, pointing out that, while it was true certain Spaniards had stayed at Hemmi, it was only to comply with the basic rules of hospitality. As for the Franciscan monks, I had had no knowledge of them, nor knew of reasons for their coming until two days before, when I had spoken to his father.

He refused to listen, but ordered me to go to Yokosuka and tell the friars that if they did not leave immediately he would dispatch soldiers to kill them without trial or explanation.

I knew these were not idle threats. Hidetada put no great value on any life and certainly the loss of a foreigner's life would not cause him the slightest qualm. I was sure it was only because his father still lived that they had not been summarily put to death.

Putting the best face I could upon his words and actions, I told him I would deliver his message immediately and was dismissed from his presence.

On the journey to Yokosuka my thoughts churned with anger. It seemed no matter what I did, I was always caught between, accused by both sides of being an enemy. My dealings with the friars, up to this time, gave me little hope they would heed my warnings. I could not blame myself for their willfulness, for if they would not obey orders of the Pope, why then would they listen to me?

At Yokosuka I found them being held as prisoners in a small house by the seashore. Going directly to the head friar, I wasted no time passing on the command of Hidetada. I believe my abruptness, more than anything else, convinced him that I spoke the truth.

Under different circumstances all would have been willing to die for their religion. Here they had not even been allowed to speak, therefore their deaths would serve no purpose.

Their ship was still lying offshore and they agreed to embark. With many bitter words they accused me of being a heretic and threatened me with God's punishment for my actions in denying them the right to bring the truth to the heathens. I did not remind them that these orders were not mine but Hidetada's. I saw to it that they and their possessions were safely put aboard the ship and stayed until they had sailed from the harbor.

I was granted audience with Hidetada immediately upon my return. For some reason known only to himself, his mood had changed completely. Now he was kind. He thanked me for removing the friars from the soil of Japan. He gave me presents of a sword, three coats of deerskin, and other articles; then, with his own hand, he gave me the goshun for the next voyage, which relieved me greatly. The English factory had been thus far very unsuccessful, and my finances were such that I had either to come by some ready money or give up some of my holdings. Now that I had a son, I knew I must look also to his future.

54

Those at the factory at Hirado were anxiously awaiting news of my success in obtaining the goshun, so that within a day after my return to Hemmi, I sent Shoki-san with an escort of samurai to Hirado. I instructed him to make all speed to deliver into Cock's own hand the goshun and the detailed instructions for the work to be done on the ship. I promised to be in Hirado before two months to finish the work personally and make preparation to sail before the monsoon.

Now that this was off my mind I relaxed, casting all worry and doubt aside. It was spring. The sun, the green fields, the softness of the air and the sound of people working all blended into a wondrous song which echoed in my heart.

Yuriko and I drew closer together, spending the days in conversation. She had a great talent for a form of poetry called *haiku* which consists of but seventeen syllables, these seventeen syllables conveying the essence of a poem a hundred lines long.

It is an art for which I lacked ability. Sometimes I would feel I had finally achieved a haiku and would show it proudly to Yuriko. My clumsy attempts merely evoked her silvery laughter.

One day we were in the garden when she tried again to explain haiku.

"Ah, my honorable husband," she chided me. "Before you can make haiku you must understand *yugen*."

"Yugen? And what is yugen?"

"Yugen," she said softly as she stroked my face, "is that which is profound, remote and mysterious. Things which cannot be grasped or expressed in words but in symbolism. Haiku is the expression of yugen. *Sabi* is also yugen. Do you know what sabi is?"

"I know nothing more than that I love you and that you, not haiku, are the essence of love." I started to raise my head from her lap.

She pushed me gently down.

"Sabi is the love of old things. Of beauty in imperfection. Here is a sabi:

"Scent of chrysanthemums
And in Nara all the many
Ancient Buddhas."

I was enchanted by her depth of understanding, and also by the slim, cool loveliness of her body which carried within it such a fire of passion, such an art of love that merely by a look, the slightest touch of her hand, the exquisite softness of her skin, she could uncover a flowing well of desire in me that I had never dreamed existed even in my most virile youth.

Each morning, on awakening, I would look at her sleeping beside me, so graceful in repose that it seemed improbable that so short a time ago she had been all fire and delight. I would rise to meet each morning, my heart so filled with happiness that I was as drunk as ever I had been on saki.

For the first month we did not speak of the necessity for my leaving. Then, gradually, we began to discuss it. Though the thought of our impending separation was painful, Yuriko, being the woman she was and a Japanese wife as well, did not question my decision. I told her this trip, God willing, would be the last I should ever make. I would not renew my contract with the English, but would remain at home and spend my days in Hemmi where, if paradise were better, no mortal could bear the sweet joy of it.

On the day of my departure, Yuriko made it so easy for me it was as though we parted merely for the day. I kissed my son good-by and walked toward the gate with Yuriko. The horses, servants and six samurai waited in readiness. Her hand rested lightly on my arm.

When we came to the gate I felt that, for just a moment longer I must be alone with her. I drew her into the gateman's hut where I caressed her face, trying with the touch of my hand and with my eyes to tell her how much this parting grieved me. For a long time she looked at me. Then, dropping gracefully to her knees, she put her forehead to the floor and said:

"Go now, my Lord. Each day I will pray to Amida to protect you, and to Hotei to bring you good fortune. May your journey be quick and your return to me safe. And if our Lord God be kind, in myself will there grow an added joy for you and me. Sayonara, my Lord."

"Sayonara, Yuriko-san. My heart will never go beyond this gate." And, not being able to bear this parting any longer without showing weakness and shaming her by it, I left without a further word, hardly seeing the line of servants who had come out to bid me farewell.

Through the day we traveled fast, as if to outdistance the pain of parting.

55

It seemed now as if God smiled on our venture. At Hirado I found the *Sea Adventure* sturdy and in good repair, though the cost had been great. There we performed the ceremony of stepping and raising the new mast. Both the Dutch and the Spaniards were now more friendly with the English since the departure of Saris. When our vessel was laden we had a feast along with many Japanese friends.

In our cargo we had cloth of the India type, cattans—which are swords of fine workmanship—and many pieces of beautiful lacquer work in which the Japanese are proficient.

The weather favored us though we did run into one gale in which we lost our pump. Under clear skies again, we arrived at the Menam

River on January 10, 1616, after a voyage of less than two months.

Proceeding up the river to Bangkok, Tempest Peacock took a boat to the capital, called Ayuthia, to visit the king. Within seven days we had permission to bring the junk to the capital, where we found a factory of the East India Company newly set up.

The Siamese people are small of stature, quick-moving and sharp to trade with. We obtained audience with the Siamese king, giving him a number of gifts, including a sword of fine workmanship, a number of beautifully balanced lances, and some lacquer boxes for looking glasses and jewelry.

The king was amiable and gave us a pass and ordered that we be treated fairly in every way. We sold our cargo to Jeremy Lee, who was in charge of the East India Company factory. With the profits from this and six hundred pounds which had been delivered to me by Cock, we purchased wood and skins very cheaply.

Buying more than we could carry in the *Sea Adventure*, Tempest Peacock chartered another junk, of which he took charge. I bought a third junk from a Chinese merchant on which I paid part, with the understanding I would pay the rest at a later date. As captain for this junk I employed a Dutchman, who seemed a competent seaman.

We left the Menam River in consort. The weather continued fine day after day and we on the *Sea Adventure* arrived back at Hirado on July 22, 1616.

Within three days the other two junks came into port also. We all were happy over our good fortune and ready to celebrate when I was stricken by the news that on the first day of June Iyeyasu had died. I grieved as I had grieved when Thomas lost his life. Iyeyasu had been most dear to my heart. In him was the wisdom of the great, and a deep love of country. In truth, few such men as Iyeyasu have ever lived.

Since drink did not alleviate my sorrow, I plunged into work, counting our profits like any greedy merchant, determined to receive such a return that I would never have to think of finance again. On the *Sea Adventure* alone I brought in 2,350 piculs of Siam wood and 3,700 deerskins, all in fine condition. For these we almost tripled the price we had paid. The cargo of the other two junks we sent farther down the coast and made even more profit. This was a new lease on life for the English factory, for a poor voyage would have meant failure. On this voyage we made enough profit to cover all the costs which the English company had spent up to now and showed a large profit in addition.

My grief for Iyeyasu was a lonely one that I could not share with my countrymen. They made casual mention that they were sorry, as they understood we had been friends. Not one of them could understand the depth of the friendship I had shared with Iyeyasu. There was no point in saying anything further. I continued with the business at hand. At a meeting with Richard Cock, Eaton, and Peacock, they admitted now that I had been right from the beginning in that we should move to a new factory, somewhere close to Yedo, maintaining this one for the time being.

In spite of the cupidity of John Saris, the clause I had written when first discussing the contract with Richard Cock had been left in. This gave the English leave to trade anywhere in Japan if they should so desire. On this basis I hoped to see them able to expand.

As for myself, my contract with the company was now terminated. Though they desired me to renew it I explained I did not care to. I offered to assist them wherever possible but I no longer wanted to make any further voyages.

As we made preparations to leave for Yedo, two English ships were announced offshore and we piloted them into the Bay at Hirado, giving them a great welcome. They were the *Advice* and the *Thomas*, both from London. The arrival of these ships delayed my return for a number of days.

Shoki-san relayed the joyful tidings that Yuriko was once again with child and the birth would take place within the month. I was anxious to reach home.

All things were bright for me, except for Iyeyasu's death, which hung like a pall over the land. I wanted to finish my work quickly so that I could pay my respects to him and join the country in mourning.

When all was in order, Shoki-san, Richard Cock, and I left Hirado on the twenty-fourth of July for Yedo. The English were anxious to procure another goshun. Cock fell ill from either bad food or water and remained at Osaka to recover while Shoki-san and I went on.

As we neared Hemmi, news of our coming preceded us and I was again met by my servants on the road, with a present of food and wine. It was a most heart-warming gesture, though in truth I was impatient of the time consumed by the necessary courtesy of eating, drinking and acknowledging the honor which they did me. I was in a fever to see Yuriko again.

I was far ahead of Shoki-san when I reached Hemmi and rode my horse right to the front of the house, merely waving to those at the gate. Removing my boots, I hastened in to an inner room where Yuriko waited, heavy with child.

What we said to each other belongs to us—words that came from the heart, full of love. She was beautiful to me even though her body was heavy. I promised that never again would I leave her, that now we would be able to live quietly, enjoying the beauty of our surroundings, watching our children grow to honorable position.

I stayed at home, leaving Yuriko's side only to mourn at the tomb of Iyeyasu. Dressed in somber costume I prayed that his soul in the afterworld would dwell in happiness. I brought presents, and left at his tomb as an epitaph Yuriko's poem which Shoki-san had made into a scroll.

First I intoned the words and they seemed to fit his character as no other words could.

> "Here's the top peak, the multitude below
> Lives, for they can there.
> This man decided not to live but know.
> Bury this man there.
> Here—here's his place where the meteors shoot,
> Clouds form,
> Lightnings are loosed,
> Stars come and go. Let joy break the storm.
> Peace—let the dew send.
> Lofty designs must close in like effects
> Loftily lying.
> Leave him—still loftier than the world suspects
> Living and dying."

And so I parted with my friend Iyeyasu and returned to my home.

I was at the side of Yuriko when the baby was born. As I had hoped, it was a girl. Few babies I have seen are beautiful at birth, but this child was beautiful indeed. I gave her the name of Susanna, in English. This was the first of my children I had seen born. Nor had I been home for the ceremony, which is most important to the Japanese.

On the fourth month before birth, the child receives its soul, which is called *tamashi*. On this day, which is celebrated as "The Day of the Dog"—the dog, it is claimed, having an easy birth—the father, with his left hand, passes the maternity belt, called *yuwata-obi*, to the mother, who takes it in her right hand. The grandmother then helps to wind it around her body. This band is of silk, about eight feet in length, and is used to help the mother support the child in her womb.

I was present for the O-Shichi-ya festival. This occurs on the seventh day after birth, when all the family gathers around with presents for the baby, and the name is announced. We named her Yuriko, her mother's name, which means "Lily." Yuriko's grandfather jestingly said that her future would be good, now that she had two names.

At this ceremony Richard Cock and the two captains from the English ships were my guests at Hemmi. They were interested observers in the ceremony and enjoyed watching the priest and the family on this happy name-giving day.

We had a bountiful feast for all. Captain Keeling of the *Advice* and Captain Bright of the *Thomas* were impressed by the extent of my holdings and the respect shown me, not only by the peasants, but by the nobility who had come from Yedo for the ceremony.

I was pleased that they had come, for Saris, on his return to England, had said many ill things of me—that I was not fit even to command a junk and that I loved the Dutch and Spaniards more than my own countrymen. I had said nothing in defense of myself, leaving it to others and to my own actions to speak in denial, always feeling that so long as my own mind knew I acted honorably, I need make apology to no one.

Richard Cock had asked me to go to Yedo and use my influence to hasten the issuance of a new goshun and obtain permission to set up a factory either at Uruga or Yokosuka. I begged off, saying I would send a message to Kozuke no Suke which I thought would be sufficient for the goshun. As for the new factory I felt this would take considerable negotiation.

I was tired of pitting myself against Hidetada and conforming to all the rules of polite deception prevalent in the court. I was tired of being the buffer in trade. My desire was to stay within the boundaries of my own lands and forget the world outside which I no longer enjoyed. This was not to be.

Within but one week, a desperate message arrived from Richard Cock pleading with me to come to the court and speak in their behalf. The Spaniards had reached the ear of Hidetada and accused the English of capturing and burning their ships. They said the English robbed and stole from all they met at sea.

Certain that these were merely more lies by the Spaniards, I went to Yedo, filled with indignation, only to find that it was true indeed. The *Advice* and the *Thomas* had captured and burned three Portugal vessels, taking their goods and putting the crew ashore on the island of Surat. None of this had been told to me.

Furiously I gave vent to my feelings to Cock and the other two captains, to the great surprise of Richard Cock. Usually, no matter what the provocation, I had been calm and helpful—only losing my temper with Saris.

Seeing the extent of my anger they tried to soothe me. They called upon my honor as an Englishman. They reminded me that although I lived in Japan, I still had a family who were English and living somewhere in England.

Feeling not much honor in being an Englishman at this time, I did, however, consent once again to use what influence I had to allay Hidetada's anger against them, but swore this would be the end.

56

I formally requested an audience with Hidetada, but now the tide ran full against me. Even my old friend Kozuke no Suke put me off. The gifts which the *Thomas* and the *Advice* had brought from England had not been accepted by Hidetada. Then, after four days, we were told we would be granted an audience. We sat through the entire day, with neither food nor drink, waiting. At the end of that day King James' greeting to Hidetada was returned with the instruction that a new and fuller translation be made. The Shogun thus was accusing me of omitting or changing parts. Hidetada was well enough versed in the English tongue to do his own translating. I went to Iyeyasu's old friend and mentor, the monk Tenkai, and with his help added a number of flowery phrases, attempting to satisfy Hidetada's sense of regal importance. This being done, we again waited. Three days later, instead of an interview, word came that due to the actions of the English they were now to be limited to selling their goods only at Hirado and Nagasaki. No more trade would be permitted the English between Siam, Cochin, China and Japan.

An order such as this would mean the ruination of the English factory. I spent the following day composing a letter of protest, citing the clauses in the agreement which had been signed between the Shogun and John Saris for the English king. It was returned to me with another letter in which Hidetada decided that even Nagasaki was to be excluded, forbidding all ships to enter that harbor, though goods would be allowed to be transported overland and sold there. This meant the expense of getting passes from the local Daimyos.

Once more I was forced to go to Tenkai and ask him to use his influence in granting me a brief audience, so that I could explain our case. This was finally granted. We came into Hidetada's presence, made the usual obeisance, and once again presented the gifts sent by the English king.

Hidetada accepted them without examination and then turned his eyes to me. In them I saw the hatred that had come to full flower, as if I represented all he detested in foreigners.

"Most Honorable Lord," I said, "one of the great faults of all mankind is how their actions and words can be twisted by hatred to mean something else. The Spaniards, in accusing the English of taking three of their ships, did speak the truth, but they did not speak of the English and Dutch ships which they have taken, stealing their goods and murdering the English crews. Whether or not my actions appear to you in a different light, I have always tried to promote trade and, far more important, an understanding between the great nation of Japan and the nations from the West."

At these words he frowned and shook his head, saying, "We need not the trade, nor the goods from the West. Such things disturb our people, causing dissension and desire for unnecessary things. Though my father was a friend of foreigners, even in his last days he came to see that all of you are an evil influence. An agreement has been written; we are people of honor and will abide by the agreement until you give us further cause to break it."

"But," said I, "the agreement which was signed between the English king and my Lord of the Eastern Sun, Hidetada, gave us the privilege of choosing a place where we would trade."

Hidetada, with a motion of his hand, had Kozuke no Suke bring forward the document. He read it and said to me, "I see nothing of it in this agreement."

He then handed it to me. The clause relating to our freedom of trade had been blacked out by an ink brush. He looked at me in silence. There was nothing more to be said on this matter.

Handing back the document, I turned to the matter of another goshun, saying that without permission of another trading venture the English factory would be ruined. He answered that he would take it under further advisement with his ministers and then dismissed us, giving me a present of a cloak of cheap cloth, which spoke more eloquently than words how low my status was at the court. The cloak was the sort of gift he would have made to a beggar.

As we backed out of the room Hidetada's smile said plainly that he had had his revenge. Hatred is a strange and unreasoning thing. Why he hated me so was perhaps clear in his own mind, though it was never entirely clear to me.

Before returning home I spoke to Richard Cock and the English captains, telling them that I had reached the end of my influence, that there was no advantage to them in my making any further efforts on their behalf. I hoped, with me out of the way, Hidetada would grant them a goshun.

Captain Keeling remarked that perhaps I would have more luck working for the Dutch or the Spaniards. His words threw me into further anger. I spoke long and feelingly about the stupidity of all foreigners, of the Spaniards, the Portugals, of Captain John Saris—how by their own actions they had caused the Japanese to turn away from them in disgust.

"Perhaps a few ships of war would change the minds of these heathens," Keeling said. This infuriated me.

"If these people be heathen," I retorted, "then I know not what suitable word would describe the peoples of Europe and of England. Because they have their own religion and refuse to have the religion of the West thrust upon them, you call them heathen? For myself, I have done. I have put myself into such disrepute with these people, fighting for all of you, that I doubt if I shall ever recover. When I went to the scholar Tenkai and pleaded with him to intervene, he asked me why he should. My answer was that you were my country-men and I wanted to see trade flourish. He, as a friend, told me this would never be. The only thing I would do by petitioning the court would be to destroy myself. I have been accused by my own coun-trymen of favoring the Dutch and the Portugals, and by them of favoring you. Now I have finished. From now on I intend to sit at home, read my books, enjoy my family and try to forget the inherent stupidity of mankind."

With that I left them and returned to Hemmi. But there I found further bedevilment.

Two Portugal traders and a Spaniard priest, disguised as a mer-chant, had sought sanctuary in my house. The priest was ill. When I came home and found them I could not turn them out. I knew that Hidetada had spies all about and would soon learn these men were at my house.

Yuriko had made them welcome and tried to keep their presence a secret. I told her this was foolish. We would let them stay, but openly, until they were well enough to leave. If we were accused of harboring a priest, our defense would be that we had offered the sanctuary of hospitality.

They well knew the danger they had put me under. Hidetada's order to destroy all Christian priests was now being diligently en-forced. Their claim was that they were merely trying to reach Hirado where the priest could escape from the country. Eventually, when he was well and all three left my house, I was happy to see them gone. Yuriko and I sat in the garden enjoying the freedom of our home again. By now we knew each other so well that I could tell what was on her mind. Yet she would not speak unless I asked her.

Taking her hand in mind I said, "Yuriko-san, let us speak of the things that trouble us and bring the words out openly in the beauty of this garden. I am sure they will thus be dispelled."

"My Lord," she said, "my grandfather and many others have spo-ken of the danger which you create for yourself. In my heart I know that your concern for all, regardless of your personal danger, is be-cause you cannot act other than in honor. It was this beauty, among other things, which made me love you. But no honor or profit, whether material or spiritual—only danger—can come from inter-fering with the laws and instructions of the Shogun. Nor do those

for whom you labor realize what you do for them. It has been said
that Lord Iyeyasu made you Japanese, but if you wish not to be
Japanese, then Hidetada will make of you an Englishman again. I
am selfish, I want the happiness and beauty of you and our family
and of living together with you at peace. Know that whatever my Lord
desires, however, I will not question. You asked me to speak: this is
what is in my heart."

I told her that I had finished. The rest of my days would be spent
quietly, in study, thought, conversation, love and the enjoyment of
our children. This, I vowed, was the truth. Never would I change my
mind.

Later in the week Cock informed me that Hidetada had issued
them the goshun. I wished him well. A fortnight later, the captain of
a Dutch ship and four merchants, one of whom was Van Sartoot,
came to Hemmi and brought with them news which not only angered me, but affected my honor and destroyed my peace.

57

Of the Dutchmen who arrived at my dwelling, I knew two, Van
Sartoot and John Yoosen, who for a time had been head of the
Dutch factory at Hirado. I had in many instances lent him aid, though
he was a man of ill tongue, given to drinking more than he should.
By this I do not mean that I am against drink—in my life I have had
more than my share. But there are some who should never drink, as
it takes away their senses and makes a fool out of them. Van Sartoot,
however, never drank. Perhaps he should have, I don't know.

John Yoosen, with his gross behavior and ill tongue, had made
many enemies. One of these was Kozuke no Suke, whom Saris, not
being able to pronounce the Japanese, called "Codskin." Yoosen had
stupidly called this gentle, educated man this name to his face and
thereby gained his undying enmity.

The captain of the Dutch ship was a large man, built like a barrel.
His name was Barkhout. I did not make them welcome but waited
for them to state their business. I knew they wanted a favor and
intended to tell them, so there would be no mistake, that I would
under no condition approach the court for any further favors.

Van Sartoot cleared his throat. "Herr Adams," he said, "I have here a letter from our company for you and also two letters from your wife which my company ordered delivered into your own hands."

His words, so unexpected, had the effect of a blow. I was so shocked I felt my heart stop. With trembling hands I reached for the letters. They were addressed to me in the cramped handwriting that I but dimly remembered.

The letter from the company was long, containing a bill for monies advanced. I barely looked at it before opening the letter from Elizabeth.

Loving Husband: As I have been in sore circumstances for monies, the Dutch merchants have loaned me five hundred guilders on my promise that I would write to you and that you would lend your help to further their trading in the heathen countries. Please, for the love of me, do all you can to assist them.

Yr. loving wife, Elizabeth.

The other letter was in the same vein. No news of England, of herself or my children. At first I was filled with fury at these letters. Then they lifted a burden from me. In my heart there had been guilt because I had not made a greater effort to return to her. These letters showed that money and comfort came first with her, as ever. I was quite sure, on reading them, that she had never intended writing an answer, except when a letter to me might be worth five hundred guilders to her. And even for five hundred guilders she could not write me a decent letter.

I turned to Van Sartoot. Crumpling the paper, I said:

"It is interesting to note that the first letters the Dutch have delivered to me are those in which there is some advantage to you. Yet I know many messages have been sent by Dutch ships and none have come to my hands. How do you account for that?"

Van Sartoot shrugged. "I speak for myself only. These letters I give to your hands. Others I know nothing of."

After reading the long letter from the Dutch company I thought in silence for a time, then explained that I was no longer in favor at the court and could help but little. I would, though, return to them the five hundred guilders. This was a considerable sum of money for me to part with at this time, amounting to about half the profit I had made on the last voyage to Siam.

This they would not hear of. Van Sartoot spoke a great deal about honor, good faith and trust, all words which sickened me, as in him I had found no hint of these things. Words such as these were used solely as a wedge on my own conscience.

I answered that I sympathized with their position, but that my appearance at court would probably do them more harm than good. However, I would write a letter to Kozuke no Suke, pleading with him to accept their gifts and beseech the Shogun to grant them audience. Their problem now seemed to be that the Daimyo of Hirado had informed them that a heavy tax was to be placed upon their goods and no goods could be sold anywhere but in Hirado. This meant that the Daimyo, through his servants, could set his own price upon the goods and the Dutch would be forced to sell.

Seeing that I was firm in my intention of not going with them to the court, they became abusive, accusing me of working only for my own countrymen. Rather than continue the discussion and lose my temper, I excused myself. I wrote a letter to Suke-san and had Shoki-san deliver it to them with my good-bys. Then I retired to the garden and sat alone. . . . All the years Elizabeth and I had been apart, and I still knew not the fate of my children. I tore up her letter and threw it to the ground, grinding it into the dirt with my heel. . . .

Some days later, I received a letter from Richard Cock informing me that a Chinese merchant wished to buy the junk I had bought in Siam and had offered twelve hundred taels for it. As this was twice the amount I had paid, it was more than a fair price. Richard Cock suggested that I come to Hirado to deal with the merchant directly, as I would have to transfer to him the document which had been issued to me by the Shogun. By now even owning a boat was difficult.

Feeling that the journey and the transaction would take no more than three weeks and I would finally be rid of all ties, I told Yuriko that I would return within that time. I explained that I wanted to dispose of all further connection with ships, sea and trade. This pleased her greatly.

I set out with Itsuke-san and the necessary number of retainers. We traveled fast. The second day from Hemmi we stopped at Yuri and there it became necessary for me to change horses, for mine had gone lame. The only horse available was a very skittish animal, but I considered myself a good horseman by now and I thought nothing of it.

Leaving Yuri early in the morning we again traveled fast. Just as the sun came up we were riding along a narrow trail when suddenly a bird flew out of a bush, directly in front of my horse. The horse reared and threw me.

It is strange that even now I can feel myself falling. I did not fall directly to the ground, but toward the side of the road and down, a distance of twenty to thirty feet. How I did not break my neck is a mystery, but the last I remember was hitting the ground and thinking to myself how sad it was that, after all the trials and tribulations of my life, it should end in such a fashion.

58

Regaining my senses, I thought I was home in Hemmi. I called for Yuriko. But it seemed they had brought me to Suruga. My arm, shoulder and head were heavily encased in bandages. Because of my size they had had difficulty in transporting me, having to go into Suruga and return with a palanquin. Itsuke-san and my retainers had taken me to the inn and had made preparations to commit seppuku if I should die.

The local Daimyo, hearing of my misfortune, had sent orders to bring me to his house. There I had received kind treatment. I was impatient to reach Hirado, but I realized it would be foolish to move before the broken bone in my shoulder had a chance to heal. Therefore I rested a week before going on. The journey was uncomfortable. The jolting of the horse, and later the rough water we encountered after leaving Osaka, caused me much pain.

At Hirado I met with the Chinese merchant and settled on a price of twelve hundred taels. He paid me the money in gold and we signed the transfer of the papers. Upon leaving his dwelling Takamon no Itsuke, with four of my retainers, set out to accompany me back to Richard Cock's residence. As we passed through the dark and narrow streets we were set upon by a group of samurai.

My palanquin was tipped over and I was seized and pushed into an alley where my injured arm was twisted cruelly and deliberately behind me so that the pain nearly caused me to lose consciousness.

Being in a crippled condition, I was almost helpless. Itsuke-san and the four others fought through to my side and effected my release. The noise of the battle and the shouts brought a large crowd of people into the streets and those who had attacked us dispersed. Two of my samurai lay dead. Itsuke-san had received a deep sword cut across his left arm.

Had I not been in such pain I would have realized that Itsuke-san felt his honor had been tarnished because he had not protected me from injury. He was mad with fury. After he had carried me to Richard Cock's, he set out to regain his face.

Days passed and I was in such pain I knew not day from night. One day Shoki-san came in and I wondered how he happened to be there. His face was gray with worry. I made light talk to relieve his mind but he still seemed stricken. Finally he burst forth with a torrent of words, including the names of Itsuke-san, Basho-san and Murizo-san.

I calmed him so that I could understand his words. He then wept, rocking back and forth, and told me Basho-san and Murizo-san had been killed, which I already knew. And then he said Itsuke-san had committed seppuku.

At first I refused to believe it. Finally it penetrated deep into me, and I, too, wept with Shoki-san. Takamon no Itsuke had been my arms and eyes. Weeping, I also cursed him for a fool. My honor had been tarnished but not enough to pay for with a life—and certainly not his. But such was the code. He had not found his enemy and had to make amends.

Though I had lived with these people for so many years and was more Japanese than English, their sense of honor and fear of losing face were so extreme I could never make sense of it. And nothing could replace Itsuke-san.

As soon as I was able I strongly protested to the Daimyo at Hirado for this assault and insisted he give my three friends burial with all the ceremony and honor owing to a true samurai fallen in battle. This he did and was apologetic. I sensed, however, that my loss of favor with Hidetada had become known.

I spent some time with Richard Cock, recovering before venturing back to Hemmi. I found myself growing more and more annoyed at his involving me in his troubles with the trading factory.

It seemed now that my temper had grown short. To those who had known me before, this was surprising. There were many reasons for my present mood. First was the death of Itsuke-san. Second, I had always told myself that the flattery of my position was unimportant. Perhaps when one has the position, flattery is not important. But respect is important and having lost the prestige I had formerly enjoyed, I now found it was of importance. I disliked intensely being treated with the disrespect that was now my lot. Two years before, had I been assaulted on the street, the Daimyo would have searched out and executed every assailant even had there been a hundred involved. But for this assault upon my person I received no more than a mild apology.

Again vowing that this would be the last time I would leave Hemmi, I made the long sad journey home with my remaining samurai and began the mourning period for Takamon no Itsuke and the others.

I visited the shrines and carried out the religious ceremony of seeing their souls safely on the way. Then I turned my face away from the world, with the firm decision never to venture forth again.

59

I had been home less than a month, however, when I received an abrupt summons from Hidetada to appear before him. From the nature of the message I knew that whatever the reason, it was important and I could not refuse to go.

Aware that further bedevilment awaited me, I made the journey to the castle of the Shogun with an uneasy mind. My neck and shoulder still gave me considerable discomfort, but the unease in my heart was harder to bear.

At the court I was kept waiting. At the end of the day, not being received in audience, I decided to stay at an inn. Since I was in disfavor, I did not want to embarrass any of my friends by my presence.

Outside the castle grounds I met with the palanquin of Daimyo Safa Kimihara. He insisted that I should come to his house and spend the night with him. In courtesy I could not refuse, though I wanted no trouble to come to him. After we had tea we spoke of past things but I could see that there was some sad problem on his mind. Finally he spoke of it.

"Daishi-san, the word of the new law of Hidetada—has it reached you?"

"Do you mean in relation to the trade of foreigners?"

He shook his head sadly and said, "No. Hidetada has now ruled that all ships with a capacity of over twelve hundred bushels of grain must be destroyed. No Japanese is to leave this land on pain of death, should he return. And"—and here he hesitated—"and all books of a foreign nature relating to the Western world are to be destroyed. This includes your books on mathematics, navigation, shipbuilding—all are being gathered and are to be burned."

His words shocked me, not because what I had written was of any great importance. My poor fund of knowledge had been increased greatly by the navigators and mathematicians of England and Europe. It was just that I felt the destruction of any knowledge is a stupid and unreasoning thing.

"Do you think that his dislike for me is the cause of this new law?"

"No. The purpose of the Shogun is to drive all foreign influence from Japan, and to close the door. Police are even now searching out all priests. When they are found, they are to be executed. The Spaniards and the Portugals have been banned from the country altogether. They have but a short time to leave. The English and the Dutch also are to be pushed out, but for the time being they will be allowed to trade at Hirado. No more goshuns will be issued for any trade between Japan, Siam or any of the neighboring countries."

I drank saki and considered his words. I was suddenly afraid that I had been summoned to Yedo to receive orders of my banishment. I tried to think what I ought to do if this was true. I doubted that the estate which had been given to me by Iyeyasu could be sold. If I should be banished, my properties would most likely be confiscated.

I could take Magome no Yuriko and the children and go to Siam to enter trade there. But it was a mean and unhealthy country and in a continual state of unrest.

"Do you know the reason why I have been summoned to the court, Kimihara-san?"

"No," he replied, "though many rumors fill the air." And, leaning toward me in warmth and friendship, he said: "Know this, Daishi-san, there are many of us who are still your friends. Though we cannot stand against the laws of the Shogun, if you need our help, I have been named to speak for all of them. We will do everything in our power. I do not think that even Hidetada would dare banish you."

In this there was some comfort, though the night I spent was one of despair—despair of the deepest sort, because if a man knows what he must face, he can set his mind and courage to meet it. Not knowing is a painful thing and the thought of having to leave this land was cruelest of all. The last thing I desired was new lands and new adventure.

It was late in the afternoon before Kozuke no Suke escorted me into the throne room where Hidetada, in all his regalia, sat cross-legged on a dais. I made the required obeisance and spoke the polite phrases of gratitude to him for admitting me to his august presence.

Iyeyasu had been right in saying that Hidetada had the strength to carry on the work for the country and that if he followed Iyeyasu's rules for government, Japan would be safe.

I sat upon a mat facing him, trying to ease my sore arm into a better position. He looked coldly down at me.

From Suke-san he took a document, reading first the law relating to the destruction of vessels of over twelve hundred bushels. Then he read his law expelling the Spaniards and Portugals. Finally he read a law limiting the trading area strictly to Hirado and the government's policy of issuing no more goshuns.

When this was done he waited for some comment from me.

I said, "Most Noble Lord, there was a time when I might have disagreed on some of these edicts. But now I am in my own mind and heart a son of Nippon. Your will, as your father's before you, is my will."

Looking sternly at me, he said, "You knew of my law against the

Christian bonzes, yet I have learned that your house is a meeting place for such persons. With your mouth you say one thing about obedience to the law of this land and your actions say another."

"Some months ago, Noble Lord," I answered, "some Spaniards and Portugals, two of whom were ill, did stop at my estate at Hemmi while I was not at home. My wife and retainers took them in as they have always done before. Upon my return, I found these men too ill to travel. I let them recover, then sent them on their way. I had received no direct orders not to do this. The laws of hospitality would not allow me, in honor, to cast them from my house. Of this, my Lord, I am guilty."

"Injin-san, my father gave you great honor. He saw in you such value which my mind cannot understand. But, as he did these things, I must respect his memory. However, to my mind, you have caused much disturbance since your arrival in this land. You have affected the welfare of our country by your actions. You will return to your estate in Hemmi, accompanied by officers from this court. There you will turn over to them all your books of foreign writings. When this is done you will be confined to your estate, not leaving without a pass written in my own hand, on pain of death. Your actions deserve much more punishment than this, but in respect to my father, I will be kind."

With that he dismissed me. I left the court free and easy in my mind. The sentence he had given me was no punishment at all. All I needed in the world was what I had at Hemmi and by his words he removed any excuse I would ever have for leaving.

At Hemmi I settled down to the life of a squire, overseeing the estate, caring for my people, happily living with Yuriko and the children, away from the world.

Shoki-san became my eyes and ears. As the weeks and months passed he brought me word of the chaos in the outside world which, at first, I dismissed, for I could do nothing about it. But as time passed, these incidents began to eat at me like a sickness in the belly.

The Spaniard priests who chose to go into hiding instead of leaving the country were sought out and, one by one, brutally crucified. All Japanese Christians had to renounce their belief or be crucified the same as the priests. Many who refused to do so forfeited their lives.

Japan now entered an era of complete change. When first I had come to this land the nobility, along with the lower classes, took to all things foreign, imitating even the dress of the Portugals and Spaniards. Now everything alien was spat upon and reviled.

Even the people in the vicinity of my estate gathered in front of my gates, speaking violently against me. My outer fields were desecrated and some of my people killed. I acquired more samurai, which was not easy to do.

I received regular appeals from Richard Cock for assistance. The English factory was almost in a state of siege. The property of the Spaniards and Portugals had been sacked and burned. Worst of all, the *Sea Adventure* had not returned. Word had come that Peacock had been taken prisoner off Siam and was being held for ransom.

Cock beseeched me to come to Hirado and take command of the *Gift of God*, the other junk we had purchased on my last trading venture, and remove those who were in hiding to safety outside the country. He pleaded with me to try to effect Peacock's release. Tempest Peacock had been a good friend. I could not sit safely, with ease of heart, while those of my own civilization were in such dire peril. Yet neither could I desert my wife and children to go off on such a mission, even for the most Christian of reasons. Not that I valued my life so much, but my duty was to my family and they would surely suffer reprisal were I to do this.

Yuriko, her mind not beset by small things and with a heart large enough to encompass all, suffered in this as much as I.

We spoke much about these problems, she saying that if I felt that by not helping my countrymen it would weaken my manhood, then in honor I should not think of my duty to her and the children and do that which I thought right.

Her selfless words strengthened my resolve not to endanger her and the children. I knew full well there was little, if any, chance of my being able to reach Hirado had I wanted to. Further, if I lost my life I would have helped none. Then my problem was solved, as most such problems often are, by fate. The die was cast for me to travel again a long and bitter road.

One night there was a loud clamor at the gate. The servants went to see what it was and Shoki-san came back, leading three exhausted and wounded priests. They had been disguised as Buddhist bonzes but had been set upon by a mob when their true identity was disclosed.

Already the mob was at the gates and I had not the time to waste in indecision. Quickly I ordered four horses saddled. Gathering together some food to take on the journey, I gave orders to see that the priests had wine and stimulants.

While I gathered the things we would need, it was Yuriko who cleansed their wounds and gave them wine. She took this parting without tears or plea, her eyes alone telling of her inward sorrow. Refusing to allow anyone else to come with me, we mounted. We went through the side gate, letting the mob become aware of our escape. Drawing them off in that manner we rode toward Osaka. All the while my eyes were wet with tears and I cursed myself for a fool.

60

Should my countrymen read this account, many may say that it has run overlong, dipped into corners, turning up people who appear and disappear, no more to be heard of again. But please remember, these pages have encompassed a lifetime. I can think now of many things of importance to me, and possibly useful to those coming after my time, that I could add to what has already been written here; but it would double the number of these pages.

I can say no more than this is a record of the long life of one man. Like the story of all men, it is filled with errors. Where wisdom should have been, there was none. I have made the same mistakes as those who have gone before me. And knowing man, I know the same mistakes will be made by those coming after me. I have known great joy; and sorrow, so deep, the scars still remain. Regrets I have and yet, in some few instances, pride. That which makes a man is not one thing, but many and varied experiences, the sum total of which denotes his true worth.

In these last days I have pondered if I had not lived so long in this land that I love, and had I not become so imbued with the Japanese concept of honor, would I have done that night what I did for those three priests? Beyond all else, they were my enemies, not only of what I believe, but because of the havoc caused by their actions.

Should I tell of the journey we made from Hemmi to Hirado, I could make from this another book and perhaps one of greater interest. For it was a long one, I trying in desperation to keep the exhausted priests from falling by the wayside. We ducked and dodged about the country like foxes eluding the hounds all about. I had the advantage of knowing the road well. I knew every check point between the provinces where people passed only with permission of the local Daimyo, or with a pass from the Shogun.

We had many narrow escapes. Once, when we were caught, a samurai let us pass only because of his friendship to me. I am sure that when we had gone he committed seppuku. In that, too, I have come to feel that he did what he felt was right, as we must all do. In aiding the priests to escape I had no time to think but reacted as my nature dictated. Only later did I curse myself for a fool.

Bone-weary, hungry, with only fear driving us on, we finally arrived at Hirado. There, my good and faithful Shoki-san, sent by Yuriko, awaited our arrival with our samurai. He had given Cock knowledge of our coming and the *Gift of God* was stored and ready for departure.

One hundred and thirty-six Spaniards, priests and traders were in hiding on a small island waiting to escape, taking with them little more than their lives.

Time pressed on us as each hour meant more danger, not only to those running from the wrath of the Shogun, but also for those Christian converts who had selflessly provided shelter and protection.

I had very little time to speak with Richard Cock and the other merchants but I warned him that he would be wise to leave with us, as, more than likely, his life would be forfeit. Yet he would not go. He was that sort of Englishman who, once having given his word, will not leave his responsibility, even though his death would mean little to the India Company of merchants in London.

I wished him luck, saying, "Once these people are brought to a safe place I will take some time to investigate the fate of Tempest Peacock and the rest. When I have found them, or learned their fate, I will return."

In amazement he asked me, "You are not mad enough to think of returning to this country, Adams? You will die for it!"

I told him yes, I would return, because now this was the only country I had—that my heart and soul and love and all things of value to

me were here, and it would be my chosen place for dying also. There
could be no other place than this Morning Land for me.

We were very crowded aboard the small vessel and there was great
unhappiness among all—the priests for leaving their work undone
and the merchants for leaving their properties and holdings. Their
attitude toward me was as if I was the prime cause of all their troubles. I had reached the point, by then, where this amused me more
than anything else. None of them would ever know what I had
given up. Because of this I felt no anger, but rather sorrow. I kept
to myself, speaking to none except to give orders concerning the ship.

The voyage to Siam was like all voyages, made up of storm and
calm and days when the weather is to the liking of seamen, all things
equaling out. Within three months we arrived at Ayuthia in Siam.
Most of my passengers did not so much as bid me farewell.

As I told Cock I would do, I now spent some time in search of
the fate of the *Sea Adventure*. We set sail toward Batam, seeking
the pirates who had taken her, with the hope of effecting a ransom. This was a very dangerous voyage for so small a ship. However,
the East India Company had provided me with new and strong
armament and a number of English, Portugal, Chinese and Spaniard
sailors who joined with me, having no other place to go than the sea.

For six months we searched. Always we were met by hostility, or
with rumors that our men were being held by some other group of
pirates who infested these waters.

The days passed and became months, until all were weary of
the unceasing danger. Had it not been for these writings, I would
have been in the same state. But putting down the things which had
gone before kept me occupied.

Finally, in the Straits of Malacca, we were set upon by three small
boats which we easily destroyed before they could board us and
managed to rescue four men from the water before the sharks took
them. From them we were assured that Peacock and the others were
dead. One of these men had upon his finger a ring bearing Peacock's
seal. By then, feeling as if I had done a penance, I ordered our course
laid for Siam.

I thought not to tarry at all, but to leave for home at once. But
here, for the first time in my life, I contracted a tropical fever which
clung to me no matter how much I was purged and bled. Some days

I would feel well again. Then it would return to wrack me so that I thought my end was near, and I was in terror of dying so far from those I loved.

Desperately I tried to gather a crew, but there were few men who cared to return to Japan. In the end I managed to get a Chinese captain and a mixed crew to sail with me, promising them they would have the *Gift of God* once I was set ashore in Japan.

My illness now was such that each day I was sure would be my last. It was only my burning desire to see my beloved Yuriko and my children that kept me alive.

At last we reached the Japanese islands, and lay out of sight of land until darkness, then worked our way slowly to Hirado in the dead of night. I was put ashore so weak I could barely stand upon my feet and, in my fever, I could not tell between this night and the first night I had come to these shores so many years before.

It was strange that the first one I saw was Shoki-san, who came to the door at my knock when I reached the English factory. I fell into his arms and he and Richard Cock bore me to a pallet where they bathed my head and gave me wine. As if in answer to my unspoken question, Shoki-san said:

"Sleep, Daishi-san. All is well. Your wife and children are safe."

When I awakened I found Shoki-san and Richard by my side. I could tell how shocked they were by my appearance. There was but little flesh left on my bones, and age had settled upon me as if ten years had been in the place of one.

They insisted that I should rest. I would not, but promised to stay for one day while they procured a boat for the journey home. I knew, without question, my days were numbered and in me there was but one desire and that was to reach Hemmi.

The memory of that journey is faint, coming in bits and snatches . . . of the sound of the rowers singing; of the wind and the sail; and of my arms clutched about the neck of a horse, the coarse mane in my face and my mind repeating over and over that I must go on until I reached home.

Then I was home and there was the touch of Yuriko's soft hand on my face. In her eyes there was great and abiding sorrow. But for both of us there is the comfort of knowing that this is not the end, but merely one station on a long journey. Somewhere, somehow, we will meet once more.

When I was well enough to sit up and talk I found that officials from the court had come the day after my arrival with a guard of samurai to take me away. After looking upon me they had left me as I was, to tell Hidetada that death sat upon my shoulders.

Hidetada, knowing of this, has seen fit to let me have these last days in peace. That which he set out to do has been done. The foreigners are gone and the doors to this land are closed. At this moment, were I asked, I would say that he is right. There is a madness in our people which Hidetada recognized and I now admit.

When the history of these days is written, the failure of the Western world to open trade with Nippon will show that it was their own fault. The storm is over and I lie now, becalmed on my mat, like a dismasted ship drifting on the sea.

I have been able to finish this writing and have told Shoki-san to deliver it into the hands of Richard Cock, who has received permission to leave. I hope that it may reach England. Being no different from anyone else, I would like my memory to live on in the minds of my countrymen and my friends in this, my adopted land.

There is no more to say except that I am at peace with myself.

Soon Yuriko will come with some broth. Before I sleep I will see my children again. There is still tonight, when we will be with each other—and in time, other tomorrows.

AUTHOR'S NOTE

Daishi-san is a novel. The dialogue and the detailing of the events are the creation of the author. Yet it is also the history of an actual person, William Adams, who reacted to his life as I have described it. The majority of the other characters also lived, the exceptions being Procopia, Ali, Itsuke-san, Shoki-san, Sweringen, and Trient.

In this book I have sincerely tried to give as accurate an accounting as possible considering the long lapse of time. This has entailed a great deal of work and research. I have taken care with Japanese history, clinging to the sequence of events. Here there will probably be disagreement, for in history there is always disagreement even among the best of historians. I do not count myself as an historian.

I am sure many will wonder why I wrote this in the first person. I have asked myself that, too, and can only answer that I felt it had to be written this way. It would have been much easier to write in the third person, giving me the chance to make Adams stand as a swashbuckler with bloody sword in the best tradition of historical novels.

In Will Adams' life and times I felt a close parallel with our own life and times. I tried to keep the story simple, seeking to show the value of tolerance and understanding, and the necessity for people of different cultures to learn to live with each other.

The sources from which I gleaned the material for this book cover a wide area. Below is a list of those I used covering the events and times of Will Adams' journey through the world.

Now that it is finished I can only hope you will like it.

Corpus Christi, Texas　　　　　　　　　　　　Robert Lund
Summer, 1960

The Awakening of Japan. Okakura-Kazuzo. Chester Springs, Pa.: Dufour Editions, 1922.

A Cruise in Japanese Waters. Captain John Sherard Osborne, 1858.

349

Eastward Ho: The First English Adventurers to the Orient. F. R. Dulles, 1931. From *The Macmillan Magazine*, 1904, Vol. 90.

The First Englishman in Japan: The Story of Will Adams, by Philip George Rogers. London: Harvell Press, 1956.

In Memory of Will Adams: The First Englishman in Japan. Arthur Diósy, F.R.G.S. From the *Transactions and Proceedings of the Japan Society*. London, Vol. 6, 1903-04.

Japan. Doré Ogrizek. New York: McGraw-Hill, 1957.

Japan: A Short Cultural History. George B. Sansom. New York: Appleton-Century-Crofts, 1937.

Letters of Will Adams. Edited by Thomas Randall, 1850.

The Log-Book of William Adams, 1614-19. Edited by C. J. Purnell. Reprinted from the *Transactions and Proceedings of the Japan Society*. London, 1916.

The New American Practical Navigator. Nathaniel Bowditch. New York: E. & G. Blunt, 1839-1865.

Principall Navigations, Voiages, and Discoveries of the English Nation. Richard Hakluyt. London, 1598-1600.

Shakespeare's England. Edited by Sir Walter Raleigh, Sir Sidney Lee, and Charles Talbut Onions. London. Oxford: Clarendon Press, 1932.

Sources of the Japanese Tradition. Compiled by Ryusaku Tsunoda, William T. Debary, and Donald Keene. New York: Columbia University Press, 1958.

William Adams, Sailing Master: The First Englishman in Japan. From the *Transactions and Proceedings of the Japan Society*. London, 1916.